Scott Foresman

Reading

Grade 2

Teacher's
Resource Book

WITHDRAWN

Scott Foresman

Editorial Offices: Glenview, Illinois • Parsippany, New Jersey • New York, New York
Sales Offices: Parsippany, New Jersey • Duluth, Georgia • Glenview, Illinois
Coppell, Texas • Ontario, California

ISBN 0-328-02231-4
ISBN 0-328-04058-4

 6 7 8 9 10-V004-10 09 08 07 06 05 04
5 6 7 8 9 10-V004-10 09 08 07 06 05 04

Table of Contents

Unit 1	Family Times	Phonics	High-Frequency Words	Comprehension	Grammar	Vocabulary	Research and Study Skills	Phonics Review	Spelling	Selection Test	Writing Process
Me + You = Special											
Franny and Ginny Daddy, Could I Have an Elephant?	1-2	3-4	5	6	7, 11 17, 18	8		9, 15	10, 16	13-14	

The Wobbly People
  in Ellen's Block House
Poppleton and the
  Grapefruit
	19-20	21-22	23	24	25, 29
					35, 36
						26		27, 33	28, 34	31-32	

The Workers Tools	37-38	39-40	41	42	43, 48 53, 54	44	45	46, 51	47, 52	49-50	
The Green Leaf Club News Three Little Bikers	55-56	57-58	59	60	61, 65 71, 72	62		63, 69	64, 70	67-68	
House Repair The Surprise	73-74	75-76	77	78	79, 84 89-90	80		81, 87	82, 88	85-86	83, 91

Unit 2

Zoom In!

	Family Times	Phonics	High-Frequency Words	Comprehension	Grammar	Vocabulary	Research and Study Skills	Phonics Review	Spelling	Selection Test	Writing Process
The Ugly Duckling / Duck	93-94	95-96	97	98	99, 104 109-110	100	101	102,107	103,108	105-106	
Eye Spy / Seeing	111-112	113-114	115	116	117,121 127-128	118		119, 125	120, 126	123-124	
Furry Mouse / Two Mice	129-130	131-132	133	134	135,139 145-146	136		137, 143	138, 144	141-142	
The Old Gollywampus / Snakes	147-148	149-150	151	152	153,157 163-164	154		155, 161	156, 162	159-160	
Spiders Up Close / Anansi and the Talking Melon	165-166	167-168	169	170	171,176 181-182	172		173, 179	174, 180	177-178	175, 183

Unit 3

Side By Side

	Family Times	Phonics	High-Frequency Words	Comprehension	Grammar	Vocabulary	Research and Study Skills	Phonics Review	Spelling	Selection Test	Writing Process
How I Beat the Giants / Play Ball	185-186	187-188	189	190	191,195 201-202	192		193, 199	194, 200	197-198	
The Storykeeper / People, People, Everywhere!	203-204	205-206	207	208	209,213 219-220	210		211, 217	212, 218	215-216	
New Best Friends / Wanted: Best Friend	221-222	223-224	225	226	227,231 237-238	228		229, 235	230, 236	233-234	
Four Clues for Chee Young Cam / Jansen and the Dinosaur Game	239-240	241-242	243	244	245, 250 255-256	246	247	248, 253	249, 254	251-252	
A Good Laugh for Cookie / Moonbear's Pet	257-258	259-260	261	262	263,268 273-274	264		265, 271	266, 272	269-270	267, 275

Unit 4

Ties Through Time

	Family Times	Phonics	High-Frequency Words	Comprehension	Grammar	Vocabulary	Research and Study Skills	Phonics Review	Spelling	Selection Test	Writing Process
Hear the Cheers / The Great Ball Game	1-2	3-4	5	6	7, 11 17-18	8		9, 15	10, 16	13-14	
Birthday Joy / The Best Older Sister	19-20	21-22	23	24	25, 29 35-36	26		27, 33	28, 34	31-32	
Treasure Pie / Bruno the Baker	37-38	39-40	41	42	43, 47 53-54	44		45, 51	46, 52	49-50	
Paul Goes to the Ball / The Rooster Who Went to His Uncle's Wedding	55-56	57-58	59	60	61, 65 71-72	62		63, 69	64, 70	67-68	
Yawning Dawn / Missing: One Stuffed Rabbit	73-74	75-76	77	78	79, 84 89-90	80		81, 87	82, 88	85-86	83, 91

Unit 5

All Aboard!

	Family Times	Phonics	High-Frequency Words	Comprehension	Grammar	Vocabulary	Research and Study Skills	Phonics Review	Spelling	Selection Test	Writing Process
Space Dreams / Man on the Moon	93-94	95-96	97	98	99, 104 109-110	100	101	102, 107	103, 108	105-106	
Two Lunches at the Mill / Going to Town	111-112	113-114	115	116	117,121 127-128	118		119, 125	120, 126	123-124	
A True Boating Family / Riding the Ferry with Captain Cruz	129-130	131-132	133	134	135,139 145-146	136		137, 143	138, 144	141-142	
Splash! / Down in the Sea: The Jellyfish	147-148	149-150	151	152	153,157 163-164	154		155, 161	156, 162	159-160	
Tex and the Big Bad T. Rex / Let's Go Dinosaur Tracking!	165-166	167-168	169	170	171,176 181-182	172		173, 179	174, 180	177-178	175, 183

Unit 6

Just Imagine!

	Family Times	Phonics	High-Frequency Words	Comprehension	Grammar	Vocabulary	Research and Study Skills	Phonics Review	Spelling	Selection Test	Writing Process
The Clubhouse Lemonade for Sale	185-186	187-188	189	190	191,196 201-202	192	193	194, 199	195, 200	197-198	
Start Collecting! It's Fun! The Puddle Pail	203-204	205-206	207	208	209,213 219-220	210		211, 217	212, 218	215-216	
Stone Soup: A Folktale Stone Soup	221-222	223-224	225	226	227,231 237-238	228		229, 235	230, 236	233-234	
A Good Idea Annie's Gifts	239-240	241-242	243	244	245,249 255-256	246		247, 253	248, 254	251-252	
Wicker School Takes Action City Green	257-258	259-260	261	262	263,268 273-274	264		265, 271	266, 272	269-270	267, 275

Family Times

Franny and Ginny   Daddy, Could I Have an Elephant?

What We Like

We like to splash . . . .
And swim all day . . . .
We like to throw . . . .
Our ball and play . . . .

We like to snack . . . .
On three fresh plums
We drink some milk . . . .
Then tap our drums . . . .

We like to clap . . . .
And play guitars . . . .
We like to sleep . . . .
Under the stars . . . .

This rhyme includes words your child is working with in school: words with short *a*, *i*, and *u* vowel sounds (*splash, drink, drums*) and blends with *l*, *r*, and *s* (*play, fresh, stars*). Sing "What We Like" with your child, and then make a list of things your family likes to do.

(fold here)

Name: _____

You are your child's first and best teacher!

Here are ways to help your child practice skills while having fun!

Day 1 Look through magazines and newspapers with your child, and cut out simple words that begin with *l*, *r*, and *s* blends. These are words like *block, drop,* or *spoon.* Glue the words on separate sheets of paper labeled with the individual blends such as *bl, cl, fl, pl, cr, dr, gr, st, sm, sn,* and so on.

Day 2 Ask your child to write or tell you a story in which he or she is the main character. Have your child include the following words the children are learning to read: *could, have, need, then, was.*

Day 3 Before reading a story together, tell your child the name of the story and have him or her look through the illustrations. Ask your child to predict what the story will be about.

Day 4 Ask your child to say or write sentences about himself or herself and draw pictures to match the sentences.

Day 5 Have your child tell you about something that he or she likes to do. Remind your child to use full sentences when speaking.

Read with your child EVERY DAY!

Spin, Read, and Rhyme

Materials   paper circle, white paper, pencil, paper clip, 1 button per player

Game Directions

1. Make a simple spinner as shown.

2. Players take turns spinning the spinner and moving their buttons on the gameboard.

3. The player reads the word on the space and says a rhyming word.

4. The first player to reach the end wins!

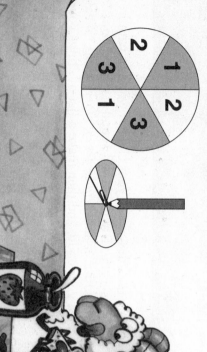

Start	tin	bun	rat
			tan
tub	pit	pal	sun
man			
cub	ram	luck	run
			fin
fish	miss	rib	nap
bit			
kiss	mat	fun	jam
			but
			End

Name _____

Say the word for each picture.
Write a, i, or **u** to finish each word.

cat   p**i**n   t**u**b

1.

n ____ t

2.

b ____ g

3.

m ____ tt

4.

b ____ g

5.

h ____ m

6.

g ____ m

7.

f ____ sh

8.

b ____ s

Draw a picture for each word.

9. rug

10. pig

Notes for Home: Your child identified words with the short *a* sound in *mat,* the short *i* sound in *win,* and the short *u* sound in *luck.* **Home Activity:** Work with your child to write a story using the words pictured above.

Level 2.1   **Phonics: Short** *a, i, u*   **3**

Name _____

Circle a word to finish each sentence.
Write the word on the line.

<u>st</u>ar

---

grabs   grins

- - - - - - - - - - - - - -

1. He _____ his things.

---

drives   drips

- - - - - - - - - - - - -

2. Al's dad _____ .

---

spring   splash

- - - - - - - - - - - - -

3. Al makes a big _____ .

---

grin   glad

- - - - - - - - - - - - -

4. Al's _____ is big.

---

swim   smell

- - - - - - - - - - - - -

5. Al likes to _____ .

Notes for Home: Your child wrote words with *l*, *r*, and *s* blends. **Home Activity:** Look through
a children's dictionary with your child to see how many words begin with the following
blends: *bl, cl, fl, gl, pl, sl, br, cr, dr, fr, gr, pr, tr, sc, sk, sm, sn, sp, st, sw,* and *str.*

Name _____

Pick a word from the box to finish each sentence.
Write the word on the line.

could	have	need	then	was

1. Bess _____ sad.

2. "I _____ a pet," she said.

3. "I _____ get a hippo."

4. "You can _____ a cat," her dad said.

5. _____ Bess was happy.

Notes for Home: This week your child is learning to read the words *could, have, need, then,* and *was.* **Home Activity:** Write these words on slips of paper. Take turns picking a word and using it in a sentence.

Name _____

Read the sentences and **look** at the pictures.
Follow the directions.

Kelly is a good ball player.
Wade passes Kelly the ball.

1. Circle the sentence that tells what will happen next.

   Kelly will not score.   Kelly will score.

2. Draw a picture to show what you think will happen next.

Chad missed the bus to the game.
Mike's mom stops to give him a ride.

3. Circle the sentence that tells what will happen next.

   Chad will get in the car.   Chad will walk home.

4. Draw a picture to show where Chad will go next.

Notes for Home: Your child made predictions about what will happen next in a story.
Home Activity: Read the beginning of a story with your child. Ask your child to tell you what
he or she thinks will happen next. Then read on to find out if the prediction came true.

6 Predicting   Level 2.1

A **sentence** is a group of words that tells a complete idea.

This is a sentence: Jon likes to play ball.
This is not a sentence: To play.

Read each group of words.
Write S if the words make a complete sentence.
Write N if the words do **not** make a complete sentence.

_____   1. Pam ran to the game.

_____   2. Met Flo there.

_____   3. Pam and Flo.

_____   4. Pam passed the ball to Flo.

Write a complete sentence about Pam and Flo.

5. _____

_____

Notes for Home: Your child identified complete sentences and wrote a complete sentence.
Home Activity: Ask your child to tell you a story. Encourage him or her to use complete sentences when speaking.

Name _____

Pick a word from the box to match each clue.
Write the word on the line.

| apartment | could | elephant | have |
| need | pianos | quiet | then |

1.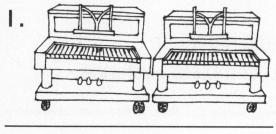

_____

2.

_____

3. hold or own

_____

4. Dogs _____ water.

_____

5. not loud

_____

6. a place to live

_____

7. was able to

_____

8. next

_____

Notes for Home: Your child wrote words that he or she learned to read this week.
Home Activity: Work with your child to write a story using as many of these words as possible.

Name _____

Say the word for each picture.
Write g or c to finish each word.

<u>g</u>erbil   <u>c</u>ircus

1.	2.	3.	4.
	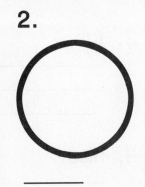		
_____ iant	_____ ircle	_____ iraffe	_____ em

5.	6.	7.	8.

_____ ym	_____ ent	_____ ereal	_____ eiling

Find the word that has the same beginning sound as the picture.
Mark the space to show your answer.

9. ⊂⊃ get
   ⊂⊃ germ
   ⊂⊃ give

10. ⊂⊃ center
    ⊂⊃ crib
    ⊂⊃ cat

 Notes for Home: Your child reviewed words with initial consonants *g* and *c* with the consonant sounds heard in *gerbil* and *circus*. **Home Activity:** Help your child use each word beginning with *g* or *c* above in a sentence.

bat   that   fit   this   cub   mug

Write the word from the box that rhymes with each word below.

1. rug
   _____
   _ _ _ _ _ _ _ _ _ _
   _____

2. tub
   _____
   _ _ _ _ _ _ _ _ _ _
   _____

3. hit
   _____
   _ _ _ _ _ _ _ _ _ _
   _____

4. hiss
   _____
   _ _ _ _ _ _ _ _ _ _
   _____

Write two words from the box that rhyme with **cat**.

5.
   _____
   _ _ _ _ _ _ _ _ _ _
   _____

6.
   _____
   _ _ _ _ _ _ _ _ _ _
   _____

Pick a word from the box to finish each sentence.
Write the word on the line.

could   have

   _____
   _ _ _ _ _ _ _ _ _

7. I asked my dad if I _____ get a gerbil.

   _____
   _ _ _ _ _ _ _ _ _

8. We _____ gerbils in my classroom at school.

Notes for Home: Your child spelled words with the short *a, i,* and *u* sound *(bat, fit,* and *cub)*
and two frequently used words: *could, have.* **Home Activity:** Say each spelling word. Have
your child use it in a sentence. Say the word again and have your child write it down.

Name _____

Match words from column A with words from column B to make complete sentences.
Write the sentences on the lines.

A	B
Sid wanted	got a fish.
He went	to a pet store.
Sid	a new pet.
It	was a big fish.
He named	it Jaws.

I. _____

2. _____

3. _____

4. _____

5. _____

Notes for Home: Your child combined words to form complete sentences.
Home Activity: Have your child write a story about an animal that would make an interesting pet. Remind your child to use complete sentences.

Test-Taking Tips

1. Write your name on the test.

2. Read each question twice.

3. Read all the answer choices for the question.

4. Mark your answer carefully.

5. Check your answer.

Part 1: Vocabulary

Find the word that best fits in each sentence.
Mark the space for your answer.

1. Sam saw the _____ at the zoo.
   - ⬭ trap
   - ⬭ must
   - ⬭ elephant

2. Lin will _____ some pie.
   - ⬭ could
   - ⬭ slip
   - ⬭ have

3. Will you please be _____ ?
   - ⬭ apartment
   - ⬭ are
   - ⬭ quiet

4. Dan and Ben are good _____ .
   - ⬭ pianos
   - ⬭ company
   - ⬭ running

5. Do I _____ a hat?
   - ⬭ hear
   - ⬭ then
   - ⬭ need

GO ON ➡

Part 2: Comprehension

Read each question.
Mark the space for your answer.

6. What is Daddy doing at first?
   - ⬭ eating
   - ⬭ sleeping
   - ⬭ jumping

7. What kind of pet will Tony get?
   - ⬭ a bird
   - ⬭ a whale
   - ⬭ a dog

8. Tony asks for a —
   - ⬭ sheep.
   - ⬭ piano.
   - ⬭ tub.

9. Why isn't an elephant a good pet for Tony?
   - ⬭ It talks too much.
   - ⬭ It likes to play.
   - ⬭ It is too big.

10. This story is mostly about —
    - ⬭ playing a game.
    - ⬭ getting a pet.
    - ⬭ feeding the elephants.

STOP

Name _____

off

gra**ss**

do**ll**

mi**tt**

Pick a word from the box to match each picture.
Write the word on the line.

| ball | bill | cliff | cuff | dress | glass | kiss | mutt |

1.
_____

2.
_____

3.
_____

4.
_____

5.
_____

6.
_____

7.
_____

8.
_____

Find the word that has the same ending sound as the picture.
Mark the space to show your answer.

9.
- ⬭ stiff
- ⬭ miss
- ⬭ cup

10.
- ⬭ class
- ⬭ grind
- ⬭ tall

Notes for Home: Your child reviewed words ending with the double consonants *ff, ss, ll,*
and *tt.* **Home Activity:** Describe a word on this page and ask your child to guess the word.
(For example: *This is something you throw.* Answer: *A ball.*)

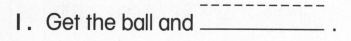

bat	that	fit	this	cub	mug

Pick a word from the box to finish each sentence.
Write the word on the line.

1. Get the ball and _____ .

2. Does the mitt _____ your hand?

Pick a word from the box to finish each rhyme.
Write the word on the line.

3. Did you see _____ ?

   It was a black cat.

4. Did you see a _____ ?

   It was in the tub.

5. What is _____ ?

   It is just a kiss.

6. Look in the _____ .

   I see a bug.

Write the word from the box that fits in each puzzle.

could	have

7. ▢▢▢▢▢

8. ▢▢▢▢

Notes for Home: Your child spelled words with short vowels *a, i,* and *u* and two frequently used words: *could, have.* **Home Activity:** Together, make up a story using the spelling words. Write it but leave blanks for the spelling words. Ask your child to fill in the blanks.

RETEACHING

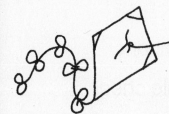

The kite   This is not a sentence.
It does not tell what the kite does.
The kite flies high. This is a sentence.
It tells what the kite does.

A **sentence** is a group of words that tells a complete idea.

Underline each group of words that is a sentence.

1. **a.** The wind blows.
   b. The wind

2. **a.** Two girls fly kites.
   b. Two girls

3. **a.** One boy
   b. One boy runs.

4. **a.** Did a string break?
   b. A string

5. **a.** His kite
   b. Does his kite go up?

6. **a.** One kite
   b. One kite falls.

7. **a.** The kite flies far.
   b. The kite

8. **a.** The girls
   b. The girls try again.

9. **a.** The boy
   b. The boy holds on tight.

10. **a.** The children have fun.
    b. The children

Notes for Home: Your child identified complete sentences. *Home Activity:* Say a sentence to your child, such as *Bob went to the park.* Ask your child whether it is a sentence or not. Do the same with an incomplete sentence, such as *The tree.*

Name _____

Circle each group of words that is a sentence.

1. Horses pull the wagons.

2. The race

3. Are the teams fast?

4. One wagon

5. Two dogs bark.

6. The people cheer.

7. The driver yells.

8. Our team wins.

Write each sentence you circled.

9. _____

10. _____

11. _____

12. _____

13. _____

14. _____

Notes for Home: Your child identified and wrote complete sentences. **Home Activity:** Write several sentences on strips of paper with your child. Cut the sentences in half, mix the papers, and have your child recombine them into sentences.

Let's Get Along

Let's get along. It's not hard to do,
If you help me, and I help you.
Let's lend a hand. Let's make the bed.
Let's paint the fence and paint the shed.
Let's lend a hand. Let's feed our pet.
Let's wash the pots. Let's not get wet.

Let's lend a hand. Let's dust and mop.
Let's make a list. Let's go and shop.
Let's stop our jobs. It's time to rest.
We get along. We do our best.
We get along. It's not hard to do,
When you help me, and I help you.

This rhyme includes words your child is working with in school: words with the short *e* sound (*b*e*d*), words with the short *o* sound (*m*o*p*), and words with final consonant blends (*along, help, hand, paint, list*). Sing "Let's Get Along" with your child. Act out the song as you sing.

(fold here)

Name: _____

1

You are your child's first and best teacher!

Here are ways to help your child practice skills while having fun!

Day 1   Write a simple short *e* word, such as *red*. Have your child change one letter to make a new word with a short *e* sound, such as *bed*. Take turns changing *bed* to *beg*, and so on. Repeat the activity with a short *o* word, such as *log*.

Day 2   Ask your child to write or say a funny story that uses any of the following words the children are learning to read: *live, made, people, taste, your*.

Day 3   After you read a story to your child, ask who the characters are. Then ask your child to tell you one or two things about each character.

Day 4   Ask your child to say or write sentences about people or objects in your home. Then have him or her identify the subject of each sentence—who or what the sentence is about.

Day 5   Draw pictures of people who are important to your child. Help your child write a complete sentence to go with each picture.

Read with your child EVERY DAY!

Phonics Go Fish

Materials index cards, markers, or crayons

Game Directions

1. Use index cards to make a set of word cards and matching picture cards as shown on page 3.

2. Use 2 players. Mix cards and give each player four cards. Place the remaining cards face down in a pile.

3. Each player takes turns asking another player for a card matching one he or she is holding.

4. If another player does not have a matching card, the player must choose one from the pile.

5. Play until one player has no cards left in his or her hand. The player with the most pairs wins!

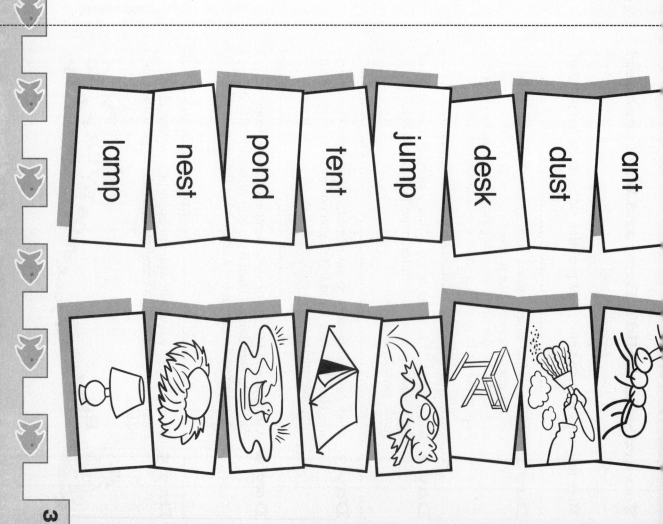

lamp nest pond tent jump desk dust ant

Name ______________________________

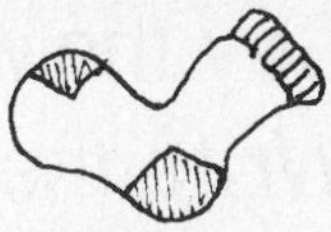

Say the word for each picture.
Write e or **o** to finish each word.

bed sock

1. h ____ n 

2. n ____ t 

3. d ____ g 

4. bl ____ ck 

5. t ____ nt 

6. m ____ n 

7. d ____ sk 

8. m ____ p 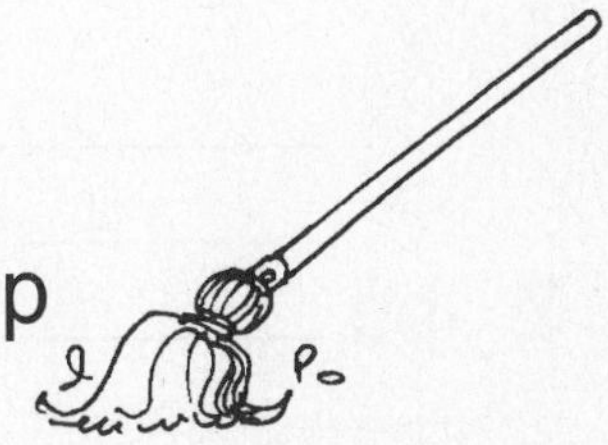

9. fr ____ g 

10. p ____ t 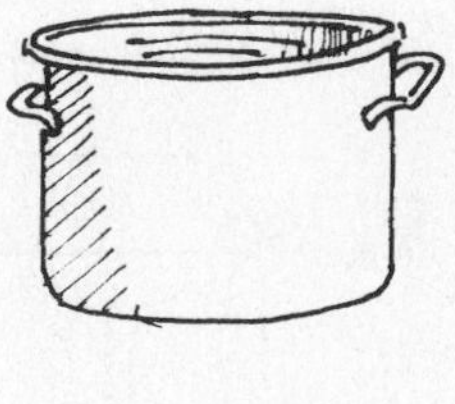

Notes for Home: Your child wrote words with the short *e* sound in *bed* and the short *o* sound in *sock*. ***Home Activity:*** Work with your child to write a story using the words pictured above.

Name _____

Say the word for each picture.
Write the letters from the box to finish each word.

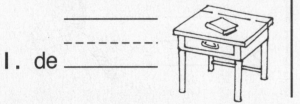
| ld | nd | sk | st | mp | nt |

a<u>nt</u>

1. de _____

2. la _____

3. chi _____

4. te _____

5. co _____

6. ju _____

7. ba _____

8. ne _____

9. sa _____

10. ce _____

Notes for Home: Your child completed words that end with the consonant blends *ld, nd, sk, st, mp,* and *nt.* **Home Activity:** Ask your child to find objects in your home with names that end with these blends. Together, write their names and draw pictures of the objects.

Name _____

Pick a word from the box to finish each sentence.
Write the word on the line.

| live | made | people | taste | your |

1. I _____ by a baker.

2. _____ go to his shop.

3. They _____ his rolls.

4. He _____ rolls for us.

5. Here is _____ roll.

Notes for Home: This week your child is learning to read the words *live, made, people, taste,* and *your.* **Home Activity:** Write these words on slips of paper and have your child practice reading them aloud to you.

Name _____

Read the story.
Follow the directions.
Answer the question.

The Park

Bill and Deb like to go to the park.

Bill sits on a bench and reads his book. Then he makes a big castle in the sandbox. Bill likes to sit still.

Deb plays on the swings. She runs and yells. She plays on the slide. Deb does *not* like to sit still.

After they finish playing, Bill and Deb ride their bikes home.

1. Circle the names of the two characters in the story.

2. Put one line under the sentences that tell what Bill does.

3. Put two lines under the sentences that tell what Deb does. _____
_____

4. Are you more like Bill or Deb? _____

5. Think of other things Bill and Deb might like to do. Draw pictures to show your ideas.

Deb | **Bill**

Notes for Home: Your child identified things that the characters in a story like to do.
Home Activity: Read a story to your child. Ask him or her to identify the characters and to tell one or two things about each one.

Name _____

The **subject** tells who or what does something.
The subject of this sentence is **man**.

The **man** fixed our door

Underline the subject in each sentence.
Draw a line from each sentence to the picture it matches.

1. The cat ran away.

2. Luke went to look for it.

3. Patty went to help Luke.

4. The cat was stuck in a tree.

5. The children helped the cat.

6.

7.

8.

9.

10.

Notes for Home: Your child identified subjects in sentences and matched each sentence to a picture. **Home Activity:** With your child, take turns saying simple sentences about something family members like to do. Then identify the subjects in the sentences.

Pick a word from the box to match each clue.
Write the word on the line.

hundred	knocked	outside
sick	taste	tears

1. eat a little bit

_____
- - - - - - - - - -

2. not inside

_____
- - - - - - - - - -

3.

_____
- - - - - - - - - -

4.

_____
- - - - - - - - - -

5. not well

_____
- - - - - - - - - -

6. what you get when you cry

_____
- - - - - - - - - -

 Notes for Home: Your child used clues to write words that he or she learned to read this week. *Home Activity:* Work with your child to write a story using as many of the listed words as possible.

Name _____

<u>c</u>one

<u>k</u>ite

clo<u>ck</u>

Say the word for each picture.
Write c, k, or ck to finish each word.

1. _____ orn

2. _____ itchen

3. _____ id

4. so _____

5. bla _____

6. du _____

7. _____ ab

8. _____ ast

Find the word that has the same beginning sound as the picture.
Mark the space to show your answer.

9. ⬭ kit
   ⬭ circus
   ⬭ tar

10. ⬭ cent
    ⬭ bar
    ⬭ came

Notes for Home: Your child reviewed words with the consonants *c, k,* and *ck,* such as *cone,*
kite, and *clock.* **Home Activity:** Have your child use words with the consonants shown above
in a sentence.

| sand | land | send | desk | lost | last |

Write the words from the box that end with each pair of letters.

sk   1. _____

st   2. _____   3. _____

nd   4. _____   5. _____   6. _____

Pick a word from the box to finish each sentence.
Write the word on the line.

7. Did you _____ Ned a letter?

8. I sent it _____ week.

Pick a word from the box to match each picture.
Write the word on the line.

taste
people

9.  _____   10. _____

Notes for Home: Your child spelled words that end with *nd, sk,* and *st* and two frequently
used words: *taste, people.* **Home Activity:** Say each spelling word twice. Have your child spell
it aloud and use it in a sentence.

Name _____

Look at the picture.
Write a subject to finish each sentence.
Use the words in the box. Use each group of words only once.

| The swings | Deb | Hal and Deb | The park | Birds |

1. _____ like to play.

2. _____ go up and down.

3. _____ pushes Hal.

4. _____ fly by the swings.

5. _____ is a fun place to play.

Notes for Home: Your child wrote subjects to complete sentences. **Home Activity:** Read a simple story with your child. Have him or her identify the subject in each sentence. Remind your child that the subject tells who or what does something.

Test-Taking Tips

1. Write your name on the test.

2. Read each question twice.

3. Read all the answer choices for the question.

4. Mark your answer carefully.

5. Check your answer.

Part 1: Vocabulary

Find the word that best fits in each sentence.
Mark the space for your answer.

1. Who _____ on the wall?
   - ⬭ quiet
   - ⬭ need
   - ⬭ knocked

2. Greg took a _____ of the cake.
   - ⬭ taste
   - ⬭ company
   - ⬭ tears

3. After he ate, he went _____ .
   - ⬭ help
   - ⬭ outside
   - ⬭ apartment

4. He jumped up and down one _____ times.
   - ⬭ could
   - ⬭ quiet
   - ⬭ hundred

5. "Oh, I feel _____ ," said Greg.
   - ⬭ have
   - ⬭ sick
   - ⬭ song

GO ON ➤

Part 2: Comprehension
Read each question.
Mark the space for your answer.

6. What does Poppleton do first?
    - ⬭ He goes to the store.
    - ⬭ He eats some grapefruit.
    - ⬭ He watches TV.

7. Why does Poppleton get some grapefruit?
    - ⬭ He wants to live a long time.
    - ⬭ He is sick.
    - ⬭ He wants to make his lips go away.

8. Where does most of this story take place?
    - ⬭ at school
    - ⬭ in Poppleton's house
    - ⬭ outside

9. Who is very old?
    - ⬭ Poppleton
    - ⬭ Uncle Bill
    - ⬭ Hudson

10. What can you tell about Poppleton from this story?
    - ⬭ He does not like grapefruit.
    - ⬭ He eats too much.
    - ⬭ He has no friends.

STOP

Pick a blend from the box to finish each word.
Write the blend on the line.

| bl | cr | dr | fr | gr | sp | st | thr |

 **gr**ape**fr**uit

---

1.

_____ apes

2.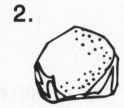

_____ one

3.

_____ ess

4.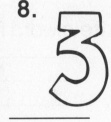

_____ og

5.

_____ ab

6.

_____ ock

7.

_____ ider

8.

_____ ee

Find the word that has the same beginning blend as the picture.
Mark the space to show your answer.

9. ⚬ trunk
⚬ three
⚬ bee

10. ⚬ press
⚬ flop
⚬ spill

 Notes for Home: Your child reviewed blends using *l, r,* and *s* as in <u>*block*</u>, <u>*crab*</u>, and *spoon*.
Home Activity: Work with your child to write words with *l, r,* and *s* blends on separate index cards. Illustrate these words on other cards. Have your child match words and pictures.

Name _____

| sand | land | send | desk | lost | last |

Write the word from the box that means the opposite of each word below.

1. first

   _____

2. found

   _____

3. get

   _____

Write two words from the box that rhyme with **hand**.

4. _____

5. _____

Write a word from the box to match the picture.

6. _____

Pick a word from the box to finish each sentence. **Write** the word on the line.

taste
people

7. I like the _____ of grapefruit.

8. Some _____ eat it every day.

Notes for Home: Your child spelled words that end with *nd, sk,* and *st* and two frequently used words: *taste, people.* **Home Activity:** Work with your child to write a short story that uses the spelling words. Encourage your child to use as many of the words as possible.

Name _____

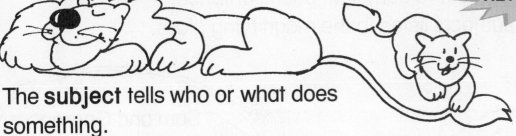

The **subject** tells who or what does something.

A lion sleeps by the tree.   **The baby** plays with the tail.

Circle the subject of each sentence.

1. The puppy brings the toy.

2. The kitten rolls the ball.

3. Birds sit on the branch.

4. A squirrel runs up a tree.

5. A fox hides in a bush.

Choose a simple subject for each sentence. **Write** it on the line.

6. The _____ crawls to a rock.

7. The _____ swims in the pond.

8. A _____ hops into the water.

9. A _____ lands on a flower.

10. A _____ makes a big splash.

duck
beaver
frog
turtle
bee

Notes for Home: Your child identified subjects as the parts of sentences that tell who or what does something. **Home Activity:** Ask your child questions about his or her classmates and what they do. Have your child identify the subjects in his or her responses.

Find the subject to complete each sentence.
Use the subjects listed in the magnifying glass.

Sam and George
Fingerprints
The cookie thieves
The cookie jar
Alex

1. _____ is missing!

2. _____ are missing too.

3. _____ will collect everyone's fingerprints.

4. _____ are never the same.

5. _____ will be found!

Notes for Home: Your child added subjects to sentences. *Home Activity:* Help your child write sentences about family members. Remind your child that the subject of a sentence tells who or what does something.

The Workers

What Will They Make?

Pete will use his tools to make
One delicious chocolate cake.
Pete will make it taste so nice.
There are cherries in each slice.

Pete will place it on a plate.
Then he'll share it. Don't be late!
Rose will use her tools to make
One white shed down by the lake.

Rose will make it in the shade.
She will work until it's made.
Rose will place her bike inside.
When it's time, she'll take a ride.

This rhyme includes words your child is working with in school: words with long vowels with final *e* (*make, nice*), and words that begin with *ch, th, sh,* and *wh.* Sing "What Will They Make?" along with your child. As you sing the rhyme, clap your hands for each word with a long vowel sound.

(fold here)

1

Name: _____

You are your child's first and best teacher!

Here are ways to help your child practice skills while having fun!

Day 1 Write *ch, th, sh,* and *wh* on separate sheets of paper. Work with your child to list words that begin with each pair of letters, such as *cherry, things, share,* and *whale.*

Day 2 Ask your child to write or say sentences that use any of the following words that the children are learning to read: *clean, many, use, work, world.*

Day 3 Before reading a book together, ask your child to look through the illustrations. Then ask your child to make predictions about the mood of the story. (Ask: *Is it happy or sad?*)

Day 4 Ask your child to draw a picture. Then have him or her write one or two sentences to describe what is happening in the picture.

Day 5 Ask your child to tell you about something he or she did in school this week. Encourage your child to use complete sentences when speaking.

Read with your child EVERY DAY!

4

Cover Up

Materials 1 game card per player, 16 buttons or other game markers per player

Game Directions

1. Use the words below to make game cards for each player like the one shown. Words should be in a different order for each card.

2. Write the 16 words below on slips of paper. Players take turns picking a word and reading it aloud.

3. Players use buttons to cover the words called.

4. The first player to cover a row of words across, down, or diagonally wins!

Game Card Words

use, rule, flute, tune, rake, make, plate, shade, bone, phone, rope, pole, slice, rice, bike, ride

use	rule	flute	tune
rake	make	plate	shade
bone	phone	rope	pole
slice	rice	bike	ride

Name _____

 g<u>a</u>te

Say the word for each picture.
Circle the words that have the same long vowel sound.

1.

cube

| mule | prune | mud |
| tube | use | bone |

2.

cake

| plane | brave | cane |
| sale | that | snake |

3.

rope

| rose | hose | stone |
| stop | phone | slope |

4.

kite

| pile | dime | slide |
| shine | kit | drip |

5.

nose

| hose | bone | flop |
| not | froze | poke |

 Notes for Home: Your child identified words with long vowel sounds that follow the pattern consonant-vowel-consonant-*e* (cube, cake, robe, kite, nose). **Home Activity:** Work with your child to write sentences using the long-vowel words listed above.

Level 2.1   **Phonics: Long Vowels with Final *e*   39**

Name _____

Say the word for each picture.
Write the letters from the box to finish each word.

cherry

| ch | sh | th | wh |

1. _____ eel

2. _____ ip

3. _____ ick

4. _____ umb

5. _____ air

6. _____ irt

7. _____ ree

8. _____ ale

Draw a picture for each word.

9. child

10. shark

Notes for Home: Your child completed words that begin with the consonants *ch, th, wh,* and *sh.* **Home Activity:** Point to the words your child completed. Have your child read each word aloud.

Pick a word from the box to finish each sentence.
Write the word on the line. Use each word only once.

| clean | many | use | work | world |

_____

1. There are _____ kinds of tools.

_____

2. Mops and brooms _____ floors.

_____

3. Farmers _____ with tractors.

_____

4. Chefs _____ tools to cook.

_____

5. People around the _____ use tools.

Notes for Home: This week your child is learning to read the words *clean, many, use, work,* and *world. Home Activity:* Write and show your child these words. Have your child use each word in a sentence and draw a picture to go with it.

Read the text below.
Follow the directions.

How to Make a Tree House
by Ted Stone

You can make a treehouse.
You need wood, a hammer, a saw,
and nails.
First you build the floor.
Next you build the walls.
Then you put on the roof.
You can paint the tree house if you like.
Then invite your friends to come play!

1. Circle the name of the author.

2. Circle the word that tells what the text is all about.

   tree houses   paint   walls

3. Underline the things you need to make a tree house.

4. Circle the part of the tree house that you build first.

5. Tell why you think the author wrote this text.

   _____
   -
   _____
   _____
   -
   _____

Notes for Home: Your child wrote about a nonfiction text and told why an author wrote it.
Home Activity: Read a nonfiction article or story to your child. Ask him or her to identify
who wrote the material and tell why the writer may have written it.

Name _____

The **predicate** tells what the subject does.
Opens the can is the predicate.

The man **opens** the **can**.

Look at each picture.
Circle a predicate to finish each sentence.

---

1. The doctor _____ .

   looks in Tim's ear

   checks Tim's nose

---

2. Stan _____ .

   cleans the stove

   washes the car

---

3. Patty _____ .

   rides her bike

   fixes the wheel

---

4. Hal _____ .

   uses a brush

   looks at his paper

---

5. Bob's mom _____ .

   drinks milk

   cuts lemons

Notes for Home: Your child chose a predicate, the part of a sentence that tells what the subject does, to complete each sentence. *Home Activity:* Take turns with your child saying simple sentences and identifying the predicate for each sentence.

Pick a word from the box to match each clue.
Write the word on the line.

| clean   easier   farm   fix   tools   use   world   write |

1.

_____

- - - - - - - - - - - - - - - -

_____

2.

_____

- - - - - - - - - - - - - - - -

_____

3. what you do to
   something broken

_____

- - - - - - - - - - - - - - - -

_____

4. what you do to
   something dirty

_____

- - - - - - - - - - - - - - - -

_____

5. what you do with a tractor

_____

- - - - - - - - - - - - - - - -

_____

6. what you do with
   a paper and pen

_____

- - - - - - - - - - - - - - - -

_____

7. not harder

_____

- - - - - - - - - - - - - - - -

_____

8. We _____ a saw to cut.

_____

- - - - - - - - - - - - - - - -

_____

Notes for Home: Your child used clues to write vocabulary words that he or she learned to read
this week. **Home Activity:** Work with your child to write a story using as many of these words
as possible.

Name _____

Read the map.
Follow the directions below.

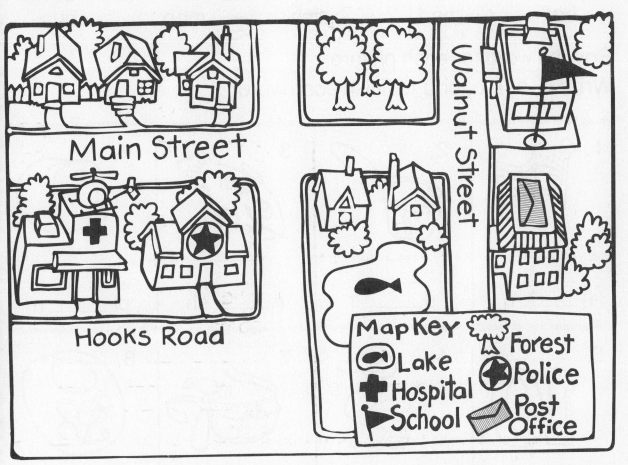

1. Color the lake blue.

2. Color the school red.

3. Circle the name of the street where the hospital is.

4. Draw a path to show how to get from the school to the hospital.

5. Put a box around the name of the street where the post office is.

Notes for Home: Your child practiced reading a simple map. **Home Activity:** Draw a simple map of your neighborhood. Take your child on a walk. Have him or her identify places on the map. Encourage your child to add to the map.

Name _____

b**a**t   b**e**d   d**i**sh   m**o**p   b**u**s

Say the word for each picture.
Write a, e, i, o, or u to finish each word.

1. fl ___ g

2. p ___ t

3. f ___ sh

4. pl ___ m

5. t ___ n

6. d ___ ck

7. b ___ lt

8. b ___ b

Find the word that has the same middle sound as the picture.
Mark the space to show your answer.

9. ⬭ drag
   ⬭ dig
   ⬭ dog

10. ⬭ boss
    ⬭ bank
    ⬭ bug

 Notes for Home: Your child reviewed words with short vowel sounds as heard in b**a**t, b**e**d, p**i**g, m**o**p, and b**u**s. **Home Activity:** Say a word with a short vowel sound. Have your child name as many rhyming words as he or she can. Try it with another vowel sound.

Name _____

| child | chin | chip | shape | ship | shut |

Write the words from the box that begin with the letters at the top of each column.

sh

1. _____

3. _____

5. _____

ch

2. _____

4. _____

6. _____

Pick a word from the box to match each clue.
Write the word on the line.

7. It is on your face.

_____

8. It is something to eat.

_____

Pick a word from the box to finish each sentence.
Write the word on the line.

use
world

9. This globe shows the _____ .

10. You can _____ it to find faraway places.

Notes for Home: Your child spelled words that begin with *ch* and *sh* (*chin*, *ship*).
Home Activity: Write each spelling word leaving two or three spaces blank in each word, for example: _ _ i l d (child). Have your child fill in the missing letters.

Name _____

Underline the predicate in each sentence.
Draw a picture to show what is happening in each sentence.

1. We use tools to cook.   2.

3. Mom cooks with a pot.   4.

5. Bill cleans the pan.   6.

7. Dad cuts the cake.   8.

9. Jan mixes with a spoon.   10.

Notes for Home: Your child identified the predicate, or action part, in sentences and drew
pictures to show each action. *Home Activity:* Read a simple story with your child. Have him
or her identify the predicates in several sentences.

Name _____

Part 1: Vocabulary

Find the word that best fits in each sentence.
Mark the space for your answer.

1. They will _____ the boat with water.
   - ⬭ write
   - ⬭ clean
   - ⬭ fix

2. My job is _____ than yours.
   - ⬭ good
   - ⬭ again
   - ⬭ easier

3. They _____ on flat land.
   - ⬭ farm
   - ⬭ tools
   - ⬭ need

4. May I _____ your bike?
   - ⬭ read
   - ⬭ use
   - ⬭ call

5. We live in a big _____ .
   - ⬭ world
   - ⬭ boy
   - ⬭ school

GO ON ➡

Part 2: Comprehension

Read each question.
Mark the space for your answer.

6. Which people use tools to dig?
   - ⬭ teachers
   - ⬭ cooks
   - ⬭ farmers

7. From this story, you can tell that —
   - ⬭ only grown-ups use tools.
   - ⬭ tools cost a lot money.
   - ⬭ tools have many uses.

8. The author wrote this story to —
   - ⬭ make fun of people.
   - ⬭ tell about tools.
   - ⬭ teach you to work faster.

9. Which sentence tells what the story is mostly about?
   - ⬭ "Tools help us in many ways."
   - ⬭ "We can even eat with tools!"
   - ⬭ "People use tools to make things."

10. People can use tools when they —
    - ⬭ read books.
    - ⬭ walk.
    - ⬭ fix cars.

Name _____

wind   **world**   **help**   **tent**

Circle the word for each picture.

1. 	2. 	3. 	4. 
child chair	bend bed	call cold	gulp gum

5. 	6. 	7. 	8. 
play plant	bad band	ant at	cell cent

Find the word that has the same ending sound as the picture.
Mark the space to show your answer.

9. ⃝ ham
   ⃝ hint
   ⃝ blind

10. ⃝ tall
    ⃝ flap
    ⃝ told

 Notes for Home: Your child reviewed words that end with *ld, lp, nd,* and *nt.* **Home Activity:** Write a word that ends with each of the blends. Have your child build new words by changing the beginning letters, *cold* becomes *mold,* for example.

| child | chin | chip | shape | ship | shut |

Pick a word from the box to match each picture.
Write the word on the line.

1.

_____
- - - - - - - - - - - - -
_____

2.

_____
- - - - - - - - - - - - -
_____

3.

_____
- - - - - - - - - - - - -
_____

Write three words from the box that have the same beginning sound as .

_____   _____   _____
- - - - - - - - - - - -   - - - - - - - - - - - -   - - - - - - - - - - - -
4. _____   5. _____   6. _____

Pick a word from the box to match each clue.
Write the word on the line.

use   world

_____
- - - - - - - - - - - - -

7. You could see this from a spaceship. _____

_____
- - - - - - - - - - - - -

8. You _____ tools to fix things. _____

Name _____

RETEACHING

The **predicate** tells what the subject is or does.

The girls **feed the fish.**

The fish **eat the food.**

Circle the predicate in each sentence.

1. Yesterday Sam called a friend.

2. His friend came over.

3. They played three games.

4. The friend went home.

5. Sam ate dinner.

Choose a predicate from the box for each sentence.
Write it on the line.

go to the lake.
swims with us.
fly in the sky.
is warm and still.

6. We _____

_____

7. The water _____

_____

8. Mom _____

_____

9. The birds _____

Notes for Home: Your child identified and wrote predicates in sentences. *Home Activity:* Write two sentences. Have your child underline the predicate in each sentence. Then have your child write two new sentences, using the same predicates.

Grammar: Predicates **53**

Draw a line from each subject to the predicate that matches it.

1. The fall   is a pretty time of year.

2. Many colorful leaves   rakes the leaves.

3. My brother   hide nuts in trees.

4. Sarah and I   jump in the leaves.

5. Some squirrels   are on the ground.

Write a predicate to finish each sentence.

6. My friends and I _____

_____

_____ .

7. At school we _____

_____

_____ .

Notes for Home: Your child identified and wrote predicates in sentences. *Home Activity:* Write three sentences, and cut the paper between the subject and predicate. Have your child put the sentences back together correctly.

The Safety Song

We're the team you need to meet.
We're the team that can't be beat!

Sneakers will protect your feet.
Check your wheels. Check your seat.

Check each tire for a leak.
Practice safely every week.

On a steep hill, watch your speed.
There are signs you need to read.

Bring a drink and lunch along.
Teach each friend this safety song!

This rhyme includes words your child is working with in school: words with the long *e* sound spelled *ee* and *ea (meet, beat)* and words ending in *ch, ng, tch*. Read "The Safety Song" aloud together. Find all the long *e* words and sort them by their *ea* or *ee* spellings.

(fold here)

Name: _____

You are your child's first and best teacher!

Here are ways to help your child practice skills while having fun!

Day 1 Write a list of long *e* words spelled *ea* and *ee*, such as *bean, flea, seat, tree, green, three*. Help your child draw pictures for these words and write a sentence for each picture.

Day 2 Ask your child to write or say sentences that use any of the following words that your child is learning to read: *should, their, through, very, would*.

Day 3 After reading a story, ask your child to tell you about the story's setting. Ask questions such as: *Where does the story take place? Does it take place today or a long time ago?*

Day 4 Choose a subject that is particularly interesting to your child, such as a favorite hobby. Take turns asking and answering questions about the subject.

Day 5 Read a nonfiction story to your child, and then discuss it. Encourage him or her to ask thoughtful questions about the subject.

Read with your child EVERY DAY!

4

Mix and Match

Materials index cards, markers or crayons

Game Directions

1. Use index cards to make a set of word cards and matching picture cards as shown.

2. Mix the cards and place each card face down. Players take turns choosing two cards to try to find a match.

3. Players keep any matching pairs. If players do not pick a match, they return the cards face down to their original positions.

4. Play until all matches have been made. The player with the most pairs at the end wins!

---

branch	bench	lunch	fish

dish	wash	moth	teeth

crutch	watch	string	king

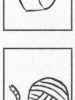

Name _____

These bees only fly past words with the **long e** sound.
Draw a line to show the path from the bees to the tree.

Start jeep tent

beans

pets

belt beet jeans

egg

bed

letter wheat

End

three 3 feet

Notes for Home: Your child identified words with long *e* sounds spelled *ea* and *ee* as in *leaf* and *tree*. **Home Activity:** Work with your child to make picture cards of the long *e* words above. Draw a picture on the front of a card and write the word for it on the back.

Name _____

Circle a word to finish each sentence.
Write the word on the line.

wren**ch**

---

wash   watch   wish
_____
- - - - - - - - - - - - -

1. Jon will _____ his bike.

---

lunch   bunch   bench
_____
- - - - - - - - - - - - -

2. He sits on a _____ to eat.

---

what   watch   wash
_____
- - - - - - - - - - - - -

3. He likes to _____ the birds.

---

pad   path   pat
_____
- - - - - - - - - - - - -

4. He rides on the _____ .

---

long   song   son
_____
- - - - - - - - - - - - -

5. He sings a _____ .

Notes for Home: Your child completed sentences by choosing words that end with *th, ch, ng, sh,* or *tch.* **Home Activity:** Read a simple story with your child. As you find words with these endings, ask your child to read the words aloud.

Name _____

Pick a word from the box to finish each sentence.
Write the word on the line.

| should | their | through | very | would |

1. Jill and Bill ride _____ bikes.

2. They ride _____ the park.

3. They know they _____ always wear helmets.

4. They are _____ safe riders.

5. They _____ like to ride every day.

Notes for Home: This week your child is learning to read the words *should, their, through, very,* and *would.* **Home Activity:** Help your child write a story using as many of the words as possible. Draw pictures to illustrate the story.

Read each story.

Underline the sentence that tells where the story takes place.

Draw a picture that shows where the story takes place.

1. Last week Anne rode her bike to the animal park. She saw seals and birds. Then she ate a snack.

2.

3. Cal and Ben slept in their backyard. They had a tent. Their mom made them some popcorn and gave them flashlights.

4.

Write the name of a story you have read.

Draw a picture that shows where the story takes place. It can be a real place or make-believe. It can take place now or long ago.

5. _____

Notes for Home: Your child identified the setting of a story. *Home Activity:* Read a story to your child. Ask questions such as: *Is this a real or make-believe place? Is it long ago or now?* Have your child tell you where and when the story takes place.

A **statement** is a sentence that tells something.
It begins with a capital letter.
It ends with a ▪.

It is fun to ride bikes.

A **question** is a sentence that asks something.
It begins with a capital letter.
It ends with a **?**.

Is it fun to ride bikes?

Read each sentence.
Write the correct end mark on the line to finish each sentence.

1. Where did Sally and Stu ride _____

2. They rode to the park _____

3. Did Sally ride up the hill _____

4. Sally did not ride up the hill _____

Write a statement that tells something about the picture.

_____

5. _____

_____

Notes for Home: Your child used periods and question marks to punctuate statements and
questions. *Home Activity:* Take turns asking each other questions and giving answers using
statements.

Pick a word from the box to match each clue.
Write the word on the line.

climb everywhere giggled should spray through

1. go from one side to another

_____

_____

2. laughed

_____

_____

3. in all places

_____

_____

4. You_____ask your mom.

_____

_____

5.

_____

_____

6.

_____

_____

Notes for Home: Your child used clues to write vocabulary words that he or she learned this
week. *Home Activity:* Work with your child to write a story using as many of these words as
possible.

Name _____

 rake   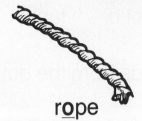 bike    rope    mule

Circle the word for each picture.

1. 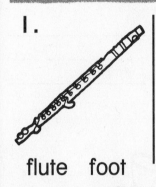	2. 	3. 	4. 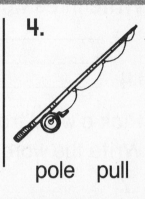
flute foot	plane plan	kit kite	pole pull

5. 	6. 	7.	8. 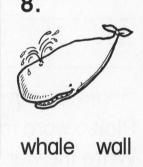
ton tune	cub cube	dim dime	whale wall

Find the word that has the same vowel sound as the picture.
Mark the space to show your answer.

9. ☐ nose
   ☐ not
   ☐ now

10. ☐ fill
    ☐ fit
    ☐ five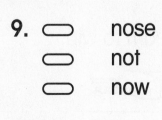

 Notes for Home: Your child identified words with long vowels that follow the pattern: consonant-vowel-consonant-*e*. **Home Activity:** Write *rake, bike, rope,* and *mule.* Challenge your child to make new long vowel words by changing one or two letters lof each word.

leaf	meal	team	deep	free	seen

Write three words from the box with **ee**.

1. _____   2. _____   3. _____

Write three words from the box with **ea**.

4. _____   5. _____   6. _____

Pick a word from the box to match each clue.
Write the word on the line.

7. _____

8. _____

Pick a word from the box to finish each sentence.
Write the word on the line.

should	their

9. Bikers _____ always wear helmets.

10. Pam and Jake want _____ team to win.

Notes for Home: Your child spelled words with the long *e* vowel sound spelled *ea* and *ee* as in *leaf* and *deep* and two frequently used words: *should, their.* **Home Activity:** Say each spelling word twice. Have your child spell the word aloud.

Look at the picture. **Read** each question.
Write a statement to answer each question.

1. What is on the seat?

_____

- -

_____

2. Is the bike on the grass or on the path?

_____

- -

_____

3. Whose bike is it?

_____

- -

_____

4. Where is Tim sitting?

_____

- -

_____

Write a question about the picture.

_____

- -

5. _____

Notes for Home: Your child wrote statements and questions. *Home Activity:* Take turns
asking and answering questions about a topic that you and your child find interesting.

Test-Taking Tips

1. Write your name on the test.

2. Read each question twice.

3. Read all the answer choices for the question.

4. Mark your answer carefully.

5. Check your answer.

Part 1: Vocabulary

Find the word that best fits in each sentence.
Mark the space for your answer.

1. I can _____ to the top.
   - ⊂⊃ fix
   - ⊂⊃ climb
   - ⊂⊃ clean

2. Jim got wet from the _____ of water.
   - ⊂⊃ spray
   - ⊂⊃ world
   - ⊂⊃ spider

3. Ali _____ at the funny story.
   - ⊂⊃ drew
   - ⊂⊃ took
   - ⊂⊃ giggled

4. You _____ eat your lunch.
   - ⊂⊃ about
   - ⊂⊃ should
   - ⊂⊃ long

5. We rode _____ the grass.
   - ⊂⊃ through
   - ⊂⊃ everywhere
   - ⊂⊃ after

GO ON ➤

Part 2: Comprehension

Read each question.
Mark the space for your answer.

6. You can tell at the beginning of the story that —
   - ⬭ it was a nice day.
   - ⬭ a storm was coming.
   - ⬭ it was almost night.

7. What made the bikers' shirts puff out like sails?
   - ⬭ the flags
   - ⬭ the wind
   - ⬭ their packs

8. The tracks in the grass were made by —
   - ⬭ the bikes' tires.
   - ⬭ three little snakes.
   - ⬭ the bikers' feet.

9. Where did the bikers spend most of their time?
   - ⬭ in a puddle
   - ⬭ on the hill
   - ⬭ in a gully

10. What helps the bikers when they ride at night?
    - ⬭ having a flag that flaps
    - ⬭ bringing a lunch
    - ⬭ turning on their headlights

STOP

Name _____

white   **sh**irt   **th**orn   **ch**est

Say the word for each picture.
Write wh, sh, th, or **ch** to finish each word.

1. _____ eep

2. _____ orts

3. _____ eel

4. _____ erry

5. _____ umb

6. _____ imp

7. _____ ovel

8. _____ ale

Find the word that has the same beginning sound as the picture.
Mark the space to show your answer.

9.
◯ cheek
◯ shine
◯ flip

10.
◯ chain
◯ plane
◯ green

 Notes for Home: Your child reviewed words that begin with *wh*, *sh*, *th*, and *ch* as in *whale*, *shirt*, *thorn*, and *chest*. **Home Activity:** Ask your child to read aloud the words above that begin with these letter pairs. Together, write a story using some of these words.

leaf	meal	team	deep	free	seen

Pick a word from the box to match each picture.
Write the word on the line.

1. _____
   _ _ _ _ _ _ _ _ _
   _____

2. _____
   _ _ _ _ _ _ _ _ _
   _____

3. _____
   _ _ _ _ _ _ _ _ _
   _____

Pick a word from the box to finish each rhyme.
Write the word on the line.

_____
_ _ _ _ _ _ _ _ _

4. Please _____ my kite from the tree.

_____
_ _ _ _ _ _ _ _ _

5. Have you ever _____ a frog that's not green?

_____
_ _ _ _ _ _ _ _ _

6. You don't hear a peep from the fish in the _____ .

Write the word from the box that fits in each puzzle.

should   their

7. | | | | |
   |-|-|-|-|

8. | | | | | |
   |-|-|-|-|-|

Notes for Home: Your child spelled words with long *e* spelled *ee* and *ea* and two frequently used words: *should, their.* **Home Activity:** Read the spelling words to your child. Have him or her write each word down and then use it in a sentence about himself or herself.

RETEACHING

One fish jumps.   Does the bear get the fish?

Begin a **statement** with a capital letter. End a statement
with a **.** . Begin a **question** with a capital letter. End a
question with a **?** .

Underline each statement.
Circle each question.

1. The deer eats leaves.

2. Squirrels find nuts.

3. Do birds eat worms?

4. Can you see the horses run?

5. Do bees like flowers?

6. Mice chew grass.

7. Does the fox hunt?

8. A bear sleeps.

Underline the correct statement or question in each pair.

9. a. The owl calls.

   b. the owl calls

10. a. a rabbit hides

    b. Can a rabbit hide?

11. a. Do you hear the bird
       sing?

    b. the bird sings

12. a. The toad hops.

    b. the toad hops

Notes for Home: Your child identified statements and questions. *Home Activity:* Pick a room
in your home and have your child ask questions about where things are in the room. Then ask
your child questions about a different room.

Name _____

Write these sentences correctly.
Use a period or a question mark at the end.

is there a gorilla in my room

_____

- - - - - - - - - - - - - - - - - - -

_____

i saw a shadow on the wall

_____

- - - - - - - - - - - - - - - - - - -

_____

it was near my bed

_____

- - - - - - - - - - - - - - - - - - -

_____

was it big

_____

- - - - - - - - - - - - - - - - - - -

_____

it was bigger than my dad

_____

- - - - - - - - - - - - - - - - - - -

_____

Notes for Home: Your child wrote statements and questions. *Home Activity:* Play a round robin question game with your child and others. Write a simple question and hand it to the next person. He or she will answer the question and write a new question.

Family Times

House Repair

The Surprise

Sally's Messy Room

Sally had a very messy room.
Robby helped her clean it with a broom.

Molly sorted shoes and folded socks.
Jimmy picked up toys and stacked the blocks.

Betty washed and brushed the tiny pet.
Tommy cleaned the fish tank with a net.

Sally had a party for us all.
We jumped and jumped and then played ball.

Sally cooked a very tasty treat.
She thanked us all. We said, "Let's eat!"

This rhyme includes words your child is working with in school: words with the long e sound spelled e and y (we, party) and words ending with -ed (jumped). Sing "Sally's Messy Room" with your child. Act out the song as you sing the words.

(fold here)

Name: _____

You are your child's first and best teacher!

Here are ways to help your child practice skills while having fun!

Day 1 Write a list of long e words spelled e and y such as we, be, she, happy, very, penny. Have your child use these words to make up sentences about helping others.

Day 2 Work with your child to write short rhyming sentences that include any of these words: house, never, off, these, took.

Day 3 When reading together, encourage your child to use the illustrations to draw conclusions about the characters' feelings and actions. Ask questions such as: Why is the boy smiling in this picture?

Day 4 Ask your child to say or write several sentences that tell something interesting about himself or herself.

Day 5 Have your child tell you a simple story. Encourage your child to make up a story with a beginning, middle, and end.

Read with your child EVERY DAY!

Race to the Top

Materials paper circle, pencil, paper clip, 1 button

Game Directions

1. Make a spinner as shown.

2. Each player takes turns spinning the spinner and moving his or her button up a ladder.

3. Player reads the word landed on and uses it in a sentence.

4. The first player who reaches the top of his or her ladder wins!

me	looked
party	jumped
penny	licked
she	cooked
very	stayed
maybe	filled
messy	helped
sandy	rolled
windy	banged
dirty	talked

Name _____

Underline the word in each sentence that has the **long e** sound.
Write the word on the line.

me   penny

1. Di has a messy room.

_____

2. She wants it to look nice.

_____

3. Bill is happy to help her.

_____

4. He likes to put toys away.

_____

5. Di is lucky to have a pal like Bill.

Notes for Home: Your child identified words with the long *e* sound spelled *e* and *y (me, penny)*. **Home Activity:** Write five simple long *e* words spelled *e* or *y*. Ask your child to read the words to you.

Level 2.1   Phonics: Long *e: e, y*   **75**

Name _____

Add -ed to the word in ( ).
Write the new word on the line to finish each sentence.

push + ed = push**ed**

1. Vera and Gail _____ in the leaves.　(play)

2. Then they _____ in the pile.　(jump)

3. Dad _____ them play.　(watch)

4. The girls _____ make a new pile.　(help)

5. The leaves _____ up two bags!　(fill)

Notes for Home: Your child formed and used words that end with *-ed* as in *picked.*
Home Activity: Write words that end with *-ed.* Have your child say each word aloud and use it in a sentence about someone in his or her family.

Name _____

Pick a word from the box to finish each sentence.
Write the word on the line.

house	never	off	these	took

1. _____ leaves are a mess!

2. Greg _____ wants to rake.

3. Becky _____ the rake.

---

4. Greg gets a bag from the _____ .

---

5. Now all the leaves are _____ the ground!

Notes for Home: This week your child is learning to read the words *house, never, off, these,* and *took.* **Home Activity:** Have your child use these words to write or say a story about helping someone.

Name _____

Look at the picture.
Circle the word that best finishes each sentence.
Write the word on the line.

sad   happy

_____
- - - - - - - - - - - - -

1. The girl is _____ .

book   mom

_____
- - - - - - - - - - - - -

2. She wants her _____ .

sad   happy

_____
- - - - - - - - - - - - -

3. The boy wants to make her _____ .

pencil   toy

_____
- - - - - - - - - - - - -

4. He gives her a _____ .

Write a sentence about how you think the girl feels now.

_____
- -

5. _____

_____
- -

Notes for Home: Your child used text and illustrations to draw conclusions about a story.
Home Activity: As you read a story to your child, stop often to ask your child to think about
what is happening or why a character is doing something.

A sentence that tells you to do something is a **command**.
In every command the subject is *you*, but *you* is not shown.
This is a command: **Pick up the socks.**

A sentence that shows surprise or strong feelings is an **exclamation**.
Put an exclamation mark **!** at the end of an exclamation.
This is an exclamation: **That is a big dog!**

Read each sentence.
Write C on the line if the sentence is a command.
Write E on the line if the sentence is an exclamation.

_____ 1. Come help us clean the yard.

_____ 2. What a mess this is!

_____ 3. Hold the bag open.

Write one command and one exclamation on the lines below.

4. _____

5. _____

Notes for Home: Your child identified commands and exclamations. *Home Activity:* Say
aloud simple sentences, including commands and exclamations. Have your child raise a hand
when he or she hears a command and tap his or her foot for each exclamation.

Pick a word from the box to match each clue.
Write the word on the line.

guess	house	never	pile
pleased	surprised	never	tomorrow

1. happy

   _____

2. not ever

   _____

3. day after today

   _____

4. a place to live

   _____

5. a stack of things

   _____

6.

7. an answer you are
   not sure of

   _____

   _____

Notes for Home: Your child used clues to write words that he or she learned to read this week. **Home Activity:** Take turns using each vocabulary word in a sentence.

Name _____

Circle the word for each picture.   <u>le</u>af   t<u>ee</u>th

1.	2.	3.	4.

 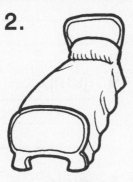  

beach bench	bead bed	suds seeds	sell seal

5.	6.	7.	8.

sheep ship	buns beans	tree trip	best bees

Find the word that has the same middle sound as the picture.
Mark the space to show your answer.

9. ⊂⊃ best
   ⊂⊃ bake
   ⊂⊃ bean

10. ⊂⊃ fed
    ⊂⊃ feed
    ⊂⊃ felt

 Notes for Home: Your child reviewed words with long *e* spelled *ea* and *ee* as in *leaf* and *teeth*. **Home Activity:** Write *leaf* and *teeth*. Have your child build new long *e* words by changing some of the consonants, for example, *leaf* becomes *lean* or *leap*.

wished	crossed	jumped	picked	pulled	pushed

Add -ed to each base word below to make a word from the box.
Write the word on the line.

1. push _____

_____

2. pull _____

_____

3. cross _____

_____

4. jump _____

_____

5. wish _____

_____

6. pick _____

_____

Pick a word from the box to finish each sentence.
Write the word on the line.

_____

7. He _____ a flower.

_____

8. She _____ rope.

Pick a word from the box to match each clue.
Write the word on the line.

house   never

_____

9. People can live in one of these.

_____

10. It means "not ever."

_____

Notes for Home: Your child spelled words that end with *-ed* and two frequently used words:
house, never. **Home Activity:** Say each base word. Have your child add *-ed.*

Name _____

Put sentences in an order that makes sense.

The room was dark.
I turned on the light.
People jumped out and yelled, "Surprise!"

Use the sentences to tell a story.
Write 1, 2, 3, 4 to show the order of the story.

_____ **a.** Then they saw land before them.

_____ **b.** The two cats jumped into a silver boat.

_____ **c.** They landed the boat on a sandy beach.

_____ **d.** They sailed for days across the blue sea.

Write a sentence that tells what might happen next.

_____
_____
_____

Notes for Home: Your child put sentences in order to tell a story. *Home Activity:* Write a paragraph from a favorite story but mix up the order of the sentences. Have your child reorder the sentences in an order that makes sense.

Read each sentence.
Underline the commands.
Circle the exclamations.

1. This room is a mess!

2. Please pick up the toys.

3. Dust the shelf.

4. Sweep the floor too.

5. This is a great surprise for Dad!

Write a **·** or an **!** to finish each sentence.

6. It sure is cold out today ____

7. Wear a hat and mittens ____

8. That's the most snow I've ever seen ____

Write one command and one exclamation.

9. _____

10. _____

Notes for Home: Your child identified and wrote commands and exclamations.
Home Activity: Have your child tell you a story about a time he or she surprised someone. Encourage your child to use both commands and exclamations in the story.

Name _____

Part I: Vocabulary

Find the word that best fits in each sentence.
Mark the space for your answer.

1. Jim lives in a big red _____ .
   ⬭ tool   ⬭ never   ⬭ house

2. Did you _____ the right answer?
   ⬭ clean   ⬭ climb   ⬭ guess

3. We will go to the zoo _____ .
   ⬭ tomorrow   ⬭ everywhere   ⬭ perfect

4. Sal put all her toys in a _____ .
   ⬭ pile   ⬭ pleased   ⬭ world

5. Leo was _____ to see a cow in school.
   ⬭ pretty   ⬭ surprised   ⬭ done

GO ON

Part 2: Comprehension

Read each question.

Mark the space for your answer.

6. Frog wanted to surprise Toad because —
   - ⬭ Frog and Toad were friends.
   - ⬭ Frog was mean.
   - ⬭ Frog did not like Toad.

7. Why did Frog run through the woods?
   - ⬭ He wanted to find a new friend.
   - ⬭ He did not want Toad to see him.
   - ⬭ He wanted to see the leaves on the trees.

8. As Frog ran through the woods, Toad was —
   - ⬭ sleeping.
   - ⬭ raking his own yard.
   - ⬭ running to Frog's house.

9. You can tell that both Frog and Toad like to —
   - ⬭ play in piles of leaves.
   - ⬭ help each other.
   - ⬭ sleep late in the morning.

10. Do you think Frog was surprised when he got home?
    - ⬭ Yes, because his front yard was clean.
    - ⬭ No, because he knew Toad had raked his yard.
    - ⬭ No, because the yard looked the same as before.

STOP

ri**ng**   tee**th**   bran**ch**   bru**sh**   wa**tch**

Pick letters from the box to finish each word.
Write the letters on the line.

ng   th   ch
sh   tch

1.

ba _____

2.

scra _____

3.

in _____

4.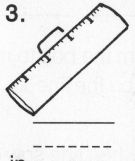

bu _____

5.

di _____

6.

wi _____

7.

ba _____

8.

pi _____

Find the word that has the same ending sound as the picture.
Mark the space to show your answer.

9. ◯ lash
        ◯ catch
        ◯ sing

10. ◯ fish
         ◯ reach
         ◯ path

 Notes for Home: Your child reviewed words that end with *ng, th, ch, sh,* and *tch.* **Home Activity:** Write words that end with these letter combinations on index cards. Hide the cards in your home. When your child finds a card, have him or her read the word aloud.

Name _____

 wished   crossed   jumped   picked   pulled   pushed

Write a word from the box to match each picture.

1.

2.

3.

_____

_____

Pick a word from the box to match each clue.
Write the word on the line.

_____

4. Jo did this when she saw a star.

_____

5. You did this to get across the street. _____

_____

6. Bob's dad did this to Bob's swing. _____

Pick a word from the box to finish each sentence.
Write the word on the line.

house
never

_____

7. Vera and her dad live in a big _____ .

_____

8. She _____ stays home alone.

 Notes for Home: Your child spelled words that end with *-ed* and two frequently used words: *house, never.* **Home Activity:** Play charades with your child. One person acts out a spelling word while the other tries to guess and spell it.

RETEACHING

Look at those trees.   What a huge forest!

Look at those trees. is a command.
It tells someone to do something.
What a huge forest! is an exclamation.
It shows strong feeling.

A **command** gives an order.
It ends with a ▮.
An **exclamation** shows strong feeling.
It ends with an ❗.

Circle each command.
Underline each exclamation.

1. Put the hammer away.

2. Pick up the crayons.

3. How tired we are!

4. How lucky that we are ready now!

5. Clear the stage.

6. What a funny play this will be!

Notes for Home: Your child identified commands and exclamations. *Home Activity:* Write simple sentences on cards. Show each card to your child and help him or her to restate the sentence as either a command or an exclamation.

Use a period after each command.
Use an exclamation mark after each exclamation.

1. Walk to that ride _____

2. What a long line _____

3. Find a seat _____

4. Lock your seat belt _____

5. How high up we are _____

6. What a fun ride _____

Write each command and exclamation.
Use a capital letter and the correct end mark.

7. look for Aunt Meg

_____

_____

8. how far away she seems

_____

_____

9. wave to her

_____

_____

10. i'm so happy to see her

_____

_____

Notes for Home: Your child identified and wrote commands and exclamations. *Home Activity:* Together, look at pictures of friends and family members, or pictures from magazines. Have your child write one command and one exclamation about the pictures.

Name _____

Correct each sentence.
Write it on the line.
Hint: Each sentence should end with a **.** , a **?** , or an **!** .

1. Look at the big dog

_____
- -
_____

2. Is the dog nice

_____
- -
_____

3. The dog barked

_____
- -
_____

4. Go away, cats

_____
- -
_____

5. We must run fast

_____
- -
_____

 Notes for Home: Your child corrected sentences by adding end marks. *Home Activity:* Write
sentences without end marks on slips of paper. Have your child pick a slip of paper and then
rewrite the sentence, adding a question mark, a period, or an exclamation mark.

Words I Can Now Read and Write

Changes Shout hooray!

There are changes every day.
Night is turning into day.
When the blue sky turns to gray,
Clouds will hide the sun away.
Rain will make the daisies grow.
Rainbows may appear, you know!

There are changes every day.
April's turning into May.
My friend Ray has moved away.
I am feeling sad today.
I grow older on this day.
It's my birthday

This rhyme includes words your child is working with in school: words with the long *a* sound spelled *a, ai,* and *ay (changes, rain, may)* and verbs that end in *-s, -es,* and *-ing (turns, changes, feeling).* Sing "Changes" with your child, raising your hands each time a long *a* word is sung.

(fold here)

Name: _____

You are your child's first and best teacher!

Here are ways to help your child practice skills while having fun!

Day 1 Write several simple sentences containing verbs that end with *-s, -es,* or *-ing,* such as *takes, pushes, falling.* Help your child read each sentence and draw a picture for it.

Day 2 Write the words *keep, mother, myself, new,* and *warm* on index cards. Take turns drawing two cards at a time. Try using both words in one sentence.

Day 3 Find two pictures of two different settings, such as New York City and Yosemite National Park. Challenge your child to think of how the places are alike and different.

Day 4 Make up sentences and leave blanks where the nouns would be. Have your child suggest nouns, silly or serious, that might be used in their places. *A dog drove the car!*

Day 5 Your child is learning to give directions. Ask him or her to give directions for doing something interesting, such as teaching a dog a new trick.

Read with your child EVERY DAY!

Long a Rhymes

Materials   1 button per player

Game Directions

1. Players take turns tossing buttons on the gameboard and saying as many words as possible that rhyme with the word landed on.

2. Players earn 1 point for each rhyming word said. The first player to get 15 points wins!

rain

cake

pail

hay

play

face

frame

mail

Name _____

Read each sentence.
Circle the word with the **long a** sound.
Write the word on the line.

n<u>ai</u>l

1. The ducklings play in the water. _____

2. Who is that waiting in the grass? _____

3. Will the cat stay? _____

4. The big ducks are not afraid of a cat. _____

5. The cat runs away as fast as it can. _____

Notes for Home: Your child identified words in which the long *a* sound is spelled *ai* or *ay* (nail, play). **Home Activity:** Have your child read and "collect" sentences with long *a* words. Together, draw a picture illustrating each sentence.

Name _____

Use the word in ( ) to finish each sentence.
Add -s, -es, or **-ing** to the word.
Write the new word on the line.

Ben shop**s**.   He push**es** a cart.   Ben is walk**ing**.

---

1. The hen _____ on her eggs. (sit)

2. She _____ "chirp, chirp, chirp." (hear)

3. Now one egg _____ . (hatch)

4. A chick _____ its way out. (push)

5. It is _____ up. (stand)

Notes for Home: Your child added *-s, -es,* and *-ing* to verbs—words that show action *(shops, pushes, walking).* **Home Activity:** Create sentences for your child like those above. Ask your child whether he or she would add *-s, -es,* or *-ing* to the verb to finish each sentence.

Name _____

Pick a word from the box to finish each sentence.
Write the word on the line. Use each word only once.

| keep | mother | myself | new | warm |

_____

1. That big dog is the pup's _____ .

_____

2. The dogs stay _____ in their bed.

_____

3. The pup knows a _____ game.

_____

4. She thinks, "I can carry the stick _____ ."

_____

5. The pup will not get to _____ the stick.

Notes for Home: This week your child is learning to read the words *keep, mother, myself, new,* and *warm.* ***Home Activity:*** Help your child use these words to write about a baby animal that he or she has seen.

Name _____

Read the words.
Write duck if it tells something about the duck.
Write duckling if it tells something about the duckling.
Write both if it tells something about them both.

duck   **duckling**

---

1. beak   _____

2. big   _____

3. little   _____

4. fuzzy down   _____

5. webbed feet   _____

Notes for Home: Your child identified the ways in which two things are alike and different.
Home Activity: Point out two household objects that have something in common, such as a
lamp and a flashlight. Ask your child to tell how they are alike and how they are different.

Name _____

A **noun** is a word that names something.
A noun can name a person, a place, an animal, or a thing.

Duck and **lake** are nouns.   The <u>duck</u> swims in the <u>lake</u>.

Read each sentence.
Circle all the nouns in each sentence.

1. This pond is not very deep.

2. Many pretty plants grow in the pond.

3. Fish like to hide in these weeds.

4. A duck gives a loud quack.

Circle all the nouns in the sentence.
Draw a picture for the sentence.

5. Big fish eat little bugs.

Notes for Home: Your child identified nouns—words that name people, places, animals, and things. ***Home Activity:*** Help your child find some outdoor pictures in a magazine. Have your child point to the things in the pictures and say the name of each one.

Circle a word to finish each sentence.

1. I am the _____ .

mother
myself

2. I take care of the eggs all by _____ .

mother
myself

3. I sat on my eggs and kept them _____ .

warm
new

4. Now is the time for my eggs to _____ .

paddle
hatch

5. Use your _____ to chip your way out!

beak
keep

6. Five _____ ducklings leave the nest.

keep
new

7. Do you want to _____ your new home?

surface
explore

8. Come and _____ in the water.

paddle
hatch

9. Stay on the water's _____ .

surface
warm

10. _____ close to me.

Mother
Keep

Notes for Home: Your child finished sentences using vocabulary words. *Home Activity:* Write each word your child circled on a slip of paper. Then have your child draw a slip, read the word on it, and use the word in a sentence. Keep the slips and add more words each week.

Name _____

Butterball Duck	Swan
It is small.	It is large.
It makes nests in hollow trees.	It makes big nests of grass and twigs beside the water.
It lays 10–12 eggs.	It lays 4–5 eggs.
It eats mostly small sea animals.	It eats mostly plants.

Use facts from the table to answer each question.
Circle or **write** the answer.

1. Which bird is bigger?   Butterball Duck   Swan

2. Where do Butterball Ducks make their nests?

   _____

   _____

3. What do swans use to make their nests?

   _____

   _____

4. Which bird lays more eggs?   Butterball Duck   Swan

5. Which bird eats mostly plants?   Butterball Duck   Swan

Notes for Home: Your child answered questions based on information in a table. *Home Activity:* Have your child make a table to record and compare facts about two animals. Think about the size, color, sound, and diet of each animal.

daisy

h<u>e</u>

Circle the word with the **long e** sound.

1.

muddy   pen

2.

we   men

3.

my   me

4.

hurry   race

5.

puppy   pet

6.

write   study

7.

baby   nest

8.

penny   cent

Find the word that has the same **long e** sound as the picture. Mark the space to show your answer.

9. ⬭ egg
   ⬭ be
   ⬭ blue

10. ⬭ ugly
    ⬭ cry
    ⬭ play

Notes for Home: Your child reviewed words with the long *e* sound spelled *y* and *e* (*daisy* and *he*). **Home Activity:** Have your child look through a story and find words that end in *y*. Discuss whether the *y* in each word stands for the long *e* sound.

passes   passing   teaches   teaching   wishes   wishing

Add -es and **-ing** to each word to make a word from the box.

		Add -es		Add -ing
wish	1.	_____	2.	_____
pass	3.	_____	4.	_____
teach	5.	_____	6.	_____

Write the word from the box that rhymes with each word below.

7. glasses

_____

8. peaches

_____

Pick a word from the box to finish each sentence.
Write the word on the line.

mother
myself

9. "I want to swim by _____ ," said the duckling.

10. His _____ shows him how.

Notes for Home: Your child spelled words that end with *-es* or *-ing,* such as *passes* and *passing,* and two frequently used words: *mother, myself.* **Home Activity:** Have your child make up a sentence using each spelling word. Then help your child write the sentence.

Name _____

Circle the noun in each group of words.

1. have   song   too   2. says   for   beaks

3. into   no   river   4. when   trees   high

5. father   am   over   6. reeds   away   has

7. always   went   bugs   8. new   little   jam

9. seems   animals   by   10. people   how   hot

Write a noun to finish each sentence.
Use a noun from the box.

> duck   feet   grass   pond   water

11. A duck is happy in the _____ .

12. The wind blows over the _____ .

13. A _____ can swim fast in the water.

14. A little duck has little _____ .

15. We will go to the _____ when it is noon.

Notes for Home: Your child reviewed nouns—words that name people, places, animals, and things. *Home Activity:* Write some simple sentences that your child can read, leaving out a noun in each sentence. Ask your child to suggest nouns to finish the sentence.

Part I: Vocabulary

Find the word that best fits in each sentence.
Mark the space for your answer.

1. The duck eats with its _____ .
   ⬭ beak   ⬭ surface   ⬭ house

2. You can _____ that hat.
   ⬭ paddle   ⬭ explore   ⬭ keep

3. I can read that book _____ .
   ⬭ around   ⬭ myself   ⬭ many

4. The ducks _____ through the water.
   ⬭ paddle   ⬭ fix   ⬭ farm

5. Bugs land on the _____ of the water.
   ⬭ warm   ⬭ surface   ⬭ tool

GO ON ➡

Part 2: Comprehension

Read each question.
Mark the space for your answer.

6. The mother duck sits on her eggs to —
   - ⊂⊃ hide them.
   - ⊂⊃ lay them.
   - ⊂⊃ keep them warm.

7. When can the duckling walk?
   - ⊂⊃ when it is two days old
   - ⊂⊃ as soon as it hatches
   - ⊂⊃ when it is one week old

8. How is a six-week-old duckling different from a one-week-old duckling?
   - ⊂⊃ It has webbed feet.
   - ⊂⊃ It has a beak.
   - ⊂⊃ It has white feathers.

9. Ducklings get food from —
   - ⊂⊃ the mother duck.
   - ⊂⊃ the water.
   - ⊂⊃ yellow down.

10. When the ducks grow up, what will they do?
    - ⊂⊃ talk
    - ⊂⊃ read
    - ⊂⊃ take care of ducklings

STOP

Pick the word that rhymes.
Write the word on the line.

hatch**ed**

---

1. pecked

nest   next   checked

- - - - - - - - - - - - - - - -

_____

2. rowed

toad   floated   slow

- - - - - - - - - - - - - - - -

_____

---

3. stayed

play   made   waited

- - - - - - - - - - - - - - - -

_____

4. nested

west   dressed   rested

- - - - - - - - - - - - - - - -

_____

---

5. smelled

melt   held   helped

- - - - - - - - - - - - - - - -

_____

6. missed

fizz   list   sled

- - - - - - - - - - - - - - - -

_____

Find the word that has the same ending sound as **lost**.
Mark the space to show your answer.

7. ⬭ moss
   ⬭ tossed
   ⬭ posted

8. ⬭ crossed
   ⬭ tested
   ⬭ close

 Notes for Home: Your child reviewed words that end in *-ed*. **Home Activity:** Point out words like these when you read with your child. Help your child say these words aloud. Discuss the different ways that words ending in *-ed* can sound as in *played, rested,* or *missed.*

Phonics: Inflected Ending *-ed* Review

passes passing teaches teaching wishes wishing

Change one or two letters in each word to make a word from the box.
Write the new word on the line.

1. dishes

   _____

   - - - - - - - - - - - - - - - -

   _____

2. beaches

   _____

   - - - - - - - - - - - - - - - -

   _____

3. passed

   _____

   - - - - - - - - - - - - - - - -

   _____

4. fishing

   _____

   - - - - - - - - - - - - - - - -

   _____

5. reaching

   _____

   - - - - - - - - - - - - - - - -

   _____

6. tossing

   _____

   - - - - - - - - - - - - - - - -

   _____

Pick a word from the box to finish each sentence.
Write the word on the line.

mother
myself

_____

- - - - - - - - - - - - - - - -

7. My _____ is teaching me to swim.

_____

- - - - - - - - - - - - - - - -

8. Soon I will swim by _____ .

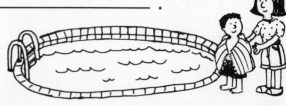

Notes for Home: Your child spelled words ending in *-es* or *-ing*, such as *passes* and *passing*, and two frequently used words: *mother, myself.* **Home Activity:** Help your child think of and spell words that rhyme with some of the spelling words on this page.

108 Spelling: Inflected Endings *-es, -ing*   Level 2.1

Name _____

RETEACHING

A **boy** rides a **bike** to his **house**.
He sees his **dog**.

The noun **boy** names a person.
The noun **house** names a place.
The noun **dog** names an animal.
The noun **bike** names a thing.

A **noun** names a person, place, animal, or thing.

Circle each noun. There may be more than one in each sentence.

1. My grandma is here.

2. Dad walks the dog.

3. My friend comes to my house.

4. My aunt calls on the telephone.

5. Mr. Jones cooks in his kitchen.

6. I play in my room.

7. Mom works in her office.

8. Grandpa works in the garden.

9. Dad shops at the store.

10. A bird sits by my window.

11. The cat licks her paw.

12. Our roof needs to be fixed.

Notes for Home: Your child identified nouns—words for people, places, animals, or things—in sentences. *Home Activity:* Read a story with your child and have him or her point out each noun on one page of the story.

Grammar: Nouns **109**

Name _____

Circle each noun that names a person or an animal.

1. My uncle lives by the sea.

2. Seagulls like to play in his yard.

3. My brother sits on the porch.

4. Sometimes my dog hides in the garage.

5. Our aunt shows us the flowers.

6. Neighbors bring food from the fair.

7. The family eats in the kitchen.

Circle each noun.
Write on each line a noun that names a place.

The father took the girl to the _____. Her friend

came too. There were many children swimming. A man pointed

to a boat and a whale in the _____. A woman

watched a baby. Some people walked to the _____.

Soon it was time to go to their _____.

Notes for Home: Your child identified nouns in sentences. *Home Activity:* Have your child
write as many nouns as possible on cards. Then he or she can categorize them as people,
places, animals, or things.

110 Grammar: Nouns

I Spy

I spy a bunny hopping by.
I spy a kite up in the sky.

I spy a star that is so bright.
I spy a bird that's taking flight.

I spy a firefly in July.
I spy a wagon rolling by.

I spy ice cream right nearby.
I spy chicken and a pizza pie.

I spy cider that I'll try.
I spy ivy that grows so high.

I spy a baby starting to cry.
Find these pictures. Play "I Spy!"

This rhyme includes words your child is working with in school: words in which the long *i* sound is spelled *i*, *igh*, *y*, and *ie (find, high, sky, pie)* and two-syllable words *(bunny, baby)*. After saying the rhyme, play "I Spy." Offer clues to items in the room with the long *i* sound for your child to guess.

(fold here)

Name: _____

You are your child's first and best teacher!

Here are ways to help your child practice skills while having fun!

Day 1 Write some two-syllable words, such as *because, away, mirror, carry,* and *hidden.* Help your child sound out each syllable as he or she reads the words aloud.

Day 2 Have your child write sentences using the words *because, carry, don't, goes,* and *whole.* Encourage your child to write both questions and statements.

Day 3 Perform a simple task, such as changing a light bulb. Ask your child to describe in order the steps in this process.

Day 4 Help your child make an address book of friends and relatives. Point out how each proper name and title, such as *Dr. Jensen* or *Mr. Gomez,* is capitalized.

Day 5 Help your child write a news story about an exciting neighborhood happening.

Read with your child EVERY DAY!

Spin a Word

Materials paper, paper clip, pencil,
1 button per player

Game Directions

1. Make a simple spinner as shown.

2. Place buttons on Start and take turns spinning the spinner.

3. If the word ending shown on the spinner can be combined with the letter or letters on the next gameboard space to make a word, player moves button to that space.

4. The first player to reach the end wins!

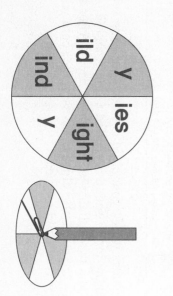

y	ies
ild	ight
ind	y

Start	Start
s	dr
cr	n
fl	r
l	wh
m	sk
f	fr
tr	sh
End	End

Name _____

Circle a word to finish each sentence.   sky   night   tie

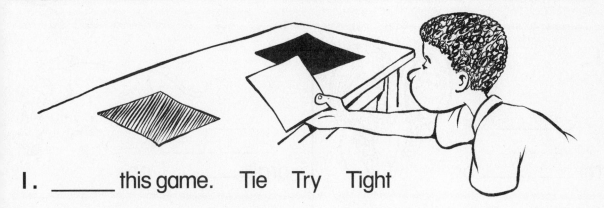

1. _____ this game.   Tie   Try   Tight

2. Play outside under a sunny _____ .   sky   sight   sigh

3. Now _____ some gray paper.   fly   fight   find

4. First put it _____ some black paper.   bright   by   hit

5. Then put it next to some white paper.
_____ does the gray paper look darker by the white paper?
Why   White   With

6. Do you think your eyes _____ ?   lie   light   lit

7. Things look darker after you see something _____ .
bright   bite   bring

Notes for Home: Your child completed sentences using long *i* sound spelled *i, igh, y,* and *ie*
(find, night, sky, tie). **Home Activity:** Say a letter. Have your child name a word that begins
with that letter and that contains the long *i* sound spelled *i, igh, y,* or *ie.*

Say the word for each picture.
Write the letter or letters from the box to finish each word.

| g | l | nd | pp | rr |

stu_d_ent

1. mi _____ or

2. dra _____ on

3. ca _____ ot

4. pu _____ y

5. ru _____ er

6. ti _____ er

7. sli _____ er

8. pa _____ a

Pick a word from the box to finish each sentence.
Write the word on the line.

| because | carry | don't | goes | whole |

1. The boy _____ to get the melon.

2. Can he _____ it?

3. I _____ think he can.

4. The _____ melon is too big.

5. He can carry a slice _____ it is small.

Notes for Home: This week your child is learning to read the words *because, carry, don't, goes,* and *whole.* **Home Activity:** Encourage your child to write an explanation of how some simple machine works, using as many of these words as possible.

Name _____

Look at the pictures. **Read** the steps.
Write a number from **1 to 5** to show the right order.
One is done for you.

_____ Tie strings through the holes.

_____ First, draw a big bowl on one side of a card.

_____ Last, use your thumbs and fingers to make the card spin fast. You will see a fish in a bowl!

3 Make a hole on one side of the card and then the other.

_____ Next, draw a fish on the other side of the card.

 Notes for Home: Your child put the steps of a process in the right order. **Home Activity:** Use an index card, string, and a hole punch to make the toy described above with your child.

Name _____

Proper nouns are special names for
people, places, animals, and things.
Proper nouns begin with **capital letters**.
Titles begin with capital letters.
Most titles end with a · .

Dr. Frank Chin

1. akron, ohio

_____

- - - - - - - - - - - - - -

2. lizzy

_____

- - - - - - - - - - - - - -

3. mrs ortiz

_____

- - - - - - - - - - - - - -

4. 12 oak drive

_____

- - - - - - - - - - - - - -

Draw a picture of a doctor.
Write a name for the doctor you drew.

5.

_____

- - - - - - - - - - - - - -

Notes for Home: Your child wrote proper nouns, including titles, using capital letters and
periods as needed. **Home Activity:** Have your child create his or her own business card,
inventing a company name. Check that capital letters and periods are used where needed.

Pick a word from the box to match each clue.
Write the word on the line.

| brain | hidden | messages | mirror | thumb | whole |

1.

_____

2.

_____

3. what you think with

_____

4. notes you write or tell
someone

_____

5. all of something

_____

6. can't be seen

_____

Notes for Home: Your child used clues to identify vocabulary words learned this week.
Home Activity: Make a picture dictionary with your child. Draw pictures and write simple
definitions for each word in the box.

Name _____

lady   mail   May

Circle the word with the **long a** sound.

1.

plant   snail

2.

radio   hand

3.

glass   tray

4.

track   train

5.

paper   pad

6.

map   crayons

7.

rag   paint

8.

hay   cat

Find the word that has the same **long a** sound as the picture.
Mark the space to show your answer.

9. ⬭ my
⬭ match
⬭ say

10. ⬭ lazy
⬭ pack
⬭ pal

Notes for Home: Your child reviewed words with the long *a* sound spelled *a, ai,* and *ay* as in *lady, mail,* and *May.* **Home Activity:** Have your child look through store ads and circle words in which the long *a* sound is spelled *a, ai,* or *ay.*

| bright | sight | line | side | sky | try |

Read the word at the top of each column.
Pick a word from the box that has the same spelling for the **long i** sound.
Write the word on the line.

why	smile	high
1. _____	3. _____	5. _____
2. _____	4. _____	6. _____

Pick a word from the box to match each clue.
Write the word on the line.

7. You see stars up there.

_____

8. star light, star _____

_____

Pick a word from the box to finish each sentence.
Write it on the line.

because
whole

9. I ate the _____ thing!

10. That's _____ it was so good!

Notes for Home: Your child spelled words with the long *i* sound spelled *igh, y,* and *i-consonant-e* as in *bright, try,* and *line* and two frequently used words: *because, whole.*
Home Activity: Have your child use the spelling words to write about looking at the stars.

Name _____

Write a proper noun that makes sense for each word below.
Use capital letters and periods as needed.
Draw a picture to match your proper noun.

1. doctor

_____

- - - - - - - - - - - - - - - - - -

_____

2.

3. dog

_____

- - - - - - - - - - - - - - - - - -

_____

4.

5. girl

_____

- - - - - - - - - - - - - - - - - -

_____

6.

7. teacher

_____

- - - - - - - - - - - - - - - - - -

_____

8.

9. state

_____

- - - - - - - - - - - - - - - - - -

_____

10.

Notes for Home: Your child wrote and drew pictures of proper nouns—special names for people, animals, places, and things. *Home Activity:* Help your child make a family tree, listing the family members by their full names.

Level 2.1

Grammar: Proper Nouns **121**

Test-Taking Tips

1. Write your name on the test.

2. Read each question twice.

3. Read all the answer choices for the question.

4. Mark your answer carefully.

5. Check your answer.

Part 1: Vocabulary

Find the word that best fits in each sentence.
Mark the space for your answer.

1. You use your _____ to think.
   ⊂⊃ beak   ⊂⊃ brain   ⊂⊃ thumb

2. Alex took two _____ for his dad.
   ⊂⊃ messages   ⊂⊃ world   ⊂⊃ surface

3. I can see you in the _____ .
   ⊂⊃ tomorrow   ⊂⊃ hidden   ⊂⊃ mirror

4. You have one _____ on each hand.
   ⊂⊃ thumb   ⊂⊃ time   ⊂⊃ beak

5. My sister ate the _____ cake!
   ⊂⊃ surprised   ⊂⊃ whole   ⊂⊃ pleased

GO ON

Part 2: Comprehension

Read each question.
Mark the space for your answer.

6. Your pupils let in just the right amount of light by changing —
   - ⬭ size.
   - ⬭ shape.
   - ⬭ color.

7. What happens first as the eye sees?
   - ⬭ Messages go to the brain.
   - ⬭ Light goes into the eye.
   - ⬭ A picture is made at the back of the eyeball.

8. Which of these did you find out from reading?
   - ⬭ Your eyeball is not really a ball.
   - ⬭ People who are far away are smaller.
   - ⬭ Your brain tries to make sense of what you see.

9. Which is a good title for this story?
   - ⬭ "Two Dogs in a Vase"
   - ⬭ "How Your Eyes Work"
   - ⬭ "Why Some Eyes Are Blue"

10. Which sentence is true?
    - ⬭ You need your brain and your eyes to see.
    - ⬭ Light goes into your brain.
    - ⬭ A friend is smaller than a thumb.

STOP

pitch**es**

play**ing**

hit**s**

Read each sentence.
Circle the verb that makes sense in the sentence.

1. Dad _____ the show.   watches watching

2. Sam _____ off his hat.   pulls   pulling

3. Kay _____ a rabbit in the hat.   puts   putting

4. Sam is _____ the hat with a wand.   taps   tapping

5. Sam is _____ a skunk out of the hat!   takes   taking

Find the word that makes sense in the sentences below.
Mark the space to show your answer.

Sam _____ his cape. | He _____ it over the hat.

6. ⬭ flings | 7. ⬭ tossing
   ⬭ flinging | ⬭ toss
   ⬭ fling | ⬭ tosses

 Notes for Home: Your child reviewed verbs with *-s, -es,* and *-ing* endings. ***Home Activity:***
Read with your child, looking for sentences with verbs ending in *-ing*. *(He is washing the dog.)* Have your child write the sentence using another form of the verb. *(He washes the dog.)*

| bright | sight | line | side | sky | try |

Change one letter in each word to make a word from the box.
Write the word on the line.

1. ride

_____

- - - - - - - - - - -

_____

2. fine

_____

- - - - - - - - - -

_____

Write two words that rhyme with .

_____

- - - - - - - - - -

3. _____

_____

- - - - - - - - - -

4. _____

Write two words from the box that rhyme with **cry**.

_____

- - - - - - - - - -

5. _____

_____

- - - - - - - - - -

6. _____

| because | whole |

Write the word from the box that fits in each puzzle.

7.

8.

Notes for Home: Your child spelled words with the long *i* sound spelled *igh, y,* and
i-consonant-e (bright, try, and *line)* and two frequently used words: *because, whole.* **Home
Activity:** Have your child sort the long *i* words according to their long *i* spellings.

Name _____

RETEACHING

Why does Brian go to Littletown?

Pepper gets a checkup from
Dr. Williams.

Proper nouns are special names for people, animals,
things, and places. They begin with capital letters.
Titles for people begin with capital letters. Most titles end
with a period.

Circle each proper noun that should begin with a capital letter.
Circle two proper nouns in each sentence.

1. wayne crane lives in the state of maine.

2. He got his dog, nick, in the city of brunswick.

3. His sister pat has a cat called matt.

Write a title or titles from the box in each sentence.

Ms.   Mr.   Mrs.   Miss   Dr.

4. Today a neighbor, _____ Ann Blatt, watches Matt.

5. _____ and _____ Crane take sick Nick to

_____ Moore.

6. _____ Susan Ko works for _____ Moore.

Notes for Home: Your child identified and capitalized proper nouns and titles for people.
Home Activity: Have your child show you his or her work on this page. Ask your child why
each proper noun is capitalized.

Circle each title and proper noun that should have a capital letter.

1. My team doctor on our basketball team is dr. john.

2. My teacher, mrs. romero, likes him too.

3. My neighbor, mr. roth, gave our team a pet dog.

4. Its name is miss sunflower.

Correct each title and proper noun and write it.

5. _____

6. _____

7. _____

8. _____

Write a proper noun that names someone you know.

9. your teacher _____

10. your friend _____

11. a pet _____

Notes for Home: Your child identified and wrote proper nouns. *Home Activity:* Talk with your child about friends and neighbors. Have your child write three of their names, using capital letters correctly.

Family Times

Furry Mouse

Two Mice

What a Perky Group!

It's party time for turtles
And birds and turkeys too.
The perky turkeys serve the food.
They've made a tasty stew.

Bert the bird stirs the stew
And perches on his swing.
When he's done he turns around
And chirps and twirls his wing.

The turtle babies drink some milk
And serve themselves some soup.
They whirl around and laugh a lot.
What a perky group!

This rhyme includes words your child is working with in school: words with *er, ir,* and *ur (serve, stirs, turtles)* and nouns that name more than one *(birds, babies)*. Say the words to "What a Perky Group!" together. Then find all the words that have the same vowel sound heard in *perky* spelled *er, ir,* and *ur.*

(fold here)

Name: _____

You are your child's first and best teacher!

Here are ways to help your child practice skills while having fun!

Day 1 Listen to the vowel sound in *her, first,* and *turn.* Together, make up lists of words with that same vowel sound spelled *er, ir,* and *ur (fern, bird, hurt).*

Day 2 Tell your child to hide an object. Then ask him or her to give you one clue at a time to help you find the object, using these words: *almost, another, around, food,* and *under.*

Day 3 Pick a simple object for you and your child to draw. Draw separate pictures. When done, have your child tell what is alike and different in the pictures you both drew.

Day 4 Read some poems with your child. Listen for words that repeat, rhyme, or represent interesting sounds.

Day 5 Help your child write a list of the contents of a kitchen or refrigerator shelf using singular nouns *(can)* and plural nouns *(boxes).*

Read with your child EVERY DAY!

Toss for Two

Materials paper, markers, scissors, bag, tape, 2 small bowls, 12 buttons per player

Game Directions

1. Copy and cut out the words shown on page 3. Put the words in a bag. Copy and cut out the word endings below. Tape one word ending to each bowl. Place the bowls on the floor.

2. Players take turns drawing a word from the bag and tossing a button into the bowl labeled with the plural ending for that word, such as -es for cherries.

3. If the button lands in the right bowl, the player spells the plural word and gets 1 point.

4. The player with the most points when the bag is empty wins!

Word Endings

| -s | -es |

baby	berry	pony
star	wheel	turkey
bug	acorn	cub
story	kitty	penny
party	monkey	toy
ant	dog	song
light	feather	friend

Name _____

Say each word.
Circle 7 words that have the same vowel sound as **shirt**.
Write these words on the lines.

sh<u>ir</u>t

1. her

_____

- - - - - - - - - - - - - - - - - -

_____

2. surf

_____

- - - - - - - - - - - - - - - - - -

_____

3. stir

_____

- - - - - - - - - - - - - - - - - -

_____

4. bird

_____

- - - - - - - - - - - - - - - - - -

_____

5. warm

_____

- - - - - - - - - - - - - - - - - -

_____

6. herd

_____

- - - - - - - - - - - - - - - - - -

_____

7. fur

_____

- - - - - - - - - - - - - - - - - -

_____

8. start

_____

- - - - - - - - - - - - - - - - - -

_____

9. wore

_____

- - - - - - - - - - - - - - - - - -

_____

10. perch

_____

- - - - - - - - - - - - - - - - - -

_____

Notes for Home: Your child identified words that contain the vowel sound in *shirt*.
Home Activity: Think of a letter. Challenge your child to name a word that begins with that
letter and that has the same vowel sound as *shirt* spelled *er, ir,* or *ur.*

Name _____

cats  boxes babies

Underline the sentence that matches each picture.

1. Look at the fat strawberry!

   Look at the fat strawberries!

2. Will the big bug eat the bush?

   Will the big bugs eat the bush?

3. Don't step on the snake.

   Don't step on the snakes.

4. Someone must water the rosebush.

   Someone must water the rosebushes.

Write a word to finish the sentence.

   _____

5. I see two _____ .

 Notes for Home: Your child read the plural forms of nouns such as *cats*, *boxes*, and *babies*. **Home Activity:** Have your child read aloud to you. Listen to be sure your child is pronouncing the *-s* or *-es* sounds of the plurals. Ask: *Is that one or more than one?*

Pick a word from the box to finish each sentence.
Write the word on the line.

| almost | another | around | food | under |

1. The cub _____ fell.

2. He hides _____ a log.

3. He sees _____ cub.

4. They run _____ the tree.

5. They eat fish for _____ .

Notes for Home: This week your child is learning to read the words *almost, another, around,*
food, and *under.* **Home Activity:** Watch a wildlife show or look at a wildlife book with your
child. Have your child use some of these words to write about what he or she saw.

Name _____

jay

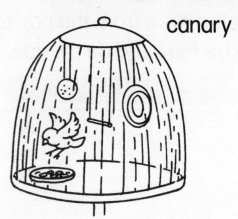
canary

Look for ways in which the jay is **not** like the canary.
Write two sentences about the jay.

1. _____

2. _____

Write one sentence that tells how both birds are alike.

3. _____

Look for ways in which the canary is **not** like the jay.
Write two sentences about the canary.

4. _____

5. _____

Notes for Home: Your child described ways in which two things are alike and different.
Home Activity: Talk with your child about members of your own family. Encourage your child
to identify ways two or more people are alike and different.

Name _____

Write the word for each picture.

Add -s or **-es** if the picture shows more than one.

Use the words in the box to help you.

ant	cherry	dish	peach	spoon

1. _____

2. _____

3. _____

4. _____

5. _____

Notes for Home: Your child used pictures to write singular and plural nouns. ***Home Activity:*** Have your child help you write grocery shopping lists. Ask your child to identify which words name one and which name more than one.

Name _____

Pick a word from the box to match each clue.
Write the word on the line.

| another | bottle | cage | follow | food | wheel |

1.

2.

---

3. walk behind someone

---

4. one more

5.

6.

Notes for Home: Your child used clues to write vocabulary words learned this week.
Home Activity: Together, write a story about the adventures of a mouse using the
vocabulary words. Help your child read the story aloud to other family members.

Name _____

 tiger

 kn**igh**t

 fl**y**

 p**ie**

Circle the word for each picture.

1.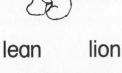

night   neat

2.

fry   free

3.

spice   spider

4.

type   tip

5.

lean   lion

6.

fling   flight

7.

tie   tin

8.

list   light

Find the word that has the same long i sound as the picture.
Mark the space to show your answer.

9.
- ⬭ lie
- ⬭ lip
- ⬭ lay

10.
- ⬭ slip
- ⬭ she
- ⬭ shy

 Notes for Home: Your child reviewed the long *i* sound spelled *i, igh, y,* and *ie*. **Home Activity:** Help your child write a story using some of the words on this page, as well as some of these words: *pilot, bicycle, mind, wild, night, fright, sight, sky, try,* and *my.*

baby   babies   bunny   bunnies   friend   friends

Read the words above each column.
Write the words from the box in the correct column.

Names One	**Names More Than One**
1. _____	2. _____
3. _____	4. _____
5. _____	6. _____

Pick a word from the box to match each clue.
Write the word on the line.

7. one pal

_____

8.   two rabbits

_____

Pick a word from the box to finish each sentence.
Write the word on the line.

another   food

9. Carrots are _____ that bunnies like to eat.

10. They will always eat _____ carrot.

Notes for Home: Your child spelled singular and plural nouns, such as *baby* and *babies,* and two frequently used words: *another, food.* **Home Activity:** Help your child make a list of his or her favorite things. Some of the words on the list should be singular, and others plural.

Name _____

Look at the picture.
Circle the word next to the picture if you see just one.
Write a plural word if you see more than one.

1. bunny

_____

- - - - - - - - - -

_____

2. bus

_____

- - - - - - - - - -

_____

3. dish

_____

- - - - - - - - - -

_____

4. cherry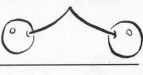

_____

- - - - - - - - - -

_____

5. wheel

_____

- - - - - - - - - -

_____

6. light

_____

- - - - - - - - - -

_____

7. boy

_____

- - - - - - - - - -

_____

8. box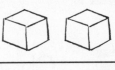

_____

- - - - - - - - - -

_____

9. egg

_____

- - - - - - - - - -

_____

10. brush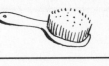

_____

- - - - - - - - - -

_____

 Notes for Home: Your child identified singular and plural nouns. ***Home Activity:*** Help your child make a list of the objects in a refrigerator, closet, or drawer. Discuss which plural nouns end in *-s* and which end in *-es*.

Test-Taking Tips

1. Write your name on the test.

2. Read each question twice.

3. Read all the answer choices for the question.

4. Mark your answer carefully.

5. Check your answer.

Part I: Vocabulary

Find the word that best fits in each sentence.
Mark the space for your answer.

1. Jen has a cat, but she wants _____ one.
   ⬭ everywhere   ⬭ many   ⬭ another

2. The baby drinks from a _____ .
   ⬭ spider   ⬭ bottle   ⬭ house

3. The cat will _____ the mouse.
   ⬭ write   ⬭ paddle   ⬭ follow

4. The dog's _____ comes in a can.
   ⬭ food   ⬭ wheel   ⬭ brain

5. My bird lives in a _____ .
   ⬭ bottle   ⬭ cage   ⬭ beak

GO ON ➡

Part 2: Comprehension

Read each question.
Mark the space for your answer.

6. In this story, the inside mouse eats —
   - ⬭ food from a bowl.
   - ⬭ rose leaves.
   - ⬭ strawberries and acorns.

7. Who almost ate the two mice?
   - ⬭ a dog
   - ⬭ a snake
   - ⬭ a cat

8. How is the outside mouse different from the inside mouse?
   - ⬭ He takes many naps.
   - ⬭ He lives in a cage.
   - ⬭ He likes to run around a lot.

9. After going out, the inside mouse was ready to —
   - ⬭ take a nap.
   - ⬭ run on the wheel.
   - ⬭ eat acorns.

10. The inside mouse probably thinks that —
    - ⬭ raccoons are friendly.
    - ⬭ outside is not a very safe place.
    - ⬭ the outside mouse wants to move inside.

STOP

Name _____

 monkey  ra**bb**it  ti**g**er

| b | ct | g | ll | lr | rr | sk | tt |

Pick a letter or a pair of letters from the box.
Write the letter or pair of letters to finish each word.

1. 	2. 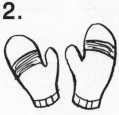	3. 	4. 
dra _____ on	mi _____ ens	wa _____ us	ro _____ ot

5. 	6. 	7. 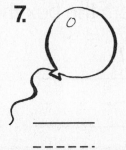	8. 
ca _____ ot	ba _____ et	ba_____oon	tra _____ or

Find the word with the same middle consonant sound as .
Mark the space to show your answer.

9. ⬭ muffin
   ⬭ kitten
   ⬭ paper

10. ⬭ butter
    ⬭ wagon
    ⬭ ruler

 Notes for Home: Your child reviewed words with more than one syllable that have one or two consonants in the middle, such as *tiger*, *monkey* and *rabbit*. *Home Activity:* Together, draw and label pictures of each word above. Practice reading these words aloud.

baby   babies   bunny   bunnies   friend   friends

Pick a word from the box to finish the math sentence.
Write the word on the line.

1. + = 2   _____

2. + = 2   _____

3. + = 3   _____

4.  − = 1   _____

Write the word from the box that rhymes with each word below.

5. bend

_____

6. maybe

_____

Pick a word from the box to match each clue.
Write the word on the line.

another   food

7. something to eat

_____

8. one more

_____

 Notes for Home: Your child spelled singular and plural nouns (*baby* and *babies*) and two frequently used words: *another, food.* **Home Activity:** Have your child draw and label pictures of these words: *ponies, dog, snakes,* and *zebra.*

Name _____

goat + s = goats

Many nouns add **-s** or **-es** to mean more than one.

Add -s or **-es** to the noun in ( ).
Write it on the line.

1. We went to see (farm).

2. Our (teacher) came with us.

3. We rode (bus).

4. We saw the chicken (coop).

5. I liked the (horse) best.

6. I hope we go on more (trip).

7. I love to see the (animal).

Notes for Home: Your child added *-s* or *-es* to nouns to make them plural. ***Home Activity:***
Have your child draw a picture of his or her room. Ask your child to label the objects in the
picture, using singular or plural nouns.

Underline each noun that means more than one.

1. One girl took out her pens.

2. Another girl found some crayons.

3. The boys wanted to draw a picture too.

4. The friends drew a spaceship.

5. They also drew two planes.

6. The teacher hung up the pictures.

Read each sentence.
Write the correct noun from the box to complete each sentence.

car	color	train
cars	colors	trains

7. I drew a picture of a _____ .

8. It had five long _____ .

9. I used many different _____ .

Notes for Home: Your child practiced using singular and plural nouns. **Home Activity:** Have your child count various objects in your home and create sentences about them. For example, *We have one refrigerator.*

146 Grammar: Singular and Plural Nouns

Moe and Joe

Outside by my treehouse,
Lives Moe the old toad.
Moe croaks in the nighttime.
Moe roams by a road.

Inside my own bedroom,
Lives my goldfish, Joe.
Joe likes his new fishbowl.
Oh, Joe told me so.

When it is midnight,
We don't hear a peep.
Then Moe starts his croaking.
We can't go to sleep.

This rhyme includes words your child is working with in school: words with the long *o* sound spelled *o*, *oa*, *ow*, and *oe* (*old*, *toad*, *fishbowl*, *Moe*) and compound words made up of two smaller words (*outside*). Say the rhyme together, stomping your foot for each long *o* word.

(fold here)

Name: _____

You are your child's first and best teacher!

Here are ways to help your child practice skills while having fun!

Day 1 Set a timer for 2 minutes and ask your child to list words that have the long *o* sound spelled *o*, *oa*, *ow*, and *oe*, such as *go*, *soap*, *grow*, and *toe*.

Day 2 Write these five words on index cards: *animals*, *before*, *between*, *knew*, and *why*. Take turns picking a word and using it in a sentence. Try to make the five sentences tell a story.

Day 3 Your child is learning to read and create charts, tables, graphs, and maps. Work with your child to create a simple map that shows the route your child takes to school.

Day 4 Find a photograph that shows your family having fun. Have your child make a short speech to you about the experience, referring to the photograph as he or she speaks.

Day 5 Write a general statement about an animal. (For example: *It is hard being a skunk.*) Have your child write sentences that give details to support the idea.

Read with your child EVERY DAY!

Combining Words

Materials 2 buttons per player, paper, pencil

Game Directions

1. Players take turns tossing buttons on the gameboard to try to make compound words.

2. Players earn 1 point for each compound word. Do not use a word more than once. Make a list to keep track of words used.

3. The first player to earn 10 points wins!

out	sun	time	shine
day	line	side	under
any	one	body	pop
every	where	corn	ground
coat	ball	rain	no
some	in	thing	base

Name _____

Circle the word in each row with the **long o** sound.
Write the word on the line.

b**ow**l

1. toad   top   two   _____

2. cop   cost   cold   _____

3. spoon   snow   soon   _____

4. out   over   one   _____

5. most   moss   mop   _____

6. took   toss   toast   _____

7. to   toe   too   _____

8. not   nod   know   _____

9. coat   cob   could   _____

10. pop   post   pots   _____

Notes for Home: Your child identified words in which the long *o* sound is spelled *o, oa, ow,* and *oe.* **Home Activity:** Write the word endings: *-oe, -oad, -oak, -oat, -old,* and *-ow,* on slips of paper. Have your child add beginning letters to each ending to form long *o* words.

Name _____

Use the pictures to make a compound word.
Write the compound word on the line.
Look at the words in the box if you need help.

cupcake   mailbox   raincoat
starfish   sunflower

rattlesnake

1. ⭐ + 🐟 = _____

2. 🌧 + 🧥 = _____

3. ☀ + 🌻 = _____

4. ☕ + 🎂 = _____

5. ✉ + 📦 = _____

Notes for Home: Your child formed compound words—words that are made up of two
smaller words. **Home Activity:** Have fun with your child making up picture puzzles for other
compound words, such as *toothbrush*.

Name _____

Pick a word from the box to finish each sentence.
Write the word on the line.

animals	before	between	knew	Why

1. _____ did you jump back?

2. I saw some strange _____ .

3. They were _____ the rock and the dirt.

4. I _____ snakes lived under rocks.

5. But I've never seen one _____ !

Notes for Home: This week your child is learning to read the words *animals, before, between, knew,* and *why.* **Home Activity:** Read and discuss a book about reptiles with your child. Encourage your child to write a few sentences about the book, using some of these words.

Name _____

Read the table.
Answer the questions.

Animal	Things They Like to Eat
Birds	worms, bugs, berries, seeds
Bears	fish, berries
Rabbits	grass, plants, carrots
Sheep	grass
Spiders	bugs

1. Which animals like to eat bugs?

   _____
   -
   _____

2. Which animals like to eat berries?

   _____
   -
   _____

3. Which animals like to eat grass?

   _____
   -
   _____

4. Which animal likes to eat fish?

   _____
   -
   _____

Notes for Home: Your child read a table and used information in it to answer questions.
Home Activity: Help your child make a table that tells something about family members,
such as favorite foods, songs, or colors.

Name _____

Some **nouns** change to a different word to name more than one.

man

men

Change each underlined word so it names more than one.
Write the new word on the line.
Look at the words in the box if you need help.

> calves   geese   leaves   mice   oxen

At the farm, we saw a <u>mouse</u> and an <u>ox</u>.

1. _____

2. _____

The <u>goose</u> ate the <u>leaf</u>.

3. _____

4. _____

The <u>calf</u> stepped into the water.

5. _____

Notes for Home: Your child wrote words that have irregular plural forms, such as *children, men, mice,* and *teeth.* **Home Activity:** Pair the underlined words with the words in the box. With your child, draw two pictures that show one *(mouse)* and more than one *(mice)* for each pair of words.

Name _____

Circle a word to finish each sentence.

between	enemy	medicine
peels	scales	underneath

1. I sometimes see snakes crawling _____ two flowers.

   between
   peels

2. The snake is an ____ of the mouse.

   scales
   enemy

3. A snake's skin ____ off many times a year.

   peels
   between

4. I once found an old snake skin ____ a log.

   underneath
   scales

5. Cats have fur, and snakes have ____ .

   scales
   medicine

6. If you are bitten by a rattlesnake, you will need ____ .

   enemy
   medicine

Notes for Home: Your child completed sentences using vocabulary words learned this week.
Home Activity: Together, find out more about snakes. Help your child make a fact card that shows a picture of a snake and tells facts about it. Use the vocabulary words if possible.

Name _____

fern

bird

surf

Circle the word for each picture.

1.

turtle   towel

2.

short   shirt

3.

herd   hard

4.

hurt   hut

5.

dirt   drift

6.

nose   nurse

7.

desk   dessert

8.

clerk   clock

Find the word that has the same vowel sound as the picture.
Mark the space to show your answer.

9. ⬭ trunk
   ⬭ first
   ⬭ near

10. ⬭ here
    ⬭ her
    ⬭ horse

Notes for Home: Your child reviewed words with *er, ir,* and *ur* that have the same vowel
sound (*fern, bird,* and *surf*). **Home Activity:** Use some of the following words to write
sentences for your child to read aloud: *germ, herd, her, bird, chirp, dirt, burn, burst, purse.*

sold	woke	coat	soap	below	owe

Write the word from the box that rhymes with each word below.

1. toe

_____

_____

2. rope

_____

_____

3. throat

_____

_____

4. cold

_____

_____

Pick a word from the box that is the opposite of each word below.
Write the word on the line.

5. above

_____

_____

6. slept

_____

_____

Pick a word from the box to finish each sentence.
Write the word on the line.

animals
between

_____

7. Some _____ sleep when it is winter.

_____

8. One sleeps _____ two rocks.

Notes for Home: Your child spelled words with the long *o* sound spelled *o, ow,* and *oa,* as well as two frequently used words: *animals, between.* **Home Activity:** Write simple sentences on slips of paper using these spelling words. Have your child read the sentences aloud.

feet   mice   sheep   teeth

Pick a word from the box to match each picture.
Write the word on the line.

1. two top _____
_____

2. two shaggy _____
_____

3. four funny _____
_____

4. three meek _____
_____

Write a sentence to tell about the picture.
Use the word that names more than one goose.

5. _____
_____

Notes for Home: Your child reviewed nouns that form plurals in unusual ways. *Home Activity:* Have your child tell you a story using the irregular plurals *feet, mice, sheep, teeth,* and *geese.* Together, write the story and draw pictures to illustrate it.

Test-Taking Tips

1. Write your name on the test.

2. Read each question twice.

3. Read all the answer choices for the question.

4. Mark your answer carefully.

5. Check your answer.

Part 1: Vocabulary

Find the word that best fits in each sentence.
Mark the space for your answer.

1. We ran _____ the houses.
   ⊂⊃ with   ⊂⊃ between   ⊂⊃ so

2. She _____ the banana.
   ⊂⊃ peels   ⊂⊃ follows   ⊂⊃ fixes

3. This _____ will help you feel better.
   ⊂⊃ enemy   ⊂⊃ ground   ⊂⊃ medicine

4. The snake's _____ are dry.
   ⊂⊃ beaks   ⊂⊃ messages   ⊂⊃ scales

5. Ben found the ball _____ his bed.
   ⊂⊃ there   ⊂⊃ underneath   ⊂⊃ after

GO ON ➡

Part 2: Comprehension

Read each question.
Mark the space for your answer.

6. Snakes have no —
   - ⬭ eyes.
   - ⬭ legs.
   - ⬭ scales.

7. Snakes use their tongues to —
   - ⬭ lick their food.
   - ⬭ pick up smells from the air.
   - ⬭ scare people.

8. Snakes "unhook" their jaws so they can —
   - ⬭ chew their food.
   - ⬭ clean their teeth.
   - ⬭ open their mouths wide.

9. To tell other animals to stay away, some snakes try to —
   - ⬭ run fast.
   - ⬭ look scary.
   - ⬭ sing songs.

10. Which sentence about snakes is true?
    - ⬭ Snakes sleep all winter.
    - ⬭ Snakes can see and hear very well.
    - ⬭ Snakes do not help people very much.

STOP

Name _____

 bell**s**    dress**es**    pupp**ies**

Write the word for each picture.
Use the word in ( ) to help you.

1.

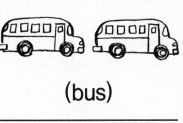

(bus)

_____

- - - - - - - - - -

2.

(tree)

_____

- - - - - - - - - -

3.

(fly)

_____

- - - - - - - - - -

4.

(fox)

_____

- - - - - - - - - -

5.

(boy)

_____

- - - - - - - - - -

6.

(dish)

_____

- - - - - - - - - -

Find the word where you would add **-es** to show more than one.
Mark the space to show your answer.

7. ⬭ bush
   ⬭ book
   ⬭ bat

8. ⬭ girl
   ⬭ glass
   ⬭ gift

 Notes for Home: Your child reviewed nouns that form plurals that end in *-s* and *-es*. **Home Activity:** Look in a catalog for pictures that show more than one thing, such as boxes. Help your child write the plural words to match these pictures.

sold	woke	coat	soap	below	owe

Change one letter in each word to make a word from the box.
Write the new word on the line.

1. soak _____

2. wake _____

3. boat _____

4. cold _____

Write two words from the box with **ow**.

5. _____

6. _____

Pick a word from the box to match each clue.
Write the word on the line.

animals
between

7. in the middle

_____

8. lions, tigers, bears

_____

Notes for Home: Your child spelled words with the long *o* sound, spelled *o, oa,* and *ow,* as well as two frequently used words: *animals, between.* **Home Activity:** Help your child use some of these words to write rhymes. For example: *I put on my <u>coat</u> and got into the <u>boat</u>.*

Name _____

RETEACHING

Some **nouns** change to a different word
to mean more than one.

One	More Than One		One	More Than One
man	men		foot	feet
woman	women		tooth	teeth
child	children		goose	geese
			mouse	mice

Look at each picture.
Circle the correct word.

1. mouse   mice

2. tooth   teeth

3. foot   feet

4. goose   geese

Change each word in ( ) to mean more than one.
Write the word in the sentence.

5. Those (man) _____ work in a hospital.

6. The (child) _____ are in their beds.

7. The (woman) _____ are doctors.

Notes for Home: Your child identified irregular plural nouns—nouns that change spelling to mean more than one. **Home Activity:** Have your child write a poem, using the following words: *teeth*, *feet*, and *children*.

Answer each clue to solve the puzzle.
Write the answers in the boxes.

Across

2. more than one man

4. more than one child

5. more than one foot

Down

1. more than one woman

2. more than one mouse

3. more than one goose

6. more than one tooth

Notes for Home: Your child practiced writing irregular plural nouns. *Home Activity:* Have your child make up a dialogue between two farmers about sheep, geese, and mice. Your child can write, record, or illustrate the dialogue.

164 Grammar: Irregular Plural Nouns

Family Times

Spiders Up Close   Anansi and the Talking Melon

Horse's House

In Horse's house a spider hides
While mouse has Moose's Swiss cheese.
Moose is huge but the mouse is wise.
He steals the cheese with ease.

There's a mouse in Horse's house.
Mouse is such a big tease.
Spider watches Horse and Moose.
They want that piece of Swiss cheese!

This rhyme includes words your child is working with in school: words that end in *ce, ge,* and *se (piece, huge, horse, tease)* and words like *Horse's* that show possession. Sing "Horse's House" with your child as you march around a room.

(fold here)

Name: _____

You are your child's first and best teacher!

Here are ways to help your child practice skills while having fun!

Day 1 Take turns writing possessives using animals, such as *a spider's web, two monkeys' bananas,* and so on.

Day 2 Help your child to create a cartoon strip about a meal time. Have your child use the words *call, enough, full, heard,* and *until* to fill in the speech balloons.

Day 3 Find some newspaper cartoon strips that your child can read. Cut each strip apart and have your child arrange the panels in order.

Day 4 Your child is learning how to write a paragraph that clearly describes a person, place, or thing. Have your child write a short descriptive paragraph that describes a pet someone has lost.

Day 5 Encourage your child to describe several friends and classmates so that you can get a good mental picture of them.

Read with your child EVERY DAY!

How Many Words?

Materials 1 button, paper, pencils, timer

Game Directions

1. Take turns tossing the button on the gameboard.

2. All players have one minute to write as many words as possible that use the letters landed on. Players earn 1 point for each word. If another player has the same word, cross out the word and no points are earned.

3. The first player to earn 10 points wins!

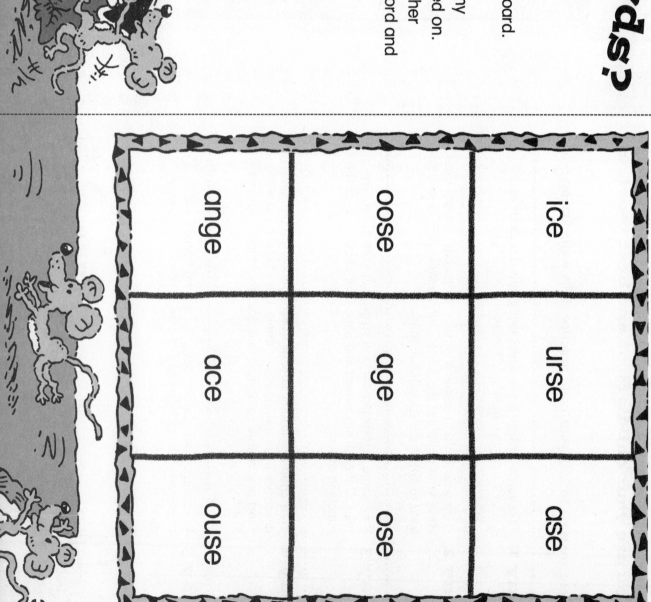

ice	urse	ase
oose	age	ose
ange	ace	ouse

Name _____

Circle the word for each picture.

mi**ce**

1.

mouth   mouse

2.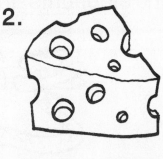

cheese   cheap

3.

ice   ink

4.

cage   case

5.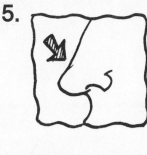

nice   nose

6.

page   place

Draw a picture of each word.

7. house

8. face

Notes for Home: Your child practiced using words that end in *ce, ge,* and *se*. **Home Activity:** Give your child practice with words that end in *-ace, -ice, -uce, -aise, -ease, -eese, -ose, -ouse,* and words that end in *-ge,* such as *cage*. Take turns writing and reading rhyming pairs of these words.

Level 2.1   Phonics: Words with *ce, ge, se* **167**

Circle the words that tell about each picture.

the **elephants'** trunks

1. the snake's hats
   the snakes' hats

2. the hog's slippers
   the hogs' slippers

3. the mice's game
   the mices' game

4. the fox's dinner
   the foxes' dinner

Draw a picture of the words below.

5. the mouse's cheese

Notes for Home: Your child identified possessives—words that show ownership.
Home Activity: Read a story with your child. Look for possessive forms of words.
Point them out and ask your child to tell you how many owners are being described.

Name _____

Pick a word from the box to finish each sentence.
Write the word on the line.

| call | enough | full | heard | until |

_____

1. All day we _____ the king and queen yell.

_____

2. They _____ out for more melons.

_____

3. They can never eat _____ melons.

_____

4. We picked melons _____ it was dark.

_____

5. We hope they will be _____ soon.

Notes for Home: This week your child is learning to read the words *call, enough, full, heard,* and *until.* **Home Activity:** Help your child use these words to write a story about some talking animals. Encourage your child to read the story to others.

Look at the pictures. **Read** the sentences.
Write 1, 2, 3, 4 to show the right order.

_____ **a.** Then, he picks up the box.

_____ **b.** Next, he opens the box.

_____ **c.** The monkey sees a box.

_____ **d.** He takes the box home.

Write a sentence that tells what might happen next.

_____

_____

_____

 Notes for Home: Your child figured out the order of events for a story. **Home Activity:** Have your child retell a favorite story. Listen to make sure that the story events are told in the correct order.

Name _____

A noun can show who owns something.

One Owner
girl**'s** bike
Chris**'s** melon
man**'s** car

More Than One Owner
girl**s'** bikes
the Cross**'s** house
men**'s** cars

Circle the words that tell who owns what.
Use the underlined words to help you.

---

1. The <u>spiders</u> are having a <u>party</u>.

spider's party
spiders' party

---

2. The <u>geese</u> are carrying a <u>melon</u>.

geese's melon
geese' melon

---

3. The <u>hippo</u> brings <u>pies</u>.

hippo's pies
hippos' pies

---

4. The <u>princes</u> wear big <u>hats</u>.

prince's hats
princes' hats

---

5. The <u>toad</u> sings a silly <u>song</u>.

toad's song
toads' song

Notes for Home: Your child identified singular and plural possessives—words that show who owns something. **Home Activity:** Using possessives *(Bob's bed, dogs' bowls)*, take turns with your child making up sentences that tell who owns what in your home.

Pick a word from the box to match each clue.
Write the letters of the word in each puzzle.
Read the circled letters to find a hidden word.

| enough | exclaimed | patch | ripe | squeeze | until |

1. press hard

2. a little bit of ground

3. Wait _____ it's dark.

4. called out in surprise

5. as much as
   is wanted

6. full grown and ready to be eaten

Riddle: What spins all day but never gets dizzy?

_____

- - - - - - - - - - - - - -

Answer: a _____

Notes for Home: Your child used clues to write vocabulary words learned this week. *Home Activity:* Challenge your child to use some of this week's vocabulary words to write a story about a rabbit that sneaked into a garden to get the farmer's vegetables.

Name _____

 cobra   b**oa**t   b**ow**    h**oe**

Circle the word for each picture.

1. cot coat	**2.** bowl bull
3. got goat	**4.** crow cross
5. soap sap	**6.** bat boat
7. toe to	**8.** tacks tacos

Find the word that has the same **long o** sound as the picture.
Mark the space to show your answer.

9. ⬭ food
   ⬭ fold
   ⬭ fox

10. ⬭ mop
    ⬭ moss
    ⬭ most

Notes for Home: Your child reviewed the long *o* sound heard in *cobra*, *boat*, *bow*, and *hoe*.
Home Activity: Help your child cut out words with this sound and these spellings from a
newspaper. Help him or her paste the words on paper and read them aloud.

Name _____

| face | twice | cage | huge | page | tease |

Read the word at the top of each column.
Write the words from the box with the same ending sound.

stage

1. _____

2. _____

3. _____

mice

4. _____

5. _____

hose

6. _____

Pick a word from the box to match each clue.
Write the word on the line.

7. very large

_____

8. two times

_____

Pick a word from the box to finish each sentence.
Write the word on the line.

until
enough

9. The king kept eating _____ it was dark.

10. He has had _____ !

 Notes for Home: Your child spelled words that end with the letters *ce*, *ge*, and *se*, such as *face*, *cage*, and *tease*, and two frequently used words: *until*, *enough*. **Home Activity:** Help your child use these spelling words to make a comic strip about a visit to a zoo.

Add words to tell more about something.

The spider spins a web.
The spider spins a **round** web.

What would make each sentence better?
Pick a word from the box to finish each sentence.
Write the word on the line. Use each word only once.

| different | eight | many | sticky |

1. Spiders have _____ legs.

2. They can catch flies in their _____ webs.

3. _____ spiders eat garden pests.

4. Spiders come in _____ sizes.

Write a sentence about a spider.
Use words that help describe it.

5. _____

_____

Notes for Home: Your child added interesting details to sentences. *Home Activity:* Help your child practice using descriptive language. Point to an object in the room and have your child describe it. Encourage your child to use interesting details to tell more about the object.

Name _____

Read each sentence.
Use the two underlined words to show who owns each thing.
Add 's or ' to one of the words.
Write the new word on the line.

1. The <u>web</u> belongs to the <u>spiders</u>.
   _____
   - - - - - - - - - - - - - - - -
   _____ web

2. The <u>crown</u> belongs to the <u>king</u>.
   _____
   - - - - - - - - - - - - - - - -
   _____ crown

3. The <u>tusks</u> belong to the <u>hog</u>.
   _____
   - - - - - - - - - - - - - - - -
   _____ tusks

4. The <u>teeth</u> belong to the <u>hippo</u>.
   _____
   - - - - - - - - - - - - - - - -
   _____ teeth

5. The <u>shells</u> belong to the <u>turtles</u>.
   _____
   - - - - - - - - - - - - - - - -
   _____ shells

Notes for Home: Your child reviewed writing possessive nouns to show who owns
something, such as *the elephant's trunk*. **Home Activity:** Look through a book with your child.
Ask your child to write descriptive sentences about the pictures (*The cat's fur is black.*).

Part I: Vocabulary

Find the word that best fits in each sentence.
Mark the space for your answer.

1. Did you have _____ to eat?
   ⊂⊃ never   ⊂⊃ enough   ⊂⊃ until

2. "Oh, no!" _____ Pat.
   ⊂⊃ exclaimed   ⊂⊃ surprised   ⊂⊃ drew

3. Please don't walk on the _____ of new grass.
   ⊂⊃ enemy   ⊂⊃ mirror   ⊂⊃ patch

4. You can eat melons when they are _____ .
   ⊂⊃ ripe   ⊂⊃ another   ⊂⊃ later

5. Len could not _____ through the hole.
   ⊂⊃ clean   ⊂⊃ peel   ⊂⊃ squeeze

GO ON ➡

Part 2: Comprehension

Read each question.
Mark the space for your answer.

6. What did Anansi use to make a hole in the melon?
   - ⬭ a rock
   - ⬭ a spoon
   - ⬭ a thorn

7. Anansi could not get out of the melon because —
   - ⬭ he was too fat from eating.
   - ⬭ the hole had gotten smaller.
   - ⬭ someone had covered the hole.

8. Which animal did Elephant see first?
   - ⬭ Warthog
   - ⬭ Hippo
   - ⬭ Ostrich

9. Why did the king get angry at the melon?
   - ⬭ The melon insulted him.
   - ⬭ The melon tasted bad.
   - ⬭ The melon would not talk to him.

10. Why will Elephant **not** take talking bananas to the king?
    - ⬭ He will want to keep the bananas for himself.
    - ⬭ He will want to share the bananas with Anansi.
    - ⬭ He will be afraid the bananas will get him in trouble.

STOP

Name _____

Say the word for each picture.
Use two words to make a compound
word that stands for the picture.
Write the compound word on the line.

wart + hog = warthog

I.

spoon   pot   table   tea

_____

- - - - - - - - - - - - - - -

_____

2.

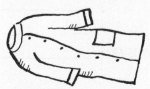

coat   shoes   rain   snow

_____

- - - - - - - - - - - - - - -

_____

3.

air   box   mail   plane

_____

- - - - - - - - - - - - - - -

_____

4.

neck   shoe   lace   tie

_____

- - - - - - - - - - - - - - -

_____

Find the word that you can put together with *meal* to make a
compound word.
Mark the space to show your answer.

5. _____ meal

- ⭘ dinner
- ⭘ oat
- ⭘ book

6. meal _____

- ⭘ time
- ⭘ spoon
- ⭘ napkin

Notes for Home: Your child reviewed compound words—words that are made up of two
smaller words, such as *warthog*. **Home Activity:** With your child, use the words listed above to
make up other compound words such as *teaspoon* or *snowshoes*.

| face | twice | cage | huge | page | tease |

Change one or two letters in each word to make a word from the box.

Write the new word on the line.

1. please _____

2. hugs _____

3. pale _____

4. slice _____

Write the word from the box to match each picture.

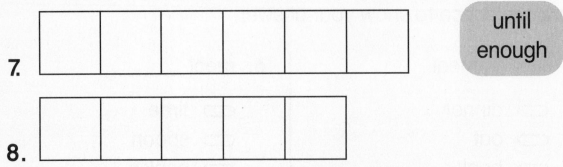

5. _____

6. _____

Write the word from the box that fits in each puzzle.

until
enough

7. ⬜⬜⬜⬜⬜

8. ⬜⬜⬜⬜

Notes for Home: Your child spelled words that end with *ce*, *ge*, and *se*, such as *face*, *cage*, and *tease*, and two frequently used words: *until*, *enough*. **Home Activity:** Have your child make new words that end with *ce*, *ge*, or *se* by changing one or two letters in each word.

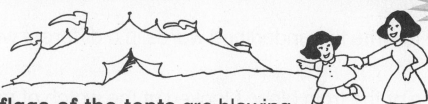

RETEACHING

The **flags of the tents** are blowing.
The **tents' flags** are blowing.
Kim holds **the hand of her mother.**
Kim holds **her mother's hand.**
The **'** shows that the flags belong to the tents. The **'s** shows that the hand belongs to the mother.

Many nouns add **'s** or **'** to show ownership.

Match the groups of words that say the same thing in a different way.

I. the face of the clown   **a.** the elephants' trunks

2. the teeth of the tiger   **b.** the clown's face

3. the trunks of the elephants   **c.** the tiger's teeth

Add 's or **'** to each noun in ( ).
Write the noun in the sentence.

4. A (clown) _____ nose is red.

5. A (lion) _____ roar is loud.

6. The (bears) _____ act was fun.

Notes for Home: Your child identified possessive nouns. *Home Activity:* Have your child make two sets of cards, one with people's names and one with names of things. Have him or her pick a card from each pile and write a sentence, using both words. *(This is Jerry's car.)*

Name _____

Read the story.

Use 's or ' to write the underlined words in a different way.

The whistle of the train blew. I looked at the watch of my mother. I could not wait to get to the city. The windows of the stores were filled with beautiful things. The eyes of my sister opened wide. We could not see the tops of the buildings. At night we saw the lights of the city. We had a good time!

1. _____

2. _____

3. _____

4. _____

5. _____

6. _____

Notes for Home: Your child wrote possessive nouns in sentences. *Home Activity:* Ask your child questions about various family members' belongings. For example, *What color is Grandma's car?* Make sure that he or she uses a possessive noun to answer.

One word in each sentence is **not** correct.
Circle the incorrect word.
Write the word correctly on the line.
Hint: Use an **'** to show ownership.

1. Ms. Goldmans class is studying insects.
   _____
   -
   _____

2. An insects head is very small.
   _____
   -
   _____

3. Marias report is about dragonflies.
   _____
   -
   _____

4. Dragonflies bodies are long and thin.
   _____
   -
   _____

5. The classs reports were all interesting.
   _____
   -
   _____

Notes for Home: Your child used apostrophes to show ownership. ***Home Activity:*** Make a
list of things that belong to members of your family. Help your child use the list to write
sentences with possessives to show ownership. (For example: *This is Bill's blue hat.*)

Name _____

Words I Can Now Read and Write

Family Times

Work Together Now!

I see fans yelling in the crowd.
I hear shouting. They're getting loud.
We are clapping. We are proud.
Watch how we work together!

I see a pitcher on the mound.
I see a player running around.
I see a baseball hitting the ground.
Watch how we work together!

I see a catcher crouching down.
I see an umpire with a frown.
I see our player dressed in brown.
Watch how we work together!

This rhyme includes words your child is working with in school: words with *ou* and *ow* (*loud*, *crowd*) and words with double consonants followed by *-ed* and *-ing* endings (*running*). After singing "Work Together Now!," make a list showing words with *ou* and *ow*.

(fold here)

Name: _____

You are your child's first and best teacher!

Here are ways to help your child practice skills while having fun!

Day 1 Name a word with *ou* or *ow* that has the same vowel sound as *house* and *crown*. Challenge your child to name a word that rhymes with it and has the same spelling for the vowel sound, such as *house/mouse* and *crown/frown*.

Day 2 Use hand puppets or stuffed animals to make up a scene where two characters talk. Try to include these words: *been, friends, show, since,* and *those.*

Day 3 Read or tell a story to your child. Have your child summarize what happens in the story using two or three sentences.

Day 4 With your child, come up with a list of action words, such as *run, hop, leap,* and *sing.* Then take turns acting out each word.

Day 5 Help your child write a paragraph that tells a brief story. The story should describe real or make-believe people working together.

Read with your child EVERY DAY!

Verb Match-Up

Materials index cards, markers

Game Directions

1. Use index cards to write the pairs of related verbs shown on page 3.

2. Mix the cards and spread each one face down on a table or the floor.

3. Players take turns turning over two cards at a time, trying to match up verb pairs.

4. Players keep matching pairs of verb cards. If a match is not made, the players return cards to their original positions.

5. Play until all matches are made. The player with the most pairs wins!

bat	batted	get	getting
grip	gripped	nod	nodded
pet	petting	rub	rubbed
run	running	sit	sitting
stop	stopped	win	winning

Name _____

Read each sentence.
Circle the word with the same vowel sound as **cow** or **house**.
Write the word on the line.

c**ow**   h**ou**se

1. I play baseball near my house.   _____

2. We are the best team in town.   _____

3. We are the Brown Bears.   _____

4. I play in the outfield.   _____

5. I went down to the park.   _____

6. There wasn't a cloud in the sky.   _____

7. The crowd was cheering.   _____

8. My teammates shouted too.   _____

9. We were about to win!   _____

10. I hit the ball out of the park!   _____

Notes for Home: Your child read and wrote words with the same vowel sound as *cow* and
house spelled *ow* and *ou*. **Home Activity:** Ask your child to draw pictures representing as
many *ou* and *ow* words as possible. Work together to label each picture.

Name _____

Read each word.
Find the base word.
Write the base word on the line.

stop + -ed = stop**ed**   hop + -ing = hopp**ing**

1. sitting _____

2. gripped _____

3. running _____

4. nodded _____

5. shopped _____

6. spinning _____

7. getting _____

8. hitting _____

Add -ed and **-ing** to each base word.
Write the new words on the line.

	+ -ed	**+ -ing**
9. bat	_____	_____
10. clip	_____	_____

Notes for Home: Your child read and wrote words whose final consonants are doubled before adding the endings -*ed* and -*ing*. **Home Activity:** Read a story together. Ask your child to point out words with -*ed* and -*ing* that have had their final consonants doubled.

Name _____

Pick a word from the box to finish each sentence.
Write the word on the line.

| been | friends | show | since | those |

1. Tom and I are best _____ .

2. We have _____ pals for a long time.

3. We don't know _____ new boys.

4. They have only lived here _____ last night.

5. We will _____ them how to play!

Notes for Home: This week your child is learning to read the words *been, friends, show, since,* and *those.* **Home Activity:** Encourage your child to write sentences about his or her best friend using these words.

Name _____

Read the story.
Answer the questions.

A New Bike for Matt

Matt had a bike. He rode his bike all over.

One day, Matt left his bike out. The next day, the bike was gone!

Matt wanted a new bike.

He did extra chores around the house. He cut the grass. Soon Matt had enough money.

Matt's dad was proud. Matt got his new bike. Now Matt always puts it in a safe place!

1. What did Matt want?

_____

- -

_____

2. Why did he want it?

_____

- -

_____

3. What did he do to get it?

_____

- -

_____

_____

- -

Notes for Home: Your child summarized what happened in a story. *Home Activity:* Watch a video or TV show with your child. Encourage your child to summarize what happened in the story in a few sentences.

Name _____

A **verb** is a word that can show action.

Sandy **kicks** the ball.

Kicks is a verb.

Circle the verb in each sentence.

1. Ann hits the ball.

2. She runs to first base.

3. Deb throws the ball to Ken.

4. He catches the ball.

5. Ann gets there just in time.

Notes for Home: Your child identified verbs that are action words. *Home Activity:* Read a story with your child. Encourage your child to point out the action words. Make a list of these words and continue adding to it as you and your child read other stories.

Pick a word from the box to match each clue.
Write the word on the line.

baseball	friend	pitching	returned
since	terrible	those	

1. pal

_____

_____

2. the ones over there

_____

_____

3. throwing a ball to a batter

_____

_____

4. gave back

_____

_____

5. awful

_____

_____

6. game played with a bat and ball

_____

_____

7. I haven't seen her _____ yesterday.

_____

_____

Notes for Home: Your child used clues to practice new vocabulary words.
Home Activity: Pretend you and your child are sports announcers at a baseball game.
Try to use these vocabulary words as you describe an imaginary game.

fen**ce**

sta**ge**

hou**se**

no**se**

Circle the word for each picture.

1.

mouse   moth

2.

face   fact

3.

rose   rope

4.

cake   cage

5.

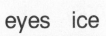

eyes   ice

6.

rack   race

7.

orange   order

8.

blouse   blue

Find the word that has the same ending sound as the picture.
Mark the space to show your answer.

9. ⬭ host
⬭ hose
⬭ hotel

10. ⬭ test
⬭ taste
⬭ tease

Notes for Home: Your child reviewed words that end in *ce, ge,* and *se.* **Home Activity:** Write *fence, stage, house,* and *nose* in a row across the top of a sheet of paper. Encourage your child to think of at least two more words that have the same ending sound as each word.

| hugged | hugging | nodded | nodding | skipped | skipping |

Add -ed or **-ing** to each word below to make a word from the box.
Write the new word on the line.

Add -ed   Add -ing

hug   1. _____   2. _____

nod   3. _____   4. _____

skip   5. _____   6. _____

Pick a word from the box to finish each sentence.
Write the word on the line.

7. We are _____ rope.

8. Before I left, I _____ my friends.

Pick a word from the box to match each clue.
Write the word on the line.

since those

9. not these

_____

10. from then until now

_____

Notes for Home: Your child practiced spelling words that end with *-ed* and *-ing* and two frequently used words: *since, those.* **Home Activity:** Have your child use each spelling word in a sentence. Work together to write each sentence.

Name _____

Read each group of words.
Circle the verb in each group.

1. sing   song   son | 2. white   with   writes

3. plaid   pail   played | 4. rang   wrong   runny

5. Chris   cries   crust | 6. cut   cot   cold

7. buns   runs   tons | 8. read   real   red

Pick one of the verbs you circled.
Draw a picture to show that verb.
Write a sentence about the picture.

9.

_____

10. _____

_____

Notes for Home: Your child practiced identifying verbs that show action. *Home Activity:*
Take a walk with your child. Point out people and objects that are doing things. Ask your
child to tell you, in a complete sentence, what action they are performing.

Test-Taking Tips

1. Write your name on the test.

2. Read each question twice.

3. Read all the answer choices for the question.

4. Mark your answer carefully.

5. Check your answer.

Part I: Vocabulary

Find the word that best fits in each sentence.
Mark the space for your answer.

1. Scott hit the _____ hard.
   - ⬭ hundred
   - ⬭ baseball
   - ⬭ terrible

2. Ken was _____ the ball fast.
   - ⬭ going
   - ⬭ pitching
   - ⬭ peeling

3. Lina _____ from her trip yesterday.
   - ⬭ returned
   - ⬭ exclaimed
   - ⬭ followed

4. I will make a cake for you _____ it is your birthday.
   - ⬭ after
   - ⬭ until
   - ⬭ since

5. I like _____ apples better than these red ones.
   - ⬭ terrible
   - ⬭ those
   - ⬭ enough

GO ON ➡

Part 2: Comprehension

Read each question.
Mark the space for your answer.

6. When it was Lionel's turn at bat, he —
   - ⬭ swung and missed.
   - ⬭ threw the ball to Ellen.
   - ⬭ hit the ball over the fence.

7. When he heard the crash, Lionel felt —
   - ⬭ terrible.
   - ⬭ glad.
   - ⬭ surprised.

8. Lionel and his friends will —
   - ⬭ pay for the broken window.
   - ⬭ help Mr. Barrie fix the window.
   - ⬭ never play baseball again.

9. Which sentence best tells what happens in this story?
   - ⬭ When Lionel breaks a window, all his friends help him.
   - ⬭ Max said that he hit the ball over the fence.
   - ⬭ Lionel tries to play baseball, but his friends know he is not very good.

10. If Lionel lost his coat, his friends probably would —
    - ⬭ tell his parents.
    - ⬭ laugh at him.
    - ⬭ help him find it.

STOP

Add 's or ' to the word in ( ) to show
who owns something.
Write the new words on the lines below.

Joe's bat

1. This is my _____ cap. (sister)

2. Here are the _____ bats. (girls)

3. Here are the _____ coaches. (teams)

4. Where is _____ mitt? (Jan)

5. I found the _____ missing ball. (boys)

6. How was _____ game? (Kim)

Find the word that shows who owns something.
Mark the space to show your answer.

7.	8.	9.	10.
⬡ crowds	⬡ fan	⬡ girls	⬡ kitten's
⬡ crowd	⬡ fans'	⬡ girl	⬡ kittens
⬡ crowd's	⬡ fans	⬡ girls'	⬡ kitten

Notes for Home: Your child reviewed possessives—words that show ownership or belonging.
Home Activity: Read a story together. Ask your child to point out any possessive words. Make
sure your child can tell the difference between possessive words and contractions.

Name _____

hugged   hugging   nodded   nodding   skipped   skipping

Check the spelling of each word below.
If the word is correct, **write** it on the line.
If the word is wrong, **correct** it and **write** it on the line.

1. skiped

_____

_____

2. huged

_____

_____

3. hugging

_____

_____

4. noding

_____

_____

5. nodded

_____

_____

6. skiping

_____

_____

Pick a word from the box to finish each sentence.
Write the word on the line.

since
those

_____

7. I have been playing baseball _____ I was five.

_____

8. I play with _____ boys over there.

Notes for Home: Your child spelled words that end with *-ed* and *-ing* and two frequently-used words: *since, those.* **Home Activity:** Work with your child to write a story using these spelling words about a group of friends.

The children **skip** to the music.

The word **skip** is a verb.
It tells what the children do.

A word that can show action is a **verb**.

Find the verb in each sentence.
Then **write** the verb.

1. The girls dance well. _____

2. They spin around the room. _____

3. All the children look. _____

4. Now some boys sing. _____

5. Friends listen to the song. _____

6. They clap loudly. _____

Notes for Home: Your child identified verbs in sentences. **Home Activity:** Watch a television show with your child. Ask him or her to tell you sentences about what people are doing. Write the sentences. Have your child circle the verbs in the sentences.

Underline the verb in each sentence.

1. We wash our hands.
2. My sisters mix the rice.
3. Mom and Dad set the table.
4. You pass the food.
5. We eat dinner.
6. Friends knock on the door.

Choose the correct word from the box.
Write it in the sentence.

gives   go   laugh   tell   play   open   sing

7. You _____ the door.

8. Our friends _____ a story.

9. We _____ at the joke.

10. We all _____ a song.

11. Then we _____ a game.

12. He _____ a gift.

13. Then our friends _____ home.

Notes for Home: Your child identified and wrote verbs in sentences. *Home Activity:* Without speaking, do an action which your child can identify and describe in a sentence. (For example: jump, write, read, wash)

Family Times

People, People, Everywhere!

The Storykeeper

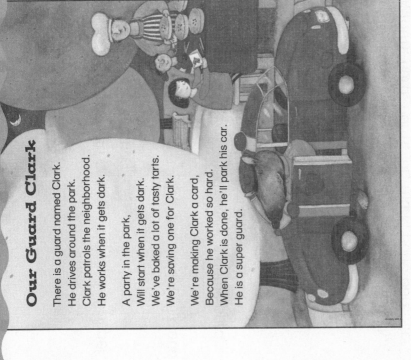

Our Guard Clark

There is a guard named Clark.
He drives around the park.
Clark patrols the neighborhood.
He works when it gets dark.

A party in the park,
Will start when it gets dark.
We've baked a lot of tasty tarts.
We're saving one for Clark.

We're making Clark a card,
Because he worked so hard.
When Clark is done, he'll park his car.
He is a super guard.

This rhyme includes words your child is working with in school: words with *ar* (*park*) and verbs that end in *-ed* and *-ing*. Sing "Our Guard Clark" with your child. Together, make a list of the words with *ar*. Then think of other *ar* words that rhyme with the words listed.

Name: _____

(fold here)

You are your child's first and best teacher!

Here are ways to help your child practice skills while having fun!

Day 1 Make a list of verbs (words that show action) that end in *e*, such as *race, ride,* or *move.* Read each one aloud. Ask your child to spell the word with an *-ed* or *-ing* ending.

Day 2 Work with your child to draw a picture and write a caption using the words *children, city, high, place,* and *room.*

Day 3 When reading together, show your child how to figure out the meaning of unfamiliar words by using context clues in nearby words, phrases, or pictures.

Day 4 Ask your child how he or she feels today. Help your child write a poem that expresses these feelings.

Day 5 Go for a walk with your child. Have your child make up sentences that describe the actions that he or she sees. Listen for the correct use of verbs to describe the actions by one person and the actions by more than one person.

Read with your child EVERY DAY!

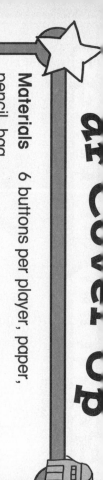

ar Cover Up

Materials 6 buttons per player, paper, pencil, bag

Game Directions

1. Copy the words with *ar* below on slips of paper. Put the words in a bag.

2. Take turns choosing a word and reading it aloud.

3. If the word appears on a player's game card, the player puts a button on it.

4. The first player to get 4 buttons in a row (across, down, or diagonally) wins!

Words with *ar*
arm, art, bark, barn, car, card, cart, Clark, dark, dart, farm, hard, harm, jar, mark, park, part, star, stars, start, tar, tart, yard, yarn

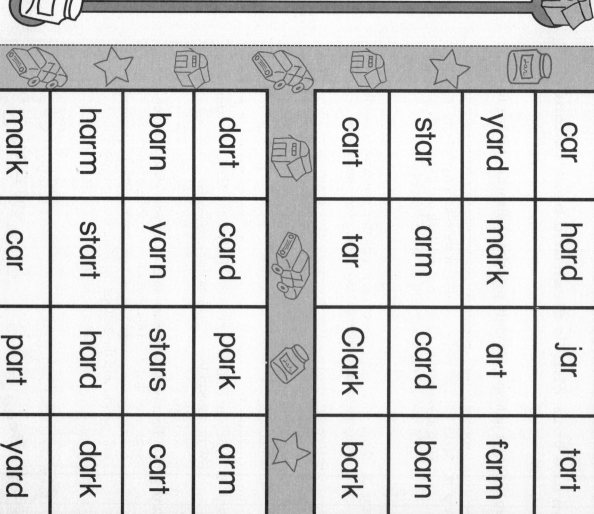

car	hard	jar	tart
star	arm	card	barn
yard	mark	art	farm
cart	tar	Clark	bark

dart	card	park	arm
barn	yarn	stars	cart
harm	start	hard	dark
mark	car	part	yard

Name _____

Circle the word for each picture.

b<u>ar</u>k

1.

pair
park

2.

barn
band

3.

arm
hair

4.

yarn
yam

5.

hard
herd

6.

cold
card

7.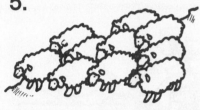

stare
star

8.

cat
cart

9.

car
care

10.

jar
jam

Notes for Home: Your child read words that contain the letters *ar* that represent the vowel sound in *car*. **Home Activity:** Name several words that contain *ar*. Challenge your child to think of a word that rhymes with each one.

Name _____

Add the ending to each word.
Write the new word on the line.

bake   bak**ed**   bak**ing**

1. race + -ing

_____

- -

_____

2. move + -ed

_____

- -

_____

3. ride + -ing

_____

- -

_____

4. rake + -ed

_____

- -

_____

5. smile + -ing

_____

- -

_____

Notes for Home: Your child wrote action words that drop the final *e* when adding the endings *-ed* and *-ing*. ***Home Activity:*** Encourage your child to make up a silly song using three or more of the action words on this page. Together write the words to the song and perform it.

Pick a word from the box to finish each sentence.
Write the word on the line.

children	city	high	place	room

1. I live in the _____ .

2. My home is way up _____ .

3. I have my own _____ .

4. I play with lots of _____ here.

5. It's a great _____ to live!

Notes for Home: This week your child is learning to read the words *children, city, high,*
place, and *room.* ***Home Activity:*** Challenge your child to make up a story using all five of
these words. Then, make a picture book of the story together.

Name _____

Look at the picture.
Read the sentence with the underlined word.
Pick the word from the box to finish the second sentence.
Write the word on the line.

| boat | car | cried | run | sells |

The <u>vendor</u> has flowers for sale.
_____
- - - - - - - - - - - -
1. A *vendor* _____ things.

We took a <u>ferry</u> across the water.
_____
- - - - - - - - - - - -
2. A *ferry* is a _____ .

The unhappy baby <u>wailed</u>.
_____
- - - - - - - - - - - -
3. *Wailed* means the same as _____ .

My mom <u>dashed</u> outside quickly.
_____
- - - - - - - - - - - -
4. To *dash* means to _____ .

We rode in a <u>taxi</u>.
_____
- - - - - - - - - - - -
5. A *taxi* is a kind of _____ .

Notes for Home: Your child used context clues (words that surround an unfamiliar word and help explain its meaning) to figure out the meanings of words. **Home Activity:** Ask your child to point out unfamiliar words in a story. Together, use context clues to help figure out their meanings.

Add **-s** to verbs that tell what
one person, animal, or thing does.
Do **not** add **-s** to verbs that tell
what two or more people,
animals, or things do.

Dad **shops** for food.

Sally and Pam **shop** for food.

Circle the correct verb to finish each sentence.
Write the verb on the line.

ride   rides
_____
- - - - - - - - - - -

1. Jim and I _____ our bikes.

race   races
_____
- - - - - - - - - - -

2. We _____ to the park.

slide   slides
_____
- - - - - - - - - -

3. Jim _____ down.

play   plays
_____
- - - - - - - - - -

4. We _____ tag.

run   runs
_____
- - - - - - - - - -

5. Tom _____ to tag me.

Notes for Home: Your child chose verbs that agree with a singular or plural subject.
Home Activity: Say a verb aloud to your child. Help him or her use the verb correctly in a
sentence to tell about the action of one person or more than one person.

Pick a word from the box to match each clue.
Write the word on the line.

children	city	country	dashing
high	place	room	sealing

1.

2.

_____

- - - - - - - - - - - -

_____

_____

- - - - - - - - - - - -

_____

3. boys and girls

4. running

_____

- - - - - - - - - - - -

_____

_____

- - - - - - - - - - - -

_____

5. not low

6. somewhere, a certain spot

_____

- - - - - - - - - - - -

_____

_____

- - - - - - - - - - - -

_____

7. part of a house

8. closing up

_____

- - - - - - - - - - - -

_____

_____

- - - - - - - - - - - -

_____

Notes for Home: Your child matched vocabulary words and picture clues.
Home Activity: Work with your child to create a simple crossword puzzle using the vocabulary words on this page.

fl<u>ow</u>ers  h<u>ou</u>se

Circle the word for each picture.

1. 	2. 	3. 	4. 
town twin	most mouse	round rope	crown core

5. 	6. 	7. 	8. 
clown crow	front frown	couch coach	grow gown

Find the word that has the same vowel sound as .
Mark the space to show your answer.

9. ⬭ shout
   ⬭ shot
   ⬭ show

10. ⬭ so
    ⬭ soap
    ⬭ sound

 Notes for Home: Your child reviewed words with *ou* and *ow* that represent the vowel sound heard in *house* and *flowers*. **Home Activity:** Have your child say and spell words that rhyme with the *ou* and *ow* words pictured on this page.

arm   barn   farm   hard   park   start

Write two words from the box that rhyme with **harm**.

1. _____   2. _____

Pick a word from the box that rhymes with each word below.
Write the word on the line.

3. yarn _____   4. part _____

5. card _____   6. dark _____

Pick a word that is the opposite of each word below.
Write the word on the line.

7. soft _____   8. stop _____

Pick a word from the box to match each clue.   city   place
Write the word on the line.

9. It rhymes with *face*.   _____

10. It is a very large town.   _____

Notes for Home: Your child spelled words with the *r*-controlled vowel *ar* where the letter *r* changes the vowel sound, as well as two frequently used words: *city, place*. **Home Activity:** Work with your child to write simple rhymes using these spelling words.

Pick a verb from the box to finish each sentence.
Write the verb on the line.

| jump | reads | rings | walk | works |

1. The girls _____ rope.

2. Mom _____ at home.

3. Tom _____ a book.

4. The phone _____ .

5. They _____ to school.

Notes for Home: Your child practiced using verbs in sentences. *Home Activity:* Read a magazine or newspaper with your child. Ask him or her to identify the verb in each sentence.

Test-Taking Tips

1. Write your name on the test.

2. Read each question twice.

3. Read all the answer choices for the question.

4. Mark your answer carefully.

5. Check your answer.

Part 1: Vocabulary

Find the word that best fits in each sentence.
Mark the space for your answer.

1. My kite will fly very _____ .
   ⬭ ripe   ⬭ place   ⬭ high

2. The _____ played in the park.
   ⬭ wheel   ⬭ children   ⬭ country

3. There is not enough _____ for all of us.
   ⬭ room   ⬭ bottle   ⬭ patch

4. Rose was _____ the leaks in the house.
   ⬭ dashing   ⬭ sealing   ⬭ pitching

5. Dick lives in the _____ .
   ⬭ city   ⬭ surface   ⬭ thumb

GO ON

Part 2: Comprehension

Read each question.

Mark the space for your answer.

6. In this story, people wait in line to —
   - ⬭ get on the bus.
   - ⬭ buy tickets.
   - ⬭ eat food.

7. You can tell from the clues in the story that vendors —
   - ⬭ sell things.
   - ⬭ clean the streets.
   - ⬭ ride in cars.

8. You can tell that the people in this story are very —
   - ⬭ busy.
   - ⬭ tired.
   - ⬭ happy.

9. How is the country different from the city?
   - ⬭ There are more cars and noise.
   - ⬭ There are more people.
   - ⬭ There is more room, and it is quiet.

10. What happens when many people move to the country?
   - ⬭ They do not work.
   - ⬭ They ride in taxis.
   - ⬭ The country starts to look like a city.

STOP

Add -ed and **-ing** to each word below.
Write the new words on the lines.

drop dropp**ing** dropp**ed**

	Add -ed		**Add -ing**
rub	1.	2.	
fix	3.	4.	
jog	5.	6.	
hop	7.	8.	

Find the word where you would double the last consonant before adding **-ed** or **-ing**.
Mark the space to show your answer.

9. ○ help
   ○ drum
   ○ ask

10. ○ stop
    ○ work
    ○ mix

Notes for Home: Your child reviewed words that end in *-ed* and *-ing*. **Home Activity:** Read a story together. Look for words that end in *-ed* or *-ing*. Challenge your child to tell you what each base word is, for example, *stop* is the base word for *stopped* and *stopping*.

arm   barn   farm   hard   park   start

Pick a word from the box to match each picture.
Write the word on the line.

1.

_____

2.

_____

3.

_____

Change one letter in each word to make a word from the box.
Write the new word on the line.

4. stars

_____

5. card

_____

6. yarn

_____

Pick a word from the box to finish each tongue twister.
Write the word on the line.

city   place

7. Polly picked a pretty _____ to play.

8. Six seals sit sipping tea in the _____ .

 Notes for Home: Your child spelled words with the *r*-controlled vowel *ar* where the letter *r* changes the vowel sound, as well as two frequently-used words: *city, place*. **Home Activity:** Work with your child to write a poem which includes these spelling words.

RETEACHING

One dog **barks.**   Two dogs **bark.**

Add **-s** to a verb to tell what one person, animal, or thing does.
Do **not** add **-s** to a verb that tells what two or more people,
animals, or things do.

Choose a verb in ( ).
Write the verb on the line.

1. Two cats (meow / meows).   _____

2. One mouse (climb / climbs).   _____

3. Three dogs (run / runs).   _____

Choose the correct verb.
Write it in the sentence.

4. Three fish (swim / swims) _____ .

5. A turtle (swim / swims) _____ fast.

Notes for Home: Your child wrote verbs which agree with the subjects of sentences. *Home Activity:* Read a story with your child and have him or her identify all the singular subjects and verbs on one page. Do the same with plural subjects and verbs.

Name _____

Match each subject to the correct predicate.
Draw a line.

1. Spotted pigs   run very fast.

2. An old cow   kicks a pail.

3. Young horses   play in mud.

4. A brown rooster   sits on a fence.

Choose the correct verb from the box.
Write it on the line to finish each sentence.

> grow   grows   taste   tastes   work   works

5. A farmer _____ in the field.

6. Farmers _____ hard.

7. They _____ corn.

8. A corn plant _____ tall.

9. The sweet corn _____ good.

Notes for Home: Your child matched subjects and verbs that agree in sentences. *Home Activity:* Say a subject. (For example: *The tiny insect*) Have your child finish the sentence by saying a verb that correctly matches the subject and adds more information.

New Best Friends

My Friend Scooter

I've got a friend named Scooter.
I'm meeting him at noon.
He's bringing his new poodle.
We will go swimming soon.

We're bringing gooey noodles.
We're bringing lots of food.
We're bringing chewy cashews,
In case we're in the mood.

Let's not forget our soup spoons,
To use this afternoon.
We'll have a little party.
Let's bring along balloons.

This rhyme includes words your child is working with in school: words with *ew, oo,* and *ou (new, spoons, soup)* and contractions. *(Let's, We'll)* Read aloud "My Friend Scooter" with your child. Make a list of the contractions in the rhyme and identify the two words each contraction represents.

(fold here)

Name: _____

You are your child's first and best teacher!

Here are ways to help your child practice skills while having fun!

Day 1 Write the letters *n't, 's, 'll, 'm, 'd, 're,* and *'ve* on slips of paper. Place them in a hat or bowl. Have your child pick a slip and name a contraction that uses those letters.

Day 2 Work with your child to create a word search puzzle using these words that your child is learning to read: *across, best, either, sometimes,* and *toward.*

Day 3 Read a story with your child. Review key events in the story and ask your child what caused each event to happen.

Day 4 Ask your child to choose a favorite character from a book or movie. Help your child write a paragraph describing how this character looks and behaves.

Day 5 Your child is practicing reading aloud. Encourage him or her to choose a favorite story or poem and read it aloud, using the punctuation to help pace his or her reading.

Read with your child EVERY DAY!

Spinning Vowels

Materials paper circle, paper clip,
pencil, 1 button per player

Game Directions

1. Make a simple spinner as shown.

2. Take turns spinning a letter pair and writing a word
that uses *ew*, *oo*, or *ou* and has the vowel sound
in *new*, *soon*, or *soup*.

3. If the word is written correctly, the player moves
his or her button the number of spaces shown on
the spinner.

4. The first player to reach the end wins!

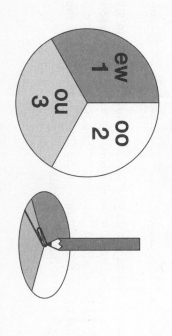

Start

End

Name _____

Circle all the words that have the same vowel sound as **new**.

 **Y<u>ou</u>** have **new** b<u>oo</u>ts!

_____

1. Barb and I have soup every day at noon.

2. You can sit with us too.

3. We'd like a few more friends in the group.

4. I knew making new friends was fun!

_____

Draw a picture of a zoo.
Write a sentence for your picture.

5.

_____
- -
_____
- -
_____

Notes for Home: Your child identified words spelled with *ew, oo,* and *ou* that have the same vowel sound. *Home Activity:* Encourage your child to make up a poem or song using as many rhyming words containing this vowel sound as possible.

Name _____

Pick the contraction that is formed from each pair of words.
Write the contraction on the line.

<u>It is</u> happy.
<u>It's</u> happy.

| don't | he'd | I'll | I'm | let's |
| she's | that's | we're | you're | you've |

1. you + are

_____
- - - - - - - - - - - - - -
_____

2. that + is

_____
- - - - - - - - - - - - - -
_____

3. I + will

_____
- - - - - - - - - - - - - -
_____

4. he + had

_____
- - - - - - - - - - - - - -
_____

5. do + not

_____
- - - - - - - - - - - - - -
_____

6. you + have

_____
- - - - - - - - - - - - - -
_____

7. let + us

_____
- - - - - - - - - - - - - -
_____

8. I + am

_____
- - - - - - - - - - - - - -
_____

9. she + has

_____
- - - - - - - - - - - - - -

10. we + are

_____
- - - - - - - - - - - - - -

Notes for Home: Your child practiced forming contractions. *Home Activity:* Work with your child to make a simple set of flashcards with a word pair (such as *do not*) on one side and the matching contraction (such as *don't*) on the other. Help your child practice contractions using the flash cards.

Name _____

Circle a word to finish each sentence.

| across | best | either | sometimes | toward |

1. We are _____ friends.   across
                                    best

2. Kim lives _____ the street.   either
                                           across

3. I play at her house _____ .   sometimes
                                           toward

4. I'm careful when I walk _____ her house.   toward
                                                         best

5. _____ my sister or my mom helps me.   Across
                                                         Either

Notes for Home: This week your child is learning to read the words *across, best, either, sometimes,* and *toward.* **Home Activity:** Encourage your child to write a story using all five of these words.

Name _____

Look at each picture.
Answer the questions.

I hurt myself **because** I fell down.

1. Why does Pat go to the doctor?

_____
___ ___ ___ ___ ___ ___ ___ ___ ___ ___ ___ ___
_____

2. Why does the baby smile?

_____
___ ___ ___ ___ ___ ___ ___ ___ ___ ___ ___ ___
_____

3. Why can't Pete play ball?

_____
___ ___ ___ ___ ___ ___ ___ ___ ___ ___ ___ ___
_____

Notes for Home: Your child looked at what happened (effect) and told why it happened (cause). **Home Activity:** Read a story with your child. Stop often to ask him or her what happened and why it happened.

Name _____

Some verbs tell what is happening **now**.
Today Jill **walks**.

Verbs with **-ed** tell what happened in the past.
Yesterday Jill **walked**.

Verbs with **will** tell about the future.
Tomorrow Jill **will walk** again.

Read each verb in the box.
Write the verb in the column where it belongs.

asked   eats   hugged   tells

Past	Now
1. _____	3. _____
2. _____	4. _____

Write a sentence about something you will do tomorrow.

5. _____

_____

Notes for Home: Your child learned to identify verbs in the present, past, and future tenses.
Home Activity: Use the verb *jump*. Ask your child to say three sentences that use this verb to tell about something happening now, in the past, and in the future.

Name _____

Circle a word to finish each sentence.

1. John moved _____ town.

across
sometimes

2. He _____ his things in a pile.

toward
dumped

3. He _____ about his new room.

complained
best

4. _____ he missed his friends.

Across
Sometimes

5. He missed his _____ friend most.

toward
best

6. Kevin will visit _____ on Saturday
or Sunday.

across
either

7. John became happy _____ the end
of the week.

toward
either

Notes for Home: Your child used new vocabulary words to complete a story.
Home Activity: Read the vocabulary words on this page aloud. Ask your child to use each
word in a sentence to tell about a good friend.

Name _____

 p**ar**k

Circle the word for each picture.

1.	2.	3.	4.
	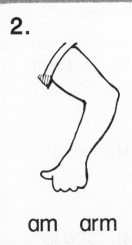		
stars stirs	am arm	shake shark	burn barn

5.	6.	7.	8.

code card	car crate	mark mask	yarn young

Find the word that has the same vowel sound as the picture.
Mark the space to show your answer.

9. ⬭ cat
   ⬭ cart
   ⬭ act

10. ⬭ spark
    ⬭ sprain
    ⬭ speak

 Notes for Home: Your child reviewed words with the *r*-controlled vowel *ar* where the letter *r* changes the vowel sound. **Home Activity:** Ask your child to think of a word that rhymes with one of the words with *ar* pictured above. Have your child spell both words.

Name _____

| I'll | I'm | can't | didn't | he's | she's |

Put each pair of words together to make a word from the box.
Write the word on the line.

1. I will _____

2. did not _____

3. I am _____

4. he is _____

5. can not _____

6. she is _____

Pick a word from the box to finish each sentence. **Write** the
word on the line. Begin with a capital letter.

7. _____ my brother.

8. _____ my sister.

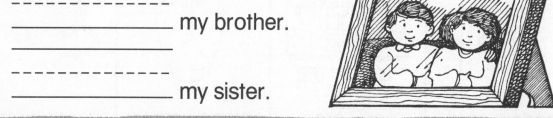

Pick a word from the box to match each clue.
Write the word on the line.

| best |
| sometimes |

9. very good _____

10. once in a while _____

Notes for Home: Your child practiced spelling contractions such as *I'll* and *can't* and two
frequently used words: *best, sometimes.* **Home Activity:** Have your child use each of these
spelling words in a sentence. Work together to write each sentence.

Name _____

Underline the verb or verbs in each sentence.
Circle now, past, or **future** to tell when the action happens.

1. Amy likes her best friend Barb.   now past future

2. Yesterday, they played at Barb's house.   now past future

3. They baked cookies with Barb's mom.   now past future

4. Tomorrow, they will swim at the pond.   now past future

5. Today, they kick a ball.   now past future

Use the verb *play*.
Write three sentences to tell about something now, in the past, and in the future.

6. (now)

_____

- -

_____

7. (past)

_____

- -

_____

8. (future)

_____

- -

_____

Notes for Home: Your child used verbs in the present, past, and future tenses. *Home Activity:* Name a simple verb that your child might know, such as *jump, walk,* or *hop.* Encourage your child to use that verb to describe actions now, in the past, and in the future.

Test-Taking Tips

1. Write your name on the test.

2. Read each question twice.

3. Read all the answer choices for the question.

4. Mark your answer carefully.

5. Check your answer.

Name _____

Part I: Vocabulary

Find the word that best fits in each sentence.
Mark the space for your answer.

1. I get to stay up late _____ .
   ⬭ sometimes   ⬭ around   ⬭ either

2. Josie _____ that she felt sick.
   ⬭ dumped   ⬭ complained   ⬭ returned

3. Mel rode her bike _____ me.
   ⬭ through   ⬭ across   ⬭ toward

4. Dad walked _____ the street.
   ⬭ since   ⬭ across   ⬭ sometimes

5. You can _____ come with us or stay home.
   ⬭ best   ⬭ once   ⬭ either

GO ON ➡

Part 2: Comprehension

Read each question.
Mark the space for your answer.

6. Why did Mouse go home?
   ⬭ Cat did not want to play crazy eights.
   ⬭ Cat had a new friend.
   ⬭ Mouse was tired of games.

7. Cat called *The Hollow Log Gazette* because he wanted to —
   ⬭ buy a newspaper.
   ⬭ try to find a friend.
   ⬭ buy a new game.

8. Who made the biggest mess in Cat's house?
   ⬭ Raccoon
   ⬭ Mouse
   ⬭ Mole

9. When Cat and Mouse play crazy eights, Cat will —
   ⬭ try to find a new friend.
   ⬭ ask Otter to come and watch.
   ⬭ be nicer to Mouse.

10. What did Cat learn in this story?
    ⬭ Mouse would never come back again.
    ⬭ Mouse was his best friend after all.
    ⬭ He could not beat Mouse at checkers.

STOP

Name _____

Add -ed and **-ing** to each word below.   smil~~e~~ + -ed = smil**ed**
Write the new words on the lines.   smil~~e~~ + -ing = smil**ing**

	Add -ed		**Add -ing**
race	1. _____	2. _____
hop	3. _____	4. _____
move	5. _____	6. _____
use	7. _____	8. _____

Find the new word that is formed by adding **-ed** or **-ing**.
Mark the space to show your answer.

9. dance + -ed =
   - ⬭ danceed
   - ⬭ danced
   - ⬭ dancced

10. give + -ing =
   - ⬭ giving
   - ⬭ givving
   - ⬭ giveing

Notes for Home: Your child reviewed words that end with *-ed* and *-ing*. **Home Activity:** Ask
your child to draw pictures showing the actions named by two or more of the words above.
Help your child write a sentence to go with each picture.

I'll   I'm   can't   didn't   he's   she's

Pick a word from the box to replace the underlined words.
Write the word on the line.

_____
- - - - - - - - - - - -
1. I <u>am</u> glad I met Gina and Tony.   _____

_____
- - - - - - - - - - - -
2. I <u>did not</u> know them last year.   _____

_____
- - - - - - - - - - - -
3. <u>He is</u> so funny.   _____

_____
- - - - - - - - - - - -
4. <u>She is</u> funny too.   _____

_____
- - - - - - - - - - - -
5. We <u>cannot</u> stop laughing sometimes.   _____

_____
- - - - - - - - - - - -
6. I <u>will</u> see them both tomorrow.   _____

Pick a word from the box to finish each sentence.
Write the word on the line.

best   sometimes

_____
- - - - - - - - - - - - - - - - -
7. Carlos is my _____ friend.

_____
- - - - - - - - - - - - - - - - -
8. We _____ play baseball together.

Notes for Home: Your child spelled contractions such as *she's* and *didn't* and two frequently
used words: *best, sometimes.* **Home Activity:** Name the two words that each contraction
represents. Have your child name the contraction and write it.

Name _____

RETEACHING

Today Karen **shows** something.
Last week Bob **showed** something.
Next week Lou **will show** something.

The verb **shows** tells about now. It ends with **-s**.
The verb **showed** tells about the past. It ends with **-ed**.
The verb **will show** tells about the future. It begins with **will**.

Underline the verb in each sentence.
Then circle **Now** or **Past**.

1. Today Karen points to a hat.	Now	Past
2. Last time she showed us a trick box.	Now	Past
3. Then Karen explained the trick.	Now	Past
4. Now she turns the hat over.	Now	Past
5. Karen picks the next person.	Now	Past

Circle the correct verb in ( ) for each sentence.

6. Now Flora (looks / looked) into the hat.

7. Next week Bob (talked / will talk) about his dog.

8. Now Karen (pulls / pulled) out a picture.

9. She (shows / will show) the picture tomorrow too.

10. Last Monday Greg (learns / learned) a new game.

Notes for Home: Your child identified verbs in the present, past, and future tenses. ***Home Activity:*** Take a walk with your child and talk about what you see and hear. Help your child use verbs in the correct tenses.

Name _____

Underline the correct verb in ( ) for each sentence.

1. Jessie says she (wants/wanted) to see a movie.

2. A few hours ago she (picks/picked) a show.

3. After that she (walks/walked) to town.

4. Now the movie (ends/ended).

5. Jessie (laughs/laughed) when the movie was over.

6. The same movie (will play/played) next week.

Add -s, -ed, or **will** to each word in the box.
Write the correct verb in each sentence.

talk	ask	learn	explain

7. Last night Jessie _____ about the movie.

8. Today Dad _____ questions.

9. Later Jessie _____ the story.

10. Jessie _____ the story well.

Notes for Home: Your child identified and wrote verbs in the present, past, and future tenses.
Home Activity: Talk with your child about a family event. Help him or her use the present, past, and future tenses correctly.

Doris and Boris

On a street corner,
At Court Street and Fourth,
Doris is running.
She hurries north.

She's a reporter,
Exploring for clues.
She takes her own notes,
Recording the news.

She looks for more clues,
And spies a good source.
The source for her story,
Is Boris, of course!

Boris gives Doris
A clue she can use.
She writes her story,
Reporting the news.

This rhyme includes words your child is working with in school: words with *or, ore,* and *our (for, more, source)* and verbs that change *y* to *i* before adding an ending *(hurries).* Sing "Doris and Boris" with your child. Underline all the words with the vowel sound heard in *D**or**is* spelled *or, ore,* and *our:*

(fold here)

Name: _____

1

You are your child's first and best teacher!

Here are ways to help your child practice skills while having fun!

Day 1 Make a list of words that have the same vowel sound heard in *st**or**m* spelled *or, ore, oor,* and *our,* such as *corner, more, door,* and *your.*

Day 2 Make up a fun song using the words children are learning to read this week: *bring, brought, next, picture,* and *read.*

Day 3 Watch a TV show with your child. Then, ask your child to tell what they learned about the characters in the show.

Day 4 Your child is learning about the importance of a story's title. Read a short story to your child without telling him or her the title. Brainstorm possible titles with your child.

Day 5 Practice using nonverbal communication with your child by playing charades. Take turns acting out a word or phrase for others to guess.

Read with your child EVERY DAY!

4

Add -ed or -es

Materials index cards, markers, coin, 1 button per player

Game Directions

1. Write the verbs shown below on index cards.

2. Take turns picking a card and flipping the coin. If heads, add -ed to the verb. If tails, add -es. Spell the new word aloud.

3. If a player spells the word correctly, the player tosses a button on the gameboard to try to earn points.

4. The first player to earn 15 points wins!

Verbs
carry, try, hurry, cry, marry, fry, worry, copy, dry

Earn 2 points!				Earn 1 point!
	Earn 1 point!		Take 2 points from other players!	Lose 2 points!
Take 2 points from other players!	Earn 3 points!		Earn 2 points!	Earn 6 points!
		Lose 4 points!		Lose 2 points!

Name _____

Pick a word from the box to match each clue.
Write the word on the line.

tore	store	horn	door
pour	fork	corn	sport

<u>Or</u>der in the c<u>our</u>t!

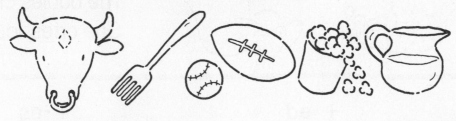

1. something you knock on

_____

2. something on a bull

_____

3. ripped

_____

4. a place where you buy things

_____

5. something to eat with

_____

6. you can play or watch this

_____

7. something you do with a pitcher

_____

8. something you can pop and eat

_____

Notes for Home: Your child read and wrote words with *or, ore, oor,* and *our* where the letter *r* changes the vowel sound. **Home Activity:** Ask your child to think of other words that rhyme with each of the words in the box.

Add -ed and **-es** to each word below.
Write the new words on the lines.

The babies cr**ied**.
She cr**ies** loudly.

Word	+ -ed	+ -es
carry	1. _____	2. _____
hurry	3. _____	4. _____
dry	5. _____	6. _____
try	7. _____	8. _____
study	9. _____	10. _____

 Notes for Home: Your child wrote words in which the final *y* changes to *i* before adding *-ed or -es*.
Home Activity: Challenge your child to use several of the words in the second and third columns in sentences. Check whether your child uses *-ed* for past actions and *-es* for present actions.

Pick a word from the box to finish each sentence.
Write the word on the line.

| bring | brought | next | picture | read |

_____
----

1. What kind of present did you _____ Lil?

_____
- - - - - - - - - - - - - - - - - - -

2. I _____ a book.

_____
- - - - - - - - - - - - - - - - - -

3. I hope she hasn't _____ it yet.

_____
- - - - - - - - - - - - - - - - - -

4. It has a nice _____ of a cat on the cover.

_____
- - - - - - - - - - - - - - - - - -

5. Lil will open my present _____ !

Notes for Home: This week your child is learning to read the words *bring, brought, next,*
picture, and *read.* **Home Activity:** Challenge your child to make up a story about a party
using these words.

Name _____

Write a word from the box to name each person.

> doctor   painter   teacher   vet

1. I help sick people. I take care of them. I help them feel well.

   _____

   I am a _____ .

   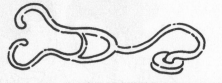

2. I help you learn. I read lots of books. I work in a school.

   _____

   I am a _____ .

3. I take care of cats and dogs. I help them feel well.

   _____

   I am a _____ .

4. I draw and paint. I use lots of pretty colors.

   _____

   I am a _____ .

Draw a picture of one of the people described.
Show something this person does.

5.

Notes for Home: Your child identified characters based on things they say and do.
Home Activity: Read a story with your child. Name characters from the story. Have your child describe each character and tell how he or she knows what the character is like.

Name _____

Be sure to use the correct verb to show something happening in the past, now, or in the future.

Today we **study**.
Yesterday she **studied**.
Tomorrow we **will study**.

Circle the correct verb to finish each sentence.
Write the verb on the line.

rains   rained

_____

1. Yesterday it _____ .

hurry   hurried

_____

2. We ran and _____ inside.

rained   will rain

_____

3. Tomorrow it _____ again.

shines   will shine

_____

4. Now the sun _____ .

play   played

_____

5. Now we _____ outside!

 Notes for Home: Your child chose the correct verb to show actions in the past, present, and future. **Home Activity:** Have your child tell you what he or she did yesterday, what he or she is doing now, and what he or she will do tomorrow. Listen for the correct verb tenses.

Name _____

Pick a word from the box to finish each sentence.
Write the word on the line.

| brought | camera | dinosaurs |
| exact | next | order |

1. We saw some _____ .

2. Mary had a _____ .

3. I _____ mine too.

4. The class stood _____ to the bones.

5. The class stood in _____ from tallest to shortest.

6. A picture is an _____ copy.

Notes for Home: Your child used new vocabulary words to complete sentences.
Home Activity: Read the vocabulary words on this page. Have your child use each word in a sentence.

Name _____

Look at the table of contents from a book of fairy tales.
Write the answer to each question.

Favorite Fairy Tales	
Contents	
Cinderella	.3
Sleeping Beauty	10
Three Little Pigs	15
Rumpelstiltskin	.21
Rapunzel	.26

1. How many stories are in this book? _____

2. What is the name of the first story?
   _____
   _____

3. On what page does "Sleeping Beauty" start? _____

4. Which story comes before "Rumpelstiltskin"?
   _____
   _____

5. What is the name of the last story?
   _____
   _____

Notes for Home: Your child read a table of contents and answered questions about it. *Home Activity:* Look through books in your home or at the library. Compare different tables of contents and talk about the information each one shows.

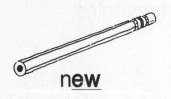 n**ew**

 ball**oo**ns

 gr**ou**p

Circle the word for each picture.

1. nose   news

2. soup   soap

3. moon   mine

4. broom   brim

5. school   skill

6. stay   stew

7. crew   cry

8. spine   spoon

Find the word that has the same vowel sound as the picture.
Mark the space to show your answer.

9. ⬭ few
   ⬭ feet
   ⬭ foot

10. ⬭ you
    ⬭ your
    ⬭ young

 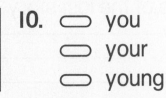

 Notes for Home: Your child reviewed words with *ew, oo,* and *ou* that have the same vowel sound (*new, balloons,* and *group*). **Home Activity:** Say one of the words with *ew, oo,* or *ou* on this page, and ask your child to say a rhyming word spelled the same way.

Name _____

| door | corn | horse | more | pour | store |

Write four words from the box that rhyme with **snore**.

1. _____

2. _____

3. _____

4. _____

Pick a word from the box to match each picture.
Write the word on the line.

5.

_____

6.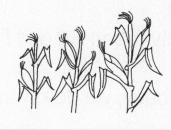

_____

Pick a word from the box to finish each sentence.
Write the word on the line.

brought
picture

7. My friend _____ her pet mouse to school.

8. Since my pet is a horse, I will bring a

_____ of him instead.

Notes for Home: Your child spelled words where the letter *r* changes the way a vowel sounds (*door, corn, more,* and *pour*) and two frequently used words: *brought, picture.* **Home Activity:** Say each word twice. Have your child spell it and use it in a sentence.

Name _____

Circle the correct verb to finish each sentence.

1. Last week, we (plays / played) a guessing game in school.

2. We (will guess / guessed) how many pencils were in a jar.

3. My friend Bill and I (studied / study) the jar all week long.

4. Today, we (talks / talk) about who will win.

5. Tomorrow, the teacher (counted / will count) the pencils.

6. The winner (walked / will walk) first in line all next week.

7. Yesterday, Bill (will change / changed) his guess.

8. Today, I (hope / hoped) that I win.

9. I (finds / will find) out tomorrow.

10. We (played / will play) another game next week!

Notes for Home: Your child chose verbs in the present, past, and future tenses. *Home Activity:* Write *today, yesterday,* and *tomorrow* on three sheets of paper. Work with your child to write sentences using present, past, and future tenses to describe different actions.

Name _____

Part 1: Vocabulary

Find the word that best fits in each sentence.
Mark the space for your answer.

1. Lee _____ a dog to school.
   ◯ drew   ◯ giggled   ◯ brought

2. Will you take a picture with my _____ ?
   ◯ order   ◯ camera   ◯ mirror

3. _____ were very big animals.
   ◯ Dinosaurs   ◯ Scales   ◯ Friends

4. Who is _____ in line?
   ◯ toward   ◯ clean   ◯ next

5. Les knew the _____ number.
   ◯ either   ◯ exact   ◯ between

GO ON ➡

Part 2: Comprehension

Read each question.
Mark the space for your answer.

6. What is special about Cam Jansen?
    - ⬭ She knows how to use a camera.
    - ⬭ She does not forget things.
    - ⬭ She gets lost.

7. What did the children do first?
    - ⬭ played musical chairs
    - ⬭ ate birthday cake
    - ⬭ wrote numbers on slips of paper

8. How did Cam know that Robert made his guess after the others?
    - ⬭ Robert told her he had guessed twice.
    - ⬭ There was some cake on the paper.
    - ⬭ Robert had the best guess.

9. How is Eric different from Robert?
    - ⬭ Eric wins every game.
    - ⬭ Eric shares the dinosaurs.
    - ⬭ Eric does not like cake.

10. Of all the children, Cam was best at —
    - ⬭ finding answers to questions.
    - ⬭ playing musical chairs.
    - ⬭ guessing the right numbers.

STOP

Name _____

Put each pair of words together to make a contraction.
Write the contraction on the line.   I + am = **I'm**

1. do not

_____

- - - - - - - - - - - - - - - - - -

_____

2. could not

_____

- - - - - - - - - - - - - - - - - -

_____

3. that is

_____

- - - - - - - - - - - - - - - - - -

_____

4. here is

_____

- - - - - - - - - - - - - - - - - -

_____

5. I will

_____

- - - - - - - - - - - - - - - - - -

_____

6. we are

_____

- - - - - - - - - - - - - - - - - -

_____

7. let us

_____

- - - - - - - - - - - - - - - - - -

_____

8. you are

_____

- - - - - - - - - - - - - - - - - -

_____

Find the contraction that is made by putting each pair of
words together.
Mark the space to show your answer.

9. we have
   - ⬭ we've
   - ⬭ wave
   - ⬭ we'd

10. it is
   - ⬭ its
   - ⬭ its'
   - ⬭ it's

Notes for Home: Your child reviewed contractions such as *don't, I'll,* and *couldn't.*
Home Activity: With your child, make a list of other contractions you know. For each
contraction you list, write the two words it represents.

| door | corn | horse | more | pour | store |

Pick a word from the box to match each clue.
Write the word on the line.

1. an animal you can ride
_____
- - - - - - - - - - - - - - -.
_____

2. a greater amount
_____
- - - - - - - - - - - - - - -.
_____

3. a place to shop
_____
- - - - - - - - - - - - - - -.
_____

4. something you eat or pop
_____
- - - - - - - - - - - - - - -.
_____

5. something you knock on
_____
- - - - - - - - - - - - - - -.
_____

6. something you do to milk
_____
- - - - - - - - - - - - - - -.
_____

Pick a word from the box to finish each sentence.
Write the word on the line.

brought
picture

_____
- - - - - - - - - - - - - - -.

7. I _____ this drawing to show you.

_____
- - - - - - - - - - - - - - -.

8. That's a great _____ of a dinosaur!

Notes for Home: Your child spelled words where the letter *r* changes the way a vowel sounds (*door, corn, more*, and *pour*) and two frequently used words: *brought, picture*. **Home Activity:** Scramble the letters of each spelling word and have your child unscramble each word.

Name _____

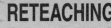

Today it **rains**.
Yesterday it **rained**.
Tomorrow it **will rain**.

Be sure to use the correct verb to show something happening now, in the past, or in the future.

Circle the verb in each sentence.
Then **write** the verb.

1. They stayed inside.

_____

2. Jason plays a game.

_____

3. Kim will watch TV.

_____

4. Ann cleaned her room.

Underline the correct verb in ( ) for each sentence.

5. Yesterday Jason (paint / painted) a picture.

6. Tomorrow Kim (color / will color) with crayons.

7. Now the dog (jumps / jumped) on them.

Notes for Home: Your child identified and wrote verbs in the correct tenses in sentences.
Home Activity: Write a sentence on a piece of paper, leaving out the verb. *(Yesterday we _____ a movie.)* Have your child write a verb in the correct tense.

Add -ed, -s, or **will** to the words in ( ).

1. An hour ago we (turn) _____ the lights off.

2. Soon Mike (walk) _____ into the room.

3. Then Barbara (yell) _____, "Surprise!"

4. Now she (hide) _____.

Complete each sentence with a verb from the box.

> **will open   play   thanked   laughed**

5. Mike _____ at our trick.

6. Soon Mike _____ his presents.

7. He _____ everyone for the surprise.

8. Now we _____ the new games.

 Notes for Home: Your child completed sentences by adding verbs in the correct tenses. **Home Activity:** Choose a verb and have your child write sentences, using that verb in the present, past, and future tenses.

When I Grow Older

My older sister likes to read a good book.
My older brother likes to stir and cook.

When I grow older, I could read this book.
When I grow older, I could learn to cook.

My older sister likes to fish in the brook.
My older brother likes to bait the hook.

When I grow older, I could fish in the brook.
When I grow older, I could bait the hook.

I am the youngest child of us all.
I look and listen because I'm small!

This rhyme includes words your child is working with in school: words with *oo* and *ou* (*book*, *could*) and words that end in *-er* and *-est*. Read aloud "When I Grow Older" with your child. Then, take turns comparing family members. For example: *My hair is longer than yours. But my sister has the longest hair of all.*

(fold here)

Name: _____

You are your child's first and best teacher!

Here are ways to help your child practice skills while having fun!

Day 1 Write the word *took* on the left side of a sheet of paper and the word *could* on the right side. List other words with *oo* and *ou* that have the same vowel sound as the word at the top of each column.

Day 2 Hold a reading bee with your child and his or her friends. Have the children read a word and use it in a sentence. Include these words: *beautiful, become, even, great,* and *together.*

Day 3 Watch a movie with your child. When you finish, encourage your child to tell what happened in the story using just a few sentences.

Day 4 Work with your child to write a paragraph comparing and contrasting two friends or family members.

Day 5 Make a set of flash cards with the verbs *is, are, was, were,* and *will be.* Have your child pick a card and use the verb in a sentence.

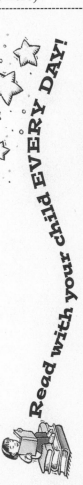

Read with your child EVERY DAY!

The Comparing Game

Materials paper circle, paper clip, pencil, marker

Game Directions

1. Make a simple spinner as shown.

2. Players take turns spinning and moving on the gameboard.

3. When a player lands on a space with a word, he or she must say and spell that word using -er and -est endings.

4. If the word is spelled correctly for both endings, the player follows the directions on the space. The first player to reach the end wins!

1	2
3	4

Start →

End

| **tall** Spin again |

| **wide** Move forward 3 spaces |

| **big** Move forward 2 spaces |

| **small** Spin again |

| **little** Move forward 4 spaces |

| **fat** Move forward 1 space |

2

3

Write the letters **oo** or **ou** on the lines to make a word.
Look at the words in the box if you need help.

cook	could	foot	look
should	took	would	wood

b<u>oo</u>k

1. sh _____ ld

2. l _____ k

3. w _____ d

4. t _____ k

5. c _____ k

6. c _____ ld

7. w _____ ld

8. f _____ t

Write two sentences.
Use a word from the box in each sentence.

9. _____

10. _____

Notes for Home: Your child wrote words with *oo* and *ou* that have the same vowel sound
(*book* and *would*). **Home Activity:** Name other words with this vowel sound. Challenge your
child to tell how each word is spelled.

Name _____

Circle a word to finish each sentence.

Spot is **big**.
Rover is **bigg_er_**.
Spike is **bigg_est_**!

---

1. Bobby is _____ than Jimmy.

sadder
saddest

---

2. The spotted one is the _____ .

smaller
smallest

---

3. Jack is _____ than Ned.

taller
tallest

---

4. Jill is the _____ of all.

wetter
wettest

---

5. This clown is _____ than that one.

fatter
fattest

Notes for Home: Your child used adjectives that end in *-er* and *-est* to complete sentences.
Home Activity: Look for objects or people in your neighborhood. Ask your child to compare
them, using adjectives such as *bigger, smallest, tallest,* and *younger.*

Pick a word from the box to finish each sentence.
Write the word on the line.

| beautiful | become | even | great | together |

_____

_ _ _ _ _ _ _ _ _ _ _ _ _ _ _

1. They keep their pets _____ .

_____

_ _ _ _ _ _ _ _ _ _ _ _ _ _ _ _

2. They have a _____ time with them.

_____

_ _ _ _ _ _ _ _ _ _ _ _ _ _ _ _

3. They _____ feed them at the same time.

_____

_ _ _ _ _ _ _ _ _ _ _ _ _ _ _ _

4. One day their pets will _____ frogs.

_____

_ _ _ _ _ _ _ _ _ _ _ _ _ _ _ _

5. Frogs are not ugly. They're _____ .

Notes for Home: This week your child is learning to read the words *beautiful, become, even, great,* and *together.* **Home Activity:** Have your child use these sentences as models for writing his or her own sentences about a pet he or she has or would like to have.

Name _____

Write a sentence that tells what each passage is mostly about.
Draw a picture that shows what each passage is mostly about.

Dogs may be different in many ways.
Some dogs are long and thin. Some are small.
Some are very big.

1. _____

2.

Barney is Terry's cat. Barney follows Terry everywhere.
He sleeps on her bed every night.
He even sits by her when she eats.

3. _____

4.

Notes for Home: Your child read a passage and wrote a sentence to tell what it was mostly about.
Home Activity: Talk about a story your child is familiar with. Ask him or her to tell what the story is mostly about in just a few sentences.

The verbs **is, are, was, were,** and **will be** do not show action.
The verbs **is** and **are** tell about now.
The verbs **was** and **were** tell about the past.
The verb **will be** tells about the future.

Circle the correct verb to finish each sentence.
Write the verb on the line.

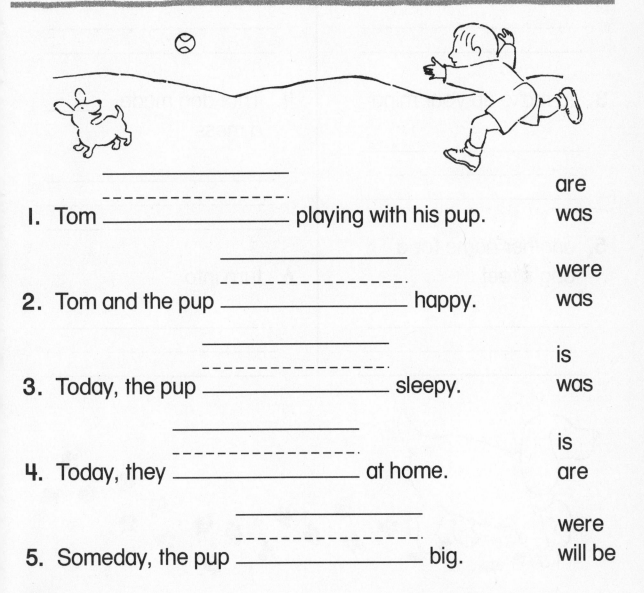

1. Tom _____ playing with his pup.   are / was

2. Tom and the pup _____ happy.   were / was

3. Today, the pup _____ sleepy.   is / was

4. Today, they _____ at home.   is / are

5. Someday, the pup _____ big.   were / will be

Notes for Home: Your child used the verbs *is, are, was, were,* and *will be* in sentences. **Home Activity:** Write *Now, Past,* and *Future* on sheets of paper. Help your child write sentences on each sheet, using the verbs *is, are, was, were,* and *will be.*

Pick a word from the box to match each clue.
Write the word on the line.

| beautiful | become | bubbles |
| decide | paws | quite |

1.  _____

_____

2. very pretty
_____

_____

3. to make up your mind
_____

_____

4. That dog made _____ a mess!
_____

_____

5. another name for a dog's feet
_____

_____

6. turn into
_____

_____

Notes for Home: Your child matched vocabulary words with word and picture clues.
Home Activity: Make a list of four or five words that your child thinks are challenging.
Work together to write a clue like those above for each word.

 th**or**n

 c**ore**

 d**oor**

 f**our**

Circle the word for each picture.

1.

acorn   actor

2.

corn   coin

3.

snore   snare

4.

floor   flower

5.

stare   store

6.

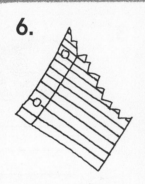

turn   torn

7.

hers   horse

8.

peer   pour

Find the word that has the same vowel sound as the picture.
Mark the space to show your answer.

9. ⬭ stork
⬭ stock
⬭ stir

10. ⬭ firm
⬭ four
⬭ few

Notes for Home: Your child reviewed words that contain the *r*-controlled vowels *or, ore, oor,* and *our,* found in *thorn, core, door,* and *four.* **Home Activity:** Ask your child to draw pictures illustrating some of the words on this page. Help your child label each picture.

| book | hood | shook | stood | took | wood |

Write three words from the box that rhyme with **good**.

1. _____ 2. _____ 3. _____

Write three words from the box that rhyme with **look**.

4. _____ 5. _____ 6. _____

Pick a word from the box to match each picture.
Write the word on the line.

7. _____

8. _____

Pick a word from the box to finish each sentence.
Write the word on the line.

become
even

9. When I read, I _____ part of the story.

10. I _____ pretend I am the hero!

Notes for Home: Your child spelled words with *oo* that have the same vowel sound heard in *book* and two frequently used words: *become, even*. **Home Activity:** Have your child use each spelling word in a sentence. Together, write each sentence.

Name _____

Use words that help show how two things are alike or different.

Cats need water.
Dogs **also** need water.

Circle a word in ( ) to finish each sentence.

1. (Both/Two) cats and dogs like living with people.

2. Cats make good pets. But lions do (know/not).

3. Pets need love just (like/same) people do.

4. A dog's needs are (same/different) from a bird's needs.

Write a sentence that compares two animals.
Use the word **both** in your sentence.

5. _____

_____

_____

Notes for Home: Your child identified words that show comparisons and contrasts. *Home Activity:* Ask your child to compare and contrast two different animals. Have him or her tell how they are alike and how they are different.

Name _____

Circle a verb in ( ) to finish each sentence.

1. Today Jill and I (is / are) playing ball.

2. Jill (is / are) my best friend.

3. Tomorrow we (was / will be) at school.

4. Last week Jill (was / will be) sick.

5. But today she (is / are) feeling better.

6. Last year, Jill and I (are / were) not friends.

7. I (was / will be) living in a different town then.

8. I hope we (were / will be) friends forever!

Write two sentences about your friends.
Use one of these verbs in each sentence: *is, are, was, were,* and *will be.*

_____
9. -
_____

_____
10. -
_____

Notes for Home: Your child practiced using the verbs *is, are, was, were,* and *will be.*
Home Activity: Write these verbs on slips of paper. Take turns picking a verb and using it in a sentence.

Part I: Vocabulary

Find the word that best fits in each sentence.
Mark the space for your answer.

1. Sue saw a _____ red bird.
   ⬭ mirror   ⬭ beautiful   ⬭ ripe

2. Ted will _____ a fireman when he grows up.
   ⬭ become   ⬭ decide   ⬭ keep

3. A dog has four _____ .
   ⬭ brains   ⬭ tools   ⬭ paws

4. Kat blew big _____ .
   ⬭ messages   ⬭ bubbles   ⬭ wheels

5. Ben is _____ tall for his age.
   ⬭ quite   ⬭ around   ⬭ between

GO ON ➡

Part 2: Comprehension

Read each question.
Mark the space for your answer.

6. What happens first in this story?
   - ⬭ Moonbear goes shopping.
   - ⬭ Splash grows four legs.
   - ⬭ Moonbear finds a pet.

7. You can tell that Bear —
   - ⬭ likes his new pet a lot.
   - ⬭ does not take good care of his pet.
   - ⬭ is mean to his new pet.

8. Little Bird thought that Splash —
   - ⬭ should be in a pool.
   - ⬭ wanted to be a bird.
   - ⬭ was growing paws.

9. How did Splash get out of the pool?
   - ⬭ She hopped out.
   - ⬭ Someone took her out.
   - ⬭ She flew out.

10. This story is about two friends who learn that —
    - ⬭ they should not fight about silly things.
    - ⬭ everyone should be a bird.
    - ⬭ fish grow up to be frogs.

STOP

Add -ed to each verb.
Write the new word on the line.

cr$\cancel{y}$ + -es = cr**ies**

cr$\cancel{y}$ + -ed = cr**ied**

1. fry _____

2. help _____

3. try _____

4. reply _____

Add -es to each verb.
Write the new word on the line.

5. hurry _____

6. dry _____

7. fix _____

8. worry _____

Find the word where **-es** has been added to a verb.
Mark the space to show your answer.

9. ⬭ cars
   ⬭ carries
   ⬭ canes

10. ⬭ mares
    ⬭ marry
    ⬭ marries

Notes for Home: Your child reviewed words that end with *-ed* and *-es,* including words where the final *y* is changed to an *i* before *-ed* or *-es* is added. **Home Activity:** Ask your child to spell other words in which *y* changes to *i* before *-ed* or *-es* is added, such as *bury, study,* and *carry.*

Name _____

Find the words from the box in the puzzle.
They may go across or down.
Circle each word in the puzzle.
Write the words on the lines.

book	hood	shook
stood	took	wood

```
s  t  o  o  d  x  g  l  b  w
b  v  y  b  o  o  k  o  p  o
t  a  c  y  u  w  e  u  i  o
o  h  o  o  d  h  q  w  y  d
o  h  j  g  o  s  y  k  e  c
k  s  s  h  o  o  k  n  y  v
```

1. _____

2. _____

3. _____

4. _____

5. _____

6. _____

Pick a word from the box to finish each sentence.
Write the word on the line.

become
even

7. A tadpole will _____ a frog.

8. It will _____ grow legs!

Notes for Home: Your child spelled words with the letters *oo* that have the same vowel sound heard in *book* and two frequently used words: *become, even.* **Home Activity:** Work with your child to write and illustrate a story using these spelling words.

Circle the word in ( ) that makes sense in each sentence.

We (are / is) going to school today.

Tomorrow I (was / will be) staying home.

The verbs **is, are, was, were,** and **will be** do not show action.
The verbs **is** and **are** tell about now.
The verbs **was** and **were** tell about the past.
The verb **will be** tells about the future.

Draw lines to connect sentence parts and make sentences.

1. The sun	is cool.	5.	The sky	are up.
2. Boats	is bright.	6.	The sails	is clear.
3. The lake	are ready.	7.	Dina	is busy.
4. The races	are today.			

Underline the correct word in ( ) for each sentence.

8. The show (was / were) exciting.

9. Many people (was / were) there.

10. It (was / were) lots of fun.

Write a sentence using **will be.**

_____

_____

_____

_____

Notes for Home: Your child wrote forms of the verb *to be,* such as *is, was, are, were,* and *will be,* in sentences. **Home Activity:** Talk with your child about what he or she did last year that is different from this year. Remind your child to use the correct forms of the verb *to be.*

Write **is, are, was, were,** or **will be** to complete each sentence correctly.

1. Dad and I _____ hiking for hours this morning.

2. When we got there, Lost Lake _____ very crowded.

3. Now Dad _____ looking for a different lake.

4. He said, "We _____ not going to camp with the crowd."

5. We _____ cold and wet when we set up the tent.

6. I _____ so happy when we go back home!

Notes for Home: Your child completed sentences by adding forms of the verb *to be (is, are, was, were, will be)*. **Home Activity:** Write *is, are, was, were,* and *will be* on cards. Have your child choose a card and write a sentence with that form of the verb *to be.*

Correct each sentence.
Write it on the line.
Hint: Make sure that verbs are used correctly.

1. They plays together.

_____
- -
_____

2. Now the big cat roll over.

_____
- -
_____

3. Now the kitten are jumping up.

_____
- -
_____
- -
_____

4. It is born last month.

_____
- -
_____

5. It is big someday.

_____
- -
_____

Notes for Home: Your child corrected verbs in sentences. *Home Activity:* Read a sentence from a story aloud to your child, leaving out the verb. Have your child give a verb that makes sense in the sentence.

Words I Can Now Read and Write

It Happens Once a Year

Our family game is almost here.
My family comes from far and near.
They bring their bats. They bring their gear.
It happens once a year.

Suddenly, dreary clouds appear.
But it will clear. We have no fear!
Our family game is almost here.
It happens once a year.

The clouds are gone. The sky is clear.
We start to play. We start to cheer.
Our family game is finally here.
It happens once a year.

This rhyme includes words your child is working with in school: words with *eer* and *ear* where the letter *r* changes the vowel sound (*cheer, near*) and words with the suffix -*ly* (*suddenly, finally*). Sing "It Happens Once a Year" together. Clap when you hear a word that rhymes with *year*.

(fold here)

Name: _____

You are your child's first and best teacher!

Here are ways to help your child practice skills while having fun!

Day 1 Work with your child to make up a silly poem using as many words as you can that rhyme with *deer* and *year*.

Day 2 Write these words on index cards: *ago, better, head, idea,* and *still*. Take turns picking a card and giving a clue about the word for the other players to guess.

Day 3 After shopping for food together, point out to your child how your food storage is organized. Then, have your child help with sorting and putting the groceries away.

Day 4 Read a story with your child. Ask your child to point out clue words that tell when something happened, such as *long ago, first, then,* or *finally.*

Day 5 Your child is learning to use adjectives that describe number (*two*), size (*large*), and shape (*round*). Point out different household objects and ask your child to describe their number, size, and shape.

Read with your child EVERY DAY!

4

Lift and Spell

Materials   20 buttons per player

Game Directions

1. Cover each of the words on the gameboard with a button.

2. Players take turns lifting a button off one word.

3. A player must add -ly to that word and spell the new word correctly to keep the button. If incorrect, the player returns the button.

4. When all the buttons have been lifted, the player with the most buttons wins!

Finish

slow	happy	sure	sudden
glad	sweet	nice	love
near	clean	angry	soft
short	swift	quick	loud
brave	kind	sharp	hungry

Name _____

Circle a word to finish each sentence.
Write the word on the line.

y**ear**   st**eer**

1. Did you _____ ?   hear
   heart

2. It was a singing _____ !   dare
   deer

3. He sat very _____ to us.   near
   next

4. I had no _____ .   fair
   fear

5. It was _____ that he was friendly.   clear
   close

Notes for Home: Your child read and wrote words with *ear* and *eer,* such as *year* and *steer.*
Home Activity: Ask your child to write a silly poem with words that rhyme with *year* and
steer. Challenge your child to use as many *ear* and *eer* words as possible.

Name _____

Add -ly to each word.
Write the new word on the line.

happi**ly**

---

1. lucky _____

2. quick _____

3. loud _____

4. near _____

5. slow _____

6. final _____

7. sure _____

8. soft _____

Draw a picture of an animal that moves slowly and one that moves quickly.

9. slowly

10. quickly

Notes for Home: Your child has learned to form words with the suffix -*ly*. **Home Activity:** Help your child make a list of words with the suffix -*ly*. Work together to use these words in sentences.

Name _____

Pick a word from the box to finish each sentence.
Write the word on the line.

| ago | better | head | idea | still |

_____
- - - - - - - - - - - - - -

1. A long time _____ there were two cold bears.

_____
- - - - - - - - - - - - - -

2. One bear had a good _____ .

_____
- - - - - - - - - - - - - -

3. He put a hat on his _____ .

_____
- - - - - - - - - - - - - -

4. But he was _____ cold.

_____
- - - - - - - - - - - - - -

5. His friend had a _____ idea.
   She used two hats!

Notes for Home: This week your child is learning to read the words *ago, better, head, idea,*
and *still.* **Home Activity:** Make up a story together that begins: *A long time ago* . . . Use the
words from the box in your story.

Name _____

Look at the words and pictures.
Write each sport on the correct line.

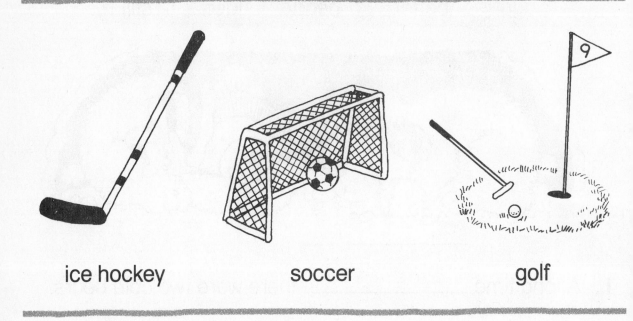

ice hockey   soccer   golf

I. sport with only a round ball

_____

- -

_____

2. sport with a stick and a puck

_____

- -

_____

3. sport with a stick and a round ball

_____

- -

_____

Notes for Home: Your child learned to classify objects. *Home Activity:* Invite your child to
help you sort clean laundry. Discuss all the ways the laundry could be sorted, i.e., pattern,
size, color, who it belongs to, kind of clothing (socks, shirts, and so on).

Name _____

An **adjective** describes a noun.
An adjective may tell how many,
what size, or what shape.

<u>Two</u> bears play ball.
A **small** bat flies by.
The ball is **round**.

Circle the adjective in each sentence.
Draw a line from each sentence to the picture it matches.

1. There is one boy walking.   a.

2. The clock is round.   b.

3. I see a big bear.   c.

4. I have three balls.   d.

5. She has a square flag.   e.

Notes for Home: Your child identified adjectives that show number, size, and shape.
Home Activity: Play an I-Spy game with your child. Take turns picking something in the
room and giving the other person clues that describe number, size, or shape.

Name _____

Pick a word from the box to match each clue.
Write the word in the puzzles. The circled letters spell two words.

| ago | better | creature | head | lose | still | team |

1. sounds like *hill*

2. where your eyes and ears are

3. not worse

4. a long, long time _____

5. animal

6. a group of people playing together

7. not win

He c**ou**ldn't reach the b**oo**ks.

Circle the word for each picture.

1.	2.	3.	4.
hood hide	hook hike	shore should	shook sock

5.	6.	7.	8.
crook creak	cork cook	could cold	fold foot

Find the word that has the same vowel sound as the picture.
Mark the space to show your answer.

9. ⬭ won
   ⬭ would
   ⬭ world

10. ⬭ took
    ⬭ top
    ⬭ too

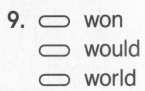

Notes for Home: Your child reviewed words with *oo* and *ou* that have the same vowel sound heard in *couldn't* and *books*. **Home Activity:** Ask your child to tell you about things he or she could do, using words with this vowel sound. *(I could look at a book.)*

| bravely | friendly | lightly | slowly | softly | weekly |

Add -ly to each word below to make a word from the box.
Write the new word on the line.

1. light

_____

- - - - - - - - - - - - - - - - - -

_____

2. week

_____

- - - - - - - - - - - - - - - - - -

_____

3. soft

_____

- - - - - - - - - - - - - - - - - -

_____

4. brave

_____

- - - - - - - - - - - - - - - - - -

_____

5. slow

_____

- - - - - - - - - - - - - - - - - -

_____

6. friend

_____

- - - - - - - - - - - - - - - - - -

_____

Pick a word from the box to finish each sentence.
Write the word on the line.

| ago | head |

_____

- - - - - - - - - - - -

7. We had a contest two days _____ .

_____

- - - - - - - - - - - -

8. I raced with a book on my _____ .

Notes for Home: Your child spelled words that end with *-ly* and two frequently used words:
ago, head. **Home Activity:** Say each spelling word, then use it in a sentence. Invite your child
to act out the sentence.

Pick an adjective from the box to finish each sentence.
Write the adjective on the line. Use each word only once.

| best | great | many | round | tall |

1. We are playing a _____ game.

2. We try to kick a _____ ball into the net.

3. Our team has two _____ players.

4. We score _____ goals.

5. Soccer is the _____ sport.

Notes for Home: Your child completed sentences using adjectives for number, size, and shape. *Home Activity:* Take turns describing an object in a room using adjectives. The other player tries to guess the object being described.

Test-Taking Tips

1. Write your name on the test.

2. Read each question twice.

3. Read all the answer choices for the question.

4. Mark your answer carefully.

5. Check your answer.

Name _____

Part 1: Vocabulary

Find the word that best fits in each sentence.
Mark the space for your answer.

1. It is time for lunch, but Meg is _____ sleeping.
   ○ still   ○ between   ○ across

2. The dinosaurs lived a long time _____ .
   ○ tomorrow   ○ quite   ○ ago

3. Jed will _____ the game.
   ○ climb   ○ lose   ○ peel

4. The ant is a tiny _____ .
   ○ surface   ○ creature   ○ picture

5. Put a hat on your _____ !
   ○ city   ○ team   ○ head

GO ON

Part 2: Comprehension

Read each question.
Mark the space for your answer.

6. The Birds and Animals have a —
   - ⬭ ball game.
   - ⬭ card game.
   - ⬭ jumping game.

7. Which one belongs on the same team as a dog?
   - ⬭ Fox
   - ⬭ Crane
   - ⬭ Hawk

8. How is Bat **not** like all the others?
   - ⬭ He has wings and teeth.
   - ⬭ He plays in the game.
   - ⬭ He can fly.

9. Who takes the ball from Crane at the end of the game?
   - ⬭ Bear
   - ⬭ Hawk
   - ⬭ Bat

10. You can tell from this story that bats do not —
    - ⬭ come out at night.
    - ⬭ fly south for the winter.
    - ⬭ use their wings much.

STOP

Name _____

big   bigg**er**   bigg**est**

Circle a word in ( ) to finish each sentence.

1. The football is (bigger / biggest) than the baseball.

2. The basketball is the (larger / largest) ball.

3. The baseball is the (smaller / smallest).

4. The (heavier / heaviest) ball is the bowling ball.

5. Jan is (taller / tallest) than Bill.

6. Jill is the (faster / fastest) runner of all.

7. Bill is (slower / slowest) than Jill.

8. Is Bill (quicker / quickest) than Jan?

Find the word that you could use to compare three things.
Mark the space to show your answer.

9. ⬭ wet
   ⬭ wetter
   ⬭ wettest

10. ⬭ loud
    ⬭ louder
    ⬭ loudest

Notes for Home: Your child reviewed words with the comparative endings *-er* and *-est,* such as *bigger* and *biggest.* **Home Activity:** Help your child write a story about bigger animals helping smaller animals play a game, using comparative *-er* and *-est* words.

bravely	friendly	lightly	slowly	softly	weekly

Pick a word from the box to match each clue.
Write the word on the line.

1. every seven days
   _____

2. without fear
   _____

3. not loudly
   _____

4. not fast
   _____

5. nice
   _____

6. with a light touch
   _____

Pick a word from the box to match each clue.
Write the word in the puzzle.

ago	head

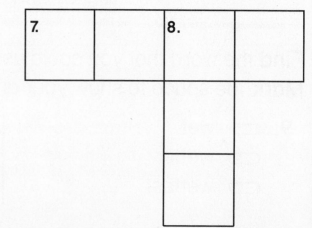

7. It is on top of your body.
8. It means "in the past."

Notes for Home: Your child spelled words ending with *-ly* and two frequently used words: *ago, head*. **Home Activity:** Have your child look through a newspaper and list words with *-ly* endings. Help your child figure out what each word means.

RETEACHING

Words for number, size, and shape are **adjectives**.

<u>Ten</u> leaves fall. The tree has <u>large</u> leaves.
The leaves have **pointed** edges.

Underline the adjective for number, size, or shape in each sentence.

1. The round leaves are gone.

2. The boy puts leaves in two piles.

3. The children collect big leaves.

4. A small squirrel climbs on the tree.

Circle the adjective for number, size, or shape in each sentence.
Write the adjective on the line.

5. The squirrel looks for large nuts.   _____

6. Its round ears hear the children.   _____

7. Two girls smile at the squirrel.   _____

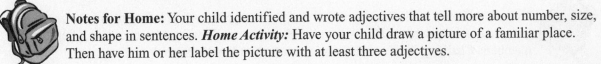

Notes for Home: Your child identified and wrote adjectives that tell more about number, size, and shape in sentences. ***Home Activity:*** Have your child draw a picture of a familiar place. Then have him or her label the picture with at least three adjectives.

Name _____

Write the adjective in ( ) on the line.

1. Chris wears a _____ hat in the school play.
   (shoe / big)

2. Kara is the girl in the _____ coat.
   (small / slowly)

3. They have _____ parrots.
   (three / fly)

Complete each sentence with an adjective from the box.

tall	little	two	square

4. Kara looks at the _____ parrots.

5. The parrots hide in a _____ tree.

6. Kara puts the parrots in _____ cages.

7. The cages have _____ doors.

Notes for Home: Your child identified and wrote adjectives that tell more about size, shape, and number in sentences. **Home Activity:** Have your child write sentences about family members. Challenge him or her to use at least one adjective in each sentence.

Family Times

Birthday Joy

The Best Older Sister

Join the Party

Join the party. It's for Roy.
Everybody bring a toy.

Let's sing songs and make some noise.
Let's play games that Roy enjoys.

Roy will make the hard-boiled eggs,
And flavorful foods like chicken legs.

Roy's mom Joy will mix and bake,
Colorful cookies and a big, round cake.

There's fun for every girl and boy.
Join the party. It's for Roy.

This rhyme includes words your child is working with in school: words with *oi* and *oy* (*Join, Roy*) and words with the suffix *-ful* (*flavorful, colorful*). Read aloud "Join the Party" with your child. Work together to write another verse for the rhyme.

(fold here)

Name: _____

You are your child's first and best teacher!

Here are ways to help your child practice skills while having fun!

Day 1 Work with your child to write an advertisement that uses words that end with *-ful*, such as *beautiful* and *wonderful*.

Day 2 Have your child draw a picture of a father and his child. Then write a sentence about the picture using words your child is learning to read: *about, different, father, important, told.*

Day 3 Read a fairy tale or folk tale to your child. Then ask your child what lesson the story might teach and how the story is like something in his or her own life.

Day 4 Describe different objects by telling how they look, feel, smell, taste, or what sounds they make. See if your child can name the objects you describe.

Day 5 Your child is learning to write a personal narrative. Ask your child to write a letter to a friend or relative telling about something he or she did that day.

Read with your child EVERY DAY!

Spell the Word

Materials index cards, 1 button per player

Game Directions

1. Copy each word shown below on index cards.

2. Take turns drawing and reading a card aloud.
   The other player must spell that word correctly.

3. If the player spells the word correctly, he or she
   moves his or her button one space.

4. The first player to reach the end wins!

toy	ton	noise	royal
paint	toil	pail	point
boys	joined	foil	nose
coins	boiling	daily	coil
oil	joyful	soil	enjoy

Start

End

Circle a word to finish each sentence.
Write the word on the line.

 b**oi**l

cans   coins

1. I have three _____ .

toy   tab

2. I wanted a new _____ .

planted   pointed

3. I _____ at it.

noise   nuts

4. It makes lots of _____ .

job   joy

5. It brings lots of _____ .

Notes for Home: Your child practiced using words with *oi* and *oy,* such as *coin* and *joy.* **Home Activity:** Work with your child to list other words with *oi* and *oy* that have the same vowel sound as *coin* and *joy.*

Add -ful to each word in ( ).
Write the word on the line to finish each sentence.

help + -ful = help**ful**

_____

1. It was a _____ party.   (wonder)

_____

2. The room looked _____ .   (joy)

_____

3. The children were _____ .   (play)

_____

4. The music was _____ .   (cheer)

_____

5. It was _____ after the party.   (peace)

Notes for Home: Your child wrote words with the suffix *-ful,* such as *helpful.* **Home Activity:**
Read a story with your child. Challenge your child to find words in the story that can have the
suffix *-ful* added to them, such as *care, help,* and *play (careful, helpful, playful).*

Name _____

Birthday Joy
The Best Older Sister

Pick a word from the box to finish each sentence.
Write the word on the line.

| about | different | father | important | told |

1. My _____ was born in Korea.

2. He has _____ me stories about Korea.

3. One is _____ a Korean boy like me.

4. Life there is a bit _____ from life here.

5. These stories are _____ to me.

 Notes for Home: This week your child is learning to read the words *about, different, father, important,* and *told.* **Home Activity:** Encourage your child to write a story with a character who is a father, using as many of these words as possible.

High-Frequency Words **23**

Name _____

Read each story. **Follow** the directions.

I have a birthday party every year. My family is all there.
My friends come too. There are games and cake.
It is a lot of fun.

1. Circle the sentence that tells the big idea of this story.

    My birthday party is always fun.

    I am growing up.

2. Underline the parts of the story that helped you tell
   the big idea.

I was going out to play, but my mom got sick. I had
to take care of my little brother. He can be a pest.
I know it is important to help out, so I didn't mind.

3. Circle the sentence that is the
   big idea of this story.

    Helping your family is important.

    A little brother can be a pest.

4. Underline the parts of the story that
   helped you tell the big idea.

Notes for Home: Your child practiced finding the big idea in a story. *Home Activity:* Work with
your child to come up with an idea you both think is important, such as: *Always plan ahead.*
Help your child write about something that has happened in his or her life that conveys that idea.

Name _____

An **adjective** describes a noun.
An adjective can tell how something looks, sounds, tastes, feels, or smells.

Apples taste **sweet**.

Circle the adjective in each sentence.
Draw a line from each adjective to the sense it goes with.

1. The ball looks red.

a.

2. The soap smells fruity.

b.

3. The tree bark feels rough.

c.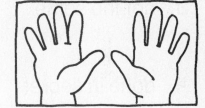

4. The music sounds loud.

d.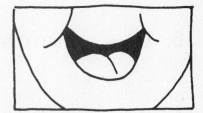

5. The stew tastes salty.

e.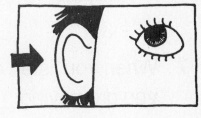

Notes for Home: Your child identified adjectives that relate to the five senses.
Home Activity: At dinner, use adjectives to describe how different foods look, taste, feel, smell, and maybe even sound.

Name _____

Pick a word from the box to match each clue.
Write the word on the line.

attention	different	important
interesting	secretly	special	told

1. I found a _____ map.

   _____

2. not boring

   _____

3. not the same

   _____

4. done in secret

   _____

5. I _____ him a story.

   _____

6. It's _____ to be on time.

   _____

7. When you listen carefully,
   you are paying _____ .

Notes for Home: Your child used word clues to practice new vocabulary words.
Home Activity: Read the vocabulary words on this page aloud. Work with your child to
use each word in a sentence.

26 Vocabulary

Level 2.2

ear

p**ee**ring

Circle the word for each picture.

1. spear   share

2. door   deer

3. rear   read

4. clear   corn

5. tires   tears

6. hear   hire

7. store   steer

8. fear   four

Find the word that has the same vowel sound as the picture.
Mark the space to show your answer.

9. ⬭ near
   ⬭ nail
   ⬭ snare

10. ⬭ yarn
    ⬭ yard
    ⬭ year

Notes for Home: Your child reviewed words with *eer* and *ear* in which the letter *r* changes the way a vowel sounds as in *ear* and *peering*. **Home Activity:** Help your child write a poem using rhyming words that have this vowel sound and these spellings.

| boil | coin | point | spoil | voice | enjoy |

Write the word from the box that rhymes with each word below.

1. choice

_____

2. toy

_____

Write two words that rhyme with **foil**.

_____   _____

3. _____   4. _____

Pick a word from the box to match each clue.
Write the word on the line.

5. a penny

_____

6. the end of a sharp pencil

_____

Pick a word from the box to finish each sentence.
Write the word on the line.

father
told

7. My _____ was born in China.

8. He _____ me stories about it.

Notes for Home: Your child spelled words with *oy* and *oi*, such as *enjoy* and *coin,* and two frequently used words: *father, told.* **Home Activity:** Say each spelling word, and use it in a sentence. Repeat the word, and have your child write it.

Name _____

Draw a line from each adjective to the sense it matches.

1. stinky

2. pretty

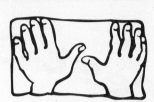

3. loud

4. warm

5. salty

Circle a word in ( ) to finish each sentence.

6. The apple looks (shut / shiny).

7. It smells (fair / fruity).

8. It tastes (sheet / sweet).

9. It feels (cold / code) in my mouth.

10. It makes a (card / crunchy) sound when I eat it.

Notes for Home: Your child identified adjectives that appeal to the five senses (sight, sound, taste, feel, and smell). **Home Activity:** When you eat or cook with your child, ask him or her to use adjectives to describe what each of the five senses can tell about the meal.

Level 2.2   **Grammar: Adjectives and Our Senses** **29**

Test-Taking Tips

1. Write your name on the test.

2. Read each question twice.

3. Read all the answer choices for the question.

4. Mark your answer carefully.

5. Check your answer.

Part 1: Vocabulary

Find the word that best fits in each sentence.
Mark the space for your answer.

1. My birthday was a _____ day.
   ⬭ guess   ⬭ next   ⬭ special

2. Amy feels it is _____ to help people.
   ⬭ across   ⬭ important   ⬭ different

3. Babies need lots of _____ .
   ⬭ attention   ⬭ creature   ⬭ thumb

4. We saw a very _____ show about ducklings.
   ⬭ ago   ⬭ interesting   ⬭ secretly

5. Peggy _____ a funny joke.
   ⬭ giggled   ⬭ lose   ⬭ told

GO ON ➡

Part 2: Comprehension

Read each question.
Mark the space for your answer.

6. After Kiju was born, Sunhi missed her time with —
   - ⬭ Robin.
   - ⬭ Halmoni.
   - ⬭ Jenny.

7. At first, Sunhi thinks that —
   - ⬭ everyone likes Kiju better than her.
   - ⬭ she is the best older sister.
   - ⬭ it would be great to have more babies.

8. Which sentence tells what this story is about?
   - ⬭ Sunhi told Halmoni about her day at school.
   - ⬭ Kiju always made such a mess.
   - ⬭ Everything changed for Sunhi when Kiju was born.

9. Why did Halmoni give Sunhi her surprise early?
   - ⬭ She could not keep it a secret.
   - ⬭ She wanted Sunhi to know that she loved her.
   - ⬭ She was afraid that Sunhi would find it.

10. In this story, Sunhi learned that —
    - ⬭ Halmoni is not her friend.
    - ⬭ it is better to be an only child.
    - ⬭ everyone is special.

STOP

Name _____

Add -ly to each word below.
Write the new word on the line.
Hint: You will need to change **y** to **i** for some words.

1. lucky
_____
- - - - - - - - - - - - - -
_____

2. friend
_____
- - - - - - - - - - - - - -
_____

3. noisy
_____
- - - - - - - - - - - - - -
_____

4. happy
_____
- - - - - - - - - - - - - -
_____

5. loud
_____
- - - - - - - - - - - - - -
_____

6. final
_____
- - - - - - - - - - - - - -
_____

7. proud
_____
- - - - - - - - - - - - - -
_____

8. love
_____
- - - - - - - - - - - - - -
_____

Find the word where **-ly** has been added correctly.
Mark the space to show your answer.

9. brave
- ○ bravely
- ○ bravly
- ○ bravelly

10. busy
- ○ busyly
- ○ busily
- ○ busilly

Notes for Home: Your child reviewed words that have the suffix *-ly*. **Home Activity:** Words with *-ly* tell how an action is done. Name some action verbs *(run, sing)* and have your child use words with the suffix *-ly* to describe how each action could be done *(swiftly, sweetly)*.

| boil | coin | point | spoil | voice | enjoy |

Pick a word from the box to match each clue.
Write the word on the line.

_____

1. You'll find it at the end of a needle. _____

_____

2. You use it to speak. _____

_____

3. You do this to water to make tea. _____

_____

4. You can use it to buy something. _____

_____

5. It means "to be happy" with something. _____

_____

6. It means "to become bad or rotten." _____

Change one letter in each word to make a word from the box.
Write the new word on the line.

| father | told |

7. gold _____

8. fatter _____

Notes for Home: Your child spelled words with *oi* and *oy*, such as *coin* and *enjoy*, and two
frequently used words: *father, told*. **Home Activity:** Write each spelling word on a slip of
paper. Take turns picking words and giving clues about each word for the other player to spell.

Name _____

RETEACHING

An **adjective** describes a person, place, animal, or thing.

An adjective can tell how something looks, sounds, tastes, feels, or smells.

The cake tastes **sweet.**

Circle the adjective in each sentence. **Draw** a line from each adjective to the sense it matches.

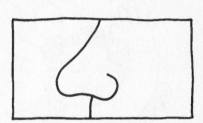

1. Our kittens feel soft. a.

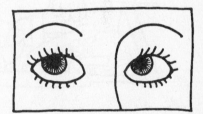

2. My soup tastes spicy. b.

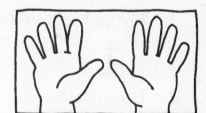

3. The trees look green. c.

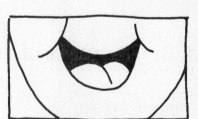

4. The air smells fresh. d.

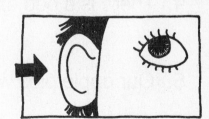

5. The drum sounds loud. e.

Notes for Home: Your child identified adjectives that relate to the five senses. *Home Activity:* Have your child close his or her eyes and taste, touch, listen to, and smell different things. Your child can guess what the things are and describe how he or she knew.

Grammar: Adjectives and Our Senses **35**

Name _____

Choose an adjective from the box that makes sense in each sentence.
Write it on the line.

| hot | sweet | wet | rotten | loud |

_____
- - - - - - - - - - - -

1. My sister's voice is _____.

_____
- - - - - - - - - - - -

2. The apples feel _____ in the water.

_____
- - - - - - - - - - - -

3. Be careful of the _____ tea on the stove!

_____
- - - - - - - - - - - -

4. There is a bad apple that smells _____.

_____
- - - - - - - - - - - -

5. Our apple pies will taste _____.

Notes for Home: Your child identified adjectives that describe sight, sound, taste, feel, and smell. *Home Activity:* Have your child choose things that he or she sees, hears, tastes, feels, and smells. Your child can write each thing on one side of a card and list adjectives on the other side.

The Bread Baker

I'll give you some bread, so you can be well fed.
And I'll spread it with butter and jam.
It's as light as a feather, and we'll eat it together.
And I'll serve you the bread with some ham.

Bread, bread, and more bread.
I'm a baker who spreads it with jam.
It's as light as a feather, and we'll eat it together.
I'm a very good baker. I am!

It's a pleasure to fix, all this bread I will mix.
And I'll use a bread timer to bake.
With my hat on my head, I will bake all the bread.
Then I'll make you a gingerbread cake.

Bread, bread, and more bread . . .

This rhyme includes words your child is working with in school: words with the short *e* sound spelled *ea* (*bread*) and words with the suffix *-er* (*baker*). Sing "The Bread Baker" together. Clap your hands for each short *e* word. Stamp your feet for each word that ends in *-er*.

(fold here)

Name: _____

You are your child's first and best teacher!

Here are ways to help your child practice skills while having fun!

Day 1 Challenge your child to list as many words that end with the suffix *-er* as he or she can think of in one minute, such as *baker* and *helper*.

Day 2 Your child is learning to read these words: *large, ready, says, today,* and *wash.* Take turns giving each other a clue and naming the word that fits the clue, such as the clue *not yesterday* for the word *today.*

Day 3 Your child is learning about realistic stories and fantasies. Read a story or two with your child. Talk about whether the events in the story could really happen.

Day 4 Provide your child with a notebook or blank diary so he or she can start a journal at home. Encourage your child to write or draw in it every few days.

Day 5 Your child is learning to make announcements. Help your child create an announcement for a family event and have him or her present it to the family.

Read with your child EVERY DAY!

Short e Spelled eq

Materials 1 button per player, 1 coin

Game Directions

1. Players place both markers on Start and take turns flipping the coin. Move ahead one space for heads, and move two spaces for tails.

2. For each space landed on, players say a short e word spelled *ea* as in *bread*. Words must begin with the letter or letters shown in the space. Some possible answers are given below.

3. The first player to reach the end wins!

Answers: lead, leather, head, health, heavy, sweat, sweater, spread, breakfast, ready, weather, thread, dread

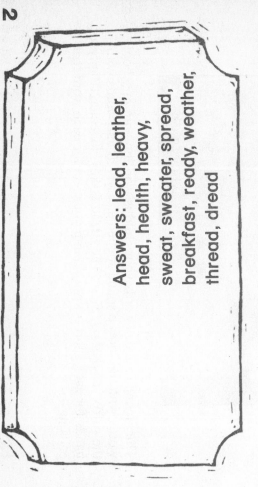

Start | l | h | sw | br | spr | r | w | thr | d | End

Name _____

Circle a word to finish each sentence.
Write the word on the line.

h**ea**d

read   rode

_____

_ _ _ _ _ _ _ _ _ _ _ _ _ _ _ _

1. I _____ a good book.

bread   braid

_____

_ _ _ _ _ _ _ _ _ _ _ _ _ _ _ _

2. It was about _____ .

healthful   helping

_____

_ _ _ _ _ _ _ _ _ _ _ _ _ _

3. Bread is _____ .

ready   reedy

_____

_ _ _ _ _ _ _ _ _ _ _ _ _

4. I'm _____ to eat!

spread   spare

_____

_ _ _ _ _ _ _ _ _ _ _ _ _

5. I _____ the jam.

 Notes for Home: Your child read and wrote words in which the short *e* sound is spelled *ea* as in *h**ea**d*. **Home Activity:** Ask your child to write short rhyming sentences using words that rhyme with *head*.

Name _____

Add -er to each word in ( ).
Write the word on the line to finish
each sentence.

run + -er = runn**er**

_____ (bake)
- - - - - - - - - - - - - - - - -
1. The _____ made bread.

_____ (mix)
- - - - - - - - - - - - - - - - -
2. He used a _____ .

_____ (time)
- - - - - - - - - - - - - - - - -
3. The _____ rang.

_____ (help)
- - - - - - - - - - - - - - - - -
4. He gave it to his _____ .

_____ (mark)
- - - - - - - - - - - - - - - - -
5. She wrote with a _____ .

Notes for Home: Your child wrote words that have the suffix *-er*. **Home Activity:** Work with
your child to make a list of words with the *-er* suffix. Ask your child to name the base word
for every word on the list. For example, *run* is the base word for *runner*.

40 Phonics: Suffix *-er*   Level 2.2

Pick a word from the box to finish each sentence.
Write the word on the line.

| large | ready | says | today | wash |

1. We will bake a pie _____.

2. We _____ the apples.

3. We'll make a _____ pie.

4. Dad _____ it will take about an hour.

5. Now we are _____ to eat!

 Notes for Home: This week your child is learning to read the words *large, ready, says, today,* and *wash.* **Home Activity:** Work with your child to write a story about some food you like to make together. Use the words in the box in your story.

Read each sentence.
Write Y if it tells something that could really happen.
Write N if it tells something that could not really happen.

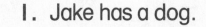

_____ 1. Jake has a dog.

_____ 2. The dog says words to Jake.

_____ 3. The dog plays with Jake.

_____ 4. Jake walks to school with the dog.

_____ 5. The dog reads stories to Jake.

 Notes for Home: Your child identified whether a story event could really happen.
Home Activity: Ask your child to make up two stories, one realistic (can really happen)
and one a fantasy (includes events that can't really happen).

Name _____

An **adjective** describes a noun.
Many adjectives come before the
nouns they describe.
Big is an adjective that describes **cake.**   He made a **big** cake.

Circle the adjective in each sentence.
Underline the noun it describes.

---

1. I smelled wonderful breads in the bakery.

2. I like the round loaves.

3. My mom bought long rolls.

4. She uses them to make huge sandwiches.

5. Her sandwiches are great!

Notes for Home: Your child has identified adjectives in sentences and the nouns they describe. *Home Activity:* Name an object in your home. Ask your child to think of adjectives to describe that object and use them in a sentence.

Pick a word from the box to match each clue.
Write the word on the line.

kitchen   large   oven   present   ready   says   today   wash

1.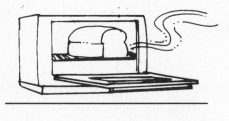

_____
- - - - - - - - - - - - - -
_____

2. a room where
you cook

_____
- - - - - - - - - - - - - -
_____

3. It comes after
yesterday.

_____
- - - - - - - - - - - - - -
_____

4. big

_____
- - - - - - - - - - - - - -
_____

5. You do this when
you are dirty.

_____
- - - - - - - - - - - - - -
_____

6.

_____
- - - - - - - - - - - - - -
_____

7. Get _____ .
Get set. Go!

_____
- - - - - - - - - - - - - -
_____

8. talks

_____
- - - - - - - - - - - - - -
_____

 Notes for Home: Your child used word and picture clues to practice new vocabulary words.
Home Activity: Ask your child to choose several vocabulary words and use them to make up
simple riddles for you to solve, such as: *This is what I do when I take a bath.*

Name _____

 coins    toys

Circle the word for each picture.

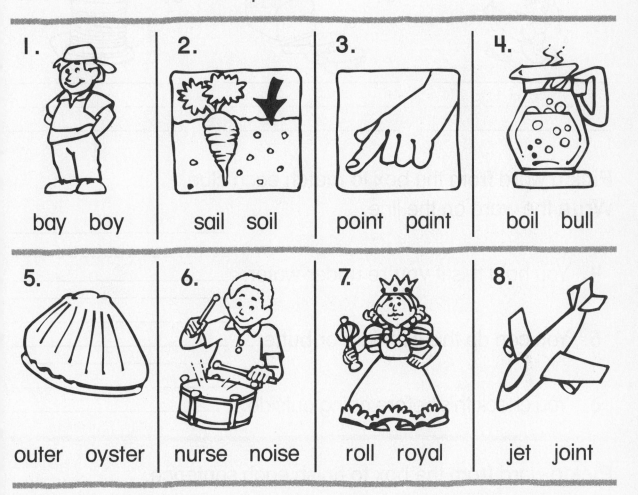

1.	2.	3.	4.
bay boy	sail soil	point paint	boil bull

5.	6.	7.	8.
outer oyster	nurse noise	roll royal	jet joint

Find the word that has the same vowel sound as the picture.
Mark the space to show your answer.

9. ⬭ spoil
    ⬭ spoon
    ⬭ snail

10. ⬭ most
     ⬭ moist
     ⬭ moose

 Notes for Home: Your child reviewed words spelled with *oi* and *oy* such as *coins* and *toys*. *Home Activity:* Have your child use the words with *oi* and *oy* in sentences. Together, draw pictures to go with the sentences.

| bread | breath | spread | sweat | thread | weather |

Pick a word from the box to match each picture.
Write the word on the line.

1. _____ 2. _____ 3. _____

_____   _____   _____

Pick a word from the box to match each clue.
Write the word on the line.

_____

4. You hold this if you're under water. _____

_____

5. You can do this with jam or butter. _____

_____

6. You check this before going outside. _____

Pick a word from the box to finish each sentence.
Write the word on the line.

| ready | today |

_____

7. _____ is Monday.

_____

8. I'm getting _____ for school.

 Notes for Home: Your child spelled words in which the short *e* sound is spelled *ea* (*bread*) and two frequently used words: *ready, today.* **Home Activity:** Help your child write new short *e* words by changing some letters in each spelling word, for example, *bread* becomes *break.*

Circle the adjective or adjectives in each sentence.

1. Dad makes wonderful desserts.

2. He bakes many, tasty pies.

3. He only uses fresh, ripe fruit.

4. The pies taste sweet.

5. I like to eat pies when they are warm.

6. I once helped Dad make ten pies.

7. They were for a big party at my school.

Write a sentence on each line about something you eat.
Use at least one adjective from the box in each sentence.

| four | good | hot | red | round | small | sweet |

8. _____

9. _____

10. _____

Notes for Home: Your child identified adjectives in sentences and wrote sentences with adjectives. **Home Activity:** Have your child write a sentence using one adjective. Then, you repeat the sentence, adding a second adjective. Switch roles and repeat.

Test-Taking Tips

1. Write your name on the test.

2. Read each question twice.

3. Read all the answer choices for the question.

4. Mark your answer carefully.

5. Check your answer.

Part 1: Vocabulary

Find the word that best fits in each sentence.
Mark the space for your answer.

1. Please _____ the dishes.
   ⬭ follow   ⬭ peel   ⬭ wash

2. Are you _____ to go?
   ⬭ high   ⬭ ready   ⬭ enough

3. That hat is too _____ for you.
   ⬭ whole   ⬭ large   ⬭ still

4. Grandma is in the _____ baking a cake.
   ⬭ oven   ⬭ kitchen   ⬭ present

5. We will go to school _____ .
   ⬭ today   ⬭ important   ⬭ until

GO ON ➡

Part 2: Comprehension

Read each question.
Mark the space for your answer.

6. Why do Bruno and Felix make a cake?
    - ⬭ Grandma tells them to make one.
    - ⬭ It is Bruno's birthday.
    - ⬭ Felix likes to mix the batter.

7. What does Bruno do first?
    - ⬭ He mixes the eggs.
    - ⬭ He turns on the oven.
    - ⬭ He puts some butter in a pan.

8. You can tell that Bruno and Felix —
    - ⬭ work well together.
    - ⬭ eat too much cake.
    - ⬭ don't like to read directions.

9. Why do Bruno's friends give him a new mixing bowl?
    - ⬭ His other bowl broke.
    - ⬭ They know he likes to bake.
    - ⬭ He needs a bowl to put flowers in.

10. Which part of the story could **not** really happen?
    - ⬭ A kitchen gets a little messy.
    - ⬭ Butter melts in a pan.
    - ⬭ Animals bake a cake.

STOP

Name _____

Add -ful to each word below.
Write the new word on the line.

a beauti**ful** cake

1. use

_____

- - - - - - - - - - - - - -

_____

2. plenty

_____

- - - - - - - - - - - - - -

_____

3. hope

_____

- - - - - - - - - - - - - -

_____

4. color

_____

- - - - - - - - - - - - - -

_____

5. help

_____

- - - - - - - - - - - - - -

_____

6. peace

_____

- - - - - - - - - - - - - -

_____

Find the base word for each word below.
Mark the space to show your answer.

7. careful
   - ⬭ car
   - ⬭ care
   - ⬭ caring

8. wonderful
   - ⬭ wonder
   - ⬭ won
   - ⬭ wand

Notes for Home: Your child reviewed words with the suffix *-ful*. **Home Activity:** Give your child some base words, such as *truth, pain, harm, fear, rest, cheer,* or *wonder.* Ask her or him to add *-ful* to each word and then use the new word in a sentence.

| bread | breath | spread | sweat | thread | weather |

Pick words from the box to finish each sentence.
Write the words on the lines.

1.–2. I like to _____

jam on _____ .

3.–4. If the _____ is hot,

I _____ a lot.

5.–6. Hold your _____ Ned.

It will help you _____ .

Write the word from the box that rhymes with each word below.

| ready | today |

7. play

_____

8. steady

_____

Notes for Home: Your child spelled words in which the short *e* sound is spelled *ea* and two frequently used words: *ready, today.* **Home Activity:** Ask your child to write a letter to a friend or relative using as many of these spelling words as possible.

RETEACHING

The kitten plays.   The **fuzzy** kitten plays.

The word **kitten** is a noun.

The adjective **fuzzy** tells more about the noun **kitten.**

An **adjective** describes a person, place, animal, or thing.

The word in ( ) is an adjective. It tells more about the noun.
Write the word in the sentence. **Read** the complete sentence.

1. Pedro pulls the _____ string. (long)

2. The _____ mouse moves. (brown)

3. The kitten chases the _____ toy. (little)

4. The toy goes under the _____ chair. (big)

5. The _____ kitten meows. (sad)

6. Now Pedro and the kitten play with a _____ ball. (blue)

Notes for Home: Your child wrote adjectives—words that describe—in sentences. ***Home Activity:*** Have your child look at pictures in magazines. Then have him or her write two sentences about the pictures, using at least one adjective in each sentence.

Grammar: Writing with Adjectives **53**

Draw one line under the adjective in each sentence.
Draw two lines under the noun it tells more about.

1. The silly movie starts.

5. A tiny donkey trots.

2. The happy children sit.

6. They step on a large hat.

3. Then fast music begins.

7. A tall cowboy comes.

4. A gray donkey runs.

8. Is he a brave man?

Choose the better adjective in ( ) to tell more about the noun.
Write the adjective in the sentence.

9. The _____ thunder crashes. (loud/quiet)

10. The _____ cattle run away. (safe/scared)

11. The cowboy calls the _____ donkey. (pink/gray)

12. The donkey chases the _____ cattle. (wild/dry)

13. The cattle sleep in the _____ barn. (tiny/big)

14. The _____ cowboy goes home. (tired/new)

Notes for Home: Your child identified and wrote adjectives—words that tell more about nouns—in sentences. *Home Activity:* Have your child draw an imaginary creature. Then help him or her write a short story about the creature, using at least four adjectives.

It's Family Time for All

Let's get together now.
It's family time for all.
My grandma makes some applesauce
As we play basketball.

Paul and Maude will climb
And even somersault.
My cousins walk and bounce a ball
While others drink their malts!

As day turns into night,
Mom knits or takes a walk.
The babies start to fall asleep.
Then we begin to talk.

This rhyme includes words your child is working with in school: words with the vowel sound heard in *Maude* and *ball* and words with silent consonants (*climb*). Sing the rhyme together. Then list all the words in the rhyme that have the same vowel sound heard in *Maude* and *ball*.

(fold here)

Name: _____

You are your child's first and best teacher!

Here are ways to help your child practice skills while having fun!

Day 1 Your child is learning to read words with *a*, *al*, and *au* that have the same vowel sound (*water*, *walk*, *sauce*). Work with your child to list words that rhyme with *walk* and *ball*.

Day 2 Work with your child to create a crossword puzzle or word search puzzle using words that your child is learning to read this week: *able*, *early*, *own*, *story*, and *thought*.

Day 3 Read a story with your child. Then ask your child to tell you what happened at the beginning, middle, and end of the story.

Day 4 Ask your child to name a favorite meal and provide details that support this opinion.

Day 5 Your child is learning about comparative and superlative adjectives (*bigger*, *biggest*). Ask your child to write an advertisement for a favorite game using adjectives that end in *-er* and *-est*.

Read with your child EVERY DAY!

Silence Is Golden

Materials   paper, pencil, bag, 1 button

Game Directions

1. Write the words below on slips of paper and put them in a bag.

2. Players take turns picking a word from the bag and reading it aloud. Players must toss a button on the gameboard and land on the picture for that word to earn a point. If a player misses, the word is put back in the bag.

3. Play continues until the bag is empty.

4. The player with the most points at the end of the game wins!

Words with Silent Consonants

comb, lamb, knife, knit, knee, knot, climb, thumb, doorknob

Name _____

Circle the word for each picture.   ch**al**k

1. 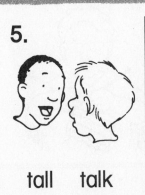	2. 	3. 	4. 
ball bell	walk wink	save sauce	well wall

5. 	6. 	7. 	8. 
tall talk	water wetter	tell tall	smell small

Draw a picture for each action.

9. falling

10. calling

Notes for Home: Your child read words with the same vowel sound as chalk spelled *a, al,* and *au.* **Home Activity:** Together, name words that rhyme with *tall.*

Name _____

Write k or b to finish each word.

 knee   **lamb**

1.

_____
nock

2.

com _____

3.

_____
nob

4.

_____
nit

5.

thum _____

6.

_____
not

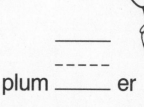

7.

crum _____ s

8.

plum _____ er

 Notes for Home: Your child read and completed words with *kn* and *mb* that have silent consonants. **Home Activity:** Work with your child to write sentences using the *kn* and *mb* words on this page.

58 Phonics: Silent Consonants *kn, mb*

Level 2.2

Pick a word from the box to finish each sentence.
Write the word on the line.

able	early	own	story	thought

1. Grandma told me a funny _____ .

2. She got ready for a party a day _____ .

3. She _____ it was on Saturday.

4. Luckily, she was _____ to go the next day.

5. It was easy because it was at her _____ house!

Notes for Home: This week your child is learning to read the words *able, early, own, story,*
and *thought.* **Home Activity:** Write these words on slips of paper. Ask your child to choose
slips at random, read each word aloud, and use it in a sentence.

Write a number next to each sentence to show the right order.

1. On July 4, everybody came with food. _____

2. For weeks, our family planned a big picnic. _____

3. We ate the food and had a lot of fun. _____

4. He played a lot and got better and better. _____

5. John started to learn to play the piano. _____

6. John won the piano contest. _____

 Notes for Home: Your child identified the order of story events. *Home Activity:* Ask your child to tell you the beginning, middle, and end of a story you have read together. Listen for your child to focus on important story events.

Name _____

Add -er to an adjective when you compare two nouns.

The striped balloon is **bigger** than the dotted balloon.

Add -est when you compare more than two nouns.

The plain balloon is the **biggest** balloon he has.

Circle a word to finish each sentence.

1. Bruno is the _____ child.

    taller
    tallest

2. This streamer is the _____ one of all.

    longer
    longest

3. This banner is _____ than last year's banner.

    smaller
    smallest

4. Kim is the _____ blower of balloons.

    faster
    fastest

5. The drum is _____ than the flute.

    louder
    loudest

Notes for Home: Your child has learned to use comparative and superlative adjectives.
Home Activity: When out with your child, point out two or more items in a group and ask
your child to compare the items.

Name _____

Pick a word from the box to match each clue.
Write the word on the line.

| able | brook | early | feathers |
| growl | own | story | |

1. I'm _____ to ride a bike.

2. not late

3. Birds have these.

4. It is often make-believe.

5. to have something

6. A bear makes this sound.

7. a small stream

Notes for Home: Your child used clues to practice new vocabulary words. *Home Activity:* Write each of the listed vocabulary words on a separate index card. Use the cards as flash cards. Ask your child to read the word on each card and use it in a sentence.

Name _____

Circle the word for each picture.   br**ea**kfast

1.	**2.**	**3.**	**4.**
head heard	heavy have	thread three	leather letter
5.	**6.**	**7.**	**8.**
father feather	swap sweat	bread braid	speed spread

Find the word that has the same **short e** sound as the picture.
Mark the space to show your answer.

9. ⬭ peach
   ⬭ weather
   ⬭ bean

10. ⬭ meeting
    ⬭ meaning
    ⬭ meadow

Notes for Home: Your child reviewed words in which the short *e* sound is spelled *ea*, as in *breakfast*. **Home Activity:** Ask your child to write a poem using words in which the short *e* sound is spelled *ea*.

climb   comb   lamb   kneel   knit   knot

Write three words from the box that begin with **kn**.

1. _____   2. _____   3. _____

Write three words from the box that end in **mb**.

4. _____   5. _____   6. _____

Pick a word from the box to match each picture.
Write the word on the line.

7. _____

8. _____

Pick a word from the box to finish each sentence.
Write the word on the line.

story   able

9. Do you want me to read you a _____ ?

10. I am _____ to read it by myself!

Notes for Home: Your child spelled words with silent consonants and two frequently used words: *story, able.* **Home Activity:** Say each spelling word, then use it in a sentence. Repeat the word, and have your child write it.

Name _____

Circle an adjective to finish each sentence.

1. I went to the (bigger / biggest) party I've ever seen.

2. It was for Jack, the (older / oldest) of all the children.

3. I am six years (younger / youngest) than he is.

4. Jack was the (hungrier / hungriest) person at the party.

5. He ate the (larger / largest) piece of cake.

---

small   fast   hard

Add -er or **-est** to each word in the box.
Write a sentence using each new adjective.

6. _____

7. _____

8. _____

Notes for Home: Your child identified and wrote comparative and superlative adjectives that end with *-er* and *-est*. **Home Activity:** Ask your child to create an advertisement for a product, real or imaginary, using adjectives such as *brightest* or *bigger*.

Test-Taking Tips

1. Write your name on the test.

2. Read each question twice.

3. Read all the answer choices for the question.

4. Mark your answer carefully.

5. Check your answer.

Part I: Vocabulary

Find the word that best fits in each sentence.
Mark the space for your answer.

1. He swims in the _____ .
   - ⃝ field
   - ⃝ brook
   - ⃝ feathers

2. Pat told us a long _____ .
   - ⃝ story
   - ⃝ able
   - ⃝ picture

3. The dog began to _____ .
   - ⃝ decide
   - ⃝ peel
   - ⃝ growl

4. Carlos got up _____ today.
   - ⃝ early
   - ⃝ between
   - ⃝ able

5. Liz has her _____ room.
   - ⃝ ripe
   - ⃝ own
   - ⃝ early

GO ON

Part 2: Comprehension

Read each question.
Mark the space for your answer.

6. What did the rooster do first?
   - ⬭ He crowed at the sun.
   - ⬭ He got ready for the wedding.
   - ⬭ He asked the grass for help.

7. The rooster got his beak dirty when he —
   - ⬭ ate some corn.
   - ⬭ walked into the brook.
   - ⬭ ate the grass.

8. The rooster talked to the grass, the lamb, and the others because he —
   - ⬭ was a friendly bird.
   - ⬭ wanted them to go to the wedding.
   - ⬭ needed some help.

9. Which of these could really happen?
   - ⬭ A dog talks.
   - ⬭ A stick burns.
   - ⬭ The grass cries.

10. Why did everyone but the sun say no to the rooster?
    - ⬭ The rooster had not done anything for them.
    - ⬭ Everyone was too busy helping someone else.
    - ⬭ They did not want to be late for the wedding.

STOP

Name _____

Add -er to each word below to make
a word that matches the picture.
Write the new word on the line.

bak**er**

---

1. time

----

2. sing

----

3. bat

----

4. farm

----

5. help

----

6. run

Find the word where the final **e** was dropped
before **-er** was added.
Mark the space to show your answer.

7. ⚬ diner
⚬ worker
⚬ drummer

8. ⚬ skater
⚬ cleaner
⚬ jogger

Notes for Home: Your child wrote words that end with *-er.* **Home Activity:** Ask your child to
make a list of different occupations that end with *-er.* Discuss what each person does and how
it relates to the base word, such as *baker* and *bake.*

Name _____

| climb | comb | lamb | kneel | knit | knot |

Pick a word from the box to match each clue.
Write the word on the line.

1. You do this to a hill. _____

2. It rhymes with *heel.* _____

Change one letter in each word to make a word from the box.
Write the new word on the line.

3. come

_____

_____

4. lame

_____

_____

5. know

_____

_____

6. knot

_____

_____

Pick a word from the box to finish each sentence.
Write the word on the line.

| story | able |

7. I know a great _____ .

8. I am _____ to tell it to you myself.

Notes for Home: Your child spelled words with *mb* and *kn* where one letter in each pair is silent *(climb, knot),* as well as two frequently used words: *story, able.* **Home Activity:** Using these spelling words, work with your child to write a story about a little lamb.

Name _____

RETEACHING

small   small**er**   small**est**

Add **-er** to an adjective to compare two persons, places, or things.

Add **-est** to an adjective to compare three or more persons, places, or things.

Add -er to each word.
Write the new word.

1. old

2. hard

3. cool

_____   _____   _____

Add -est to the word in ( ).
Write the new word in the sentence.

4. Our school has the (loud) _____ band.

5. The bells make the (soft) _____ music.

6. We play the (long) _____ song last.

Notes for Home: Your child wrote comparative and superlative adjectives in sentences. *Home Activity:* Have your child choose three objects in your home *(shoes, glasses, pictures)* and use comparative and superlative adjectives to compare the objects.

Circle a word in ( ) to complete the sentence.
Think first if two or more things are compared.

I. This car is (slower / slowest) than that car.

2. The seats are (higher / highest) than those in Jo's car.

3. Abe is the (younger / youngest) driver on the street.

4. This road is the (longer / longest) one in town.

5. That kitten is the (smaller / smallest) one in the litter.

Add -er or **-est** to each word in ( ).
Write the new word in the sentence.

6. A car is (small) _____ than a bus.

7. A train is (long) _____ than a bus.

8. This jet is the (fast) _____ of all the planes.

9. That is the (old) _____ ship I have seen.

10. My father is (tall) _____ than his brother.

Notes for Home: Your child wrote comparative and superlative adjectives. *Home Activity:*
Have your child compare family members. Remind them to use comparative and superlative
adjectives.

Family Times

Yawning Dawn   **Missing: One Stuffed Rabbit**

My Dog's Paw

We saw a sign at our local vet.
"Please take me home. I'll be your pet!"
This little dog sat on bits of straw.
We saw that he had hurt his paw.
We brought him home but he couldn't crawl.
We wrapped his paw in our mother's shawl.
When we unwrapped his little paw,
He used his paw to scratch his jaw.
Now who can jump up?
Now who can crawl?
Our little dog will come when we call.

This rhyme includes words your child is working with in school: words spelled with *aw* and *ough* (*paw, brought*) and words with *gn, wh,* and *wr,* where one consonant in each letter pair is silent (*sign, who, wrapped*). Sing "My Dog's Paw" with your child. As you sing, shout the words with *aw* and *ough.*

(fold here)

Name: _____

You are your child's first and best teacher!

Here are ways to help your child practice skills while having fun!

Day 1 Your child is learning to read words with *aw* and *ough* that have the same vowel sound (*saw, thought*). When reading together, look for words with *aw* and *ough* that have this vowel sound, such as *draw, straw, bought, brought.*

Day 2 Your child is learning to read these words: *family, finally, morning, paper,* and *really.* Challenge your child to write a sentence using as many of these words as possible.

Day 3 Read a story with your child. As you read, point out the characters' actions. Ask your child to make judgments by asking questions such as: *Why do you think that character did that? Is that a good way to act?*

Day 4 Give your child verbal instructions to follow such as: *Hop on your left foot. Wave your right hand. Pick up the blue button.*

Day 5 Work with your child to write instructions that explain how to play a favorite game.

Read with your child EVERY DAY!

Silent-Letter Spins

Materials   paper circle, paper clip, pencil, 1 button per player

Game Directions

1. Make a simple spinner as shown and take turns spinning a letter pair.

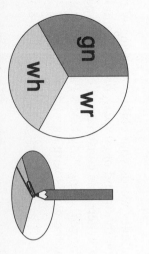

2. Toss a button on the gameboard to try to land on a word that has the same letter pair. If a player fails to land on a word with the same letter pair, the player loses his or her turn.

3. If a player lands on a word that has the same letter pair, says the word correctly, and identifies its silent consonant, he or she earns 1 point.

4. The first player to earn 5 points wins!

sign	who	wreck
write	design	whole
who's	wreath	gnaw
gnarled	whose	wrong
who'll	gnat	wrapping

Name _____

Circle a word to finish each sentence.
Write the word on the line.

He **bough**t a dr**aw**ing.

___

loan   lawn
- - - - - - - - - - - - - - - - -

1. I looked at the _____ .

saw   swamp
- - - - - - - - - - - - - - - - -

2. What do you think I _____ ?

toad   thought
- - - - - - - - - - - - - - - - -

3. I _____ it was a dragon.

claws   climbs
- - - - - - - - - - - - - - - - -

4. It had nasty _____ .

___

jays   jaws
- - - - - - - - - - - - - - - - -

5. It was Tom inside the _____ !

Notes for Home: Your child read words with *aw* and *ough* (drawing, bought). **Home Activity:** Ask your child to make up a story about an animal. Challenge your child to use words with this vowel sound and these spellings.

Level 2.2

Phonics: /ò/Vowel Patterns *aw, ough* **75**

Name _____

Circle a word to finish each sentence.
Write the word on the line.

 <u>**wr**</u>ench

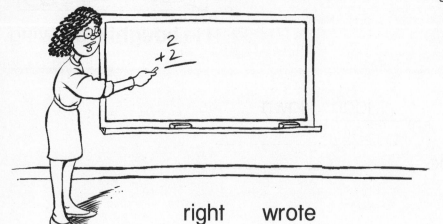

right   wrote
_____
- - - - - - - - - - - - - - -

1. The teacher _____ the problem.

hill   whole
_____
- - - - - - - - - - - - - - -

2. The _____ class watched her.

sign   swan
_____
- - - - - - - - - - - - - - -

3. She drew a plus _____ .

how   who
_____
- - - - - - - - - - - - - - -

4. She asked _____ knew the answer.

wrong   rode
_____
- - - - - - - - - - - - - - -

5. I was happy my answer wasn't _____ .

 Notes for Home: Your child read words with the letters pairs *gn, wh,* and *wr* in which one consonant is silent, as in *sign, whole,* and *write*. **Home Activity:** Ask your child to make a sign for a new household product using words with these letter pairs.

Name _____

Pick a word from the box to finish each sentence.
Write the word on the line.

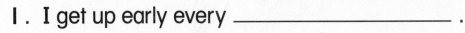

| family | finally | morning | paper | really |

1. I get up early every _____ .

2. First I get the _____ .

3. Next, my _____ cooks.

4. _____ , we eat.

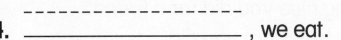

5. I _____ like mornings!

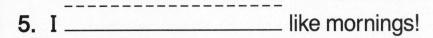

Notes for Home: This week your child is learning to read the words *family, finally, morning, paper,* and *really.* **Home Activity:** Ask your child to make the front page of a newspaper and write a story about a family activity. Encourage your child to use the listed words.

Read the story.
Answer the questions.

Judy was sick and missed school. Cathy called her to see how she was feeling. She brought Judy's homework to her house.

1. Is Cathy a good friend? _____

2. Why do you think so?

_____

_____

_____

3. **Think** about something nice you did for a friend.
   Write a sentence that tells what you did.

_____

_____

_____

_____

_____

Notes for Home: Your child made a judgment about a character in a story.
Home Activity: Read a story with your child. Ask questions about why your child thinks someone did something, and if your child thinks it was a good idea.

Name _____

Adverbs can tell how, when, or where something happens. **Quickly** is an **adverb**.

Jane runs **quickly.**

Circle the adverb in each sentence.
Write the adverb on the line.

1. Our Thanksgiving play is today.

2. We came to school early.

3. We practice inside.

4. We sing loudly.

5. We walk softly.

 Notes for Home: Your child identified adverbs—words that tell how, when, or where something happens. ***Home Activity:*** Give your child simple commands that use adverbs to tell how to do the action. *(Clap your hands softly.)*

Pick a word from the box to match each clue.
Write the word on the line.

calm	family	finally	gathered
hospital	morning	paper	really

1. a place where sick or hurt people go

_____

2. something to write on

_____

3. mother, father, brothers, and sisters

_____

4. came together

_____

5. quiet

_____

6. at last

_____

7. beginning of the day

_____

8. very much, truly

_____

 Notes for Home: Your child used word clues to practice new vocabulary words.
Home Activity: Make a simple crossword puzzle with your child using some of these
vocabulary words. Use the clues above or write your own clues.

Name _____

water

walking

sauce

Pick the word in ( ) that has the same vowel sound as **sauce**.
Circle the word to finish each sentence.

1. The water comes out of the (glass/faucet).

2. Our teacher (calls/says) hello to us.

3. I like (butter/salt) on my food.

4. I hurt my knee (because/when) I fell down.

5. He hit the (bell/ball) hard.

6. I like to draw with (markers/chalk).

7. This shirt is too (large/small).

8. We were late, and it was all my (fault/mistake).

Find the word that has the same vowel sound as the picture.
Mark the space to show your answer.

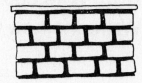

9. ⬭ told
   ⬭ talk
   ⬭ take

10. ⬭ ant
    ⬭ able
    ⬭ author

Notes for Home: Your child reviewed words that have the vowel sound heard in *sauce* spelled *a, al,* and *au.* **Home Activity:** Write some of the words with this vowel sound listed above. Have your child create new words with this vowel sound by changing a few letters in each word.

Name _____

| awful | bought | claw | draw | saw | straw |

Write four words from the box that rhyme with **jaw**.

1. _____   2. _____

3. _____   4. _____

Pick a word from the box that has nearly the same meaning as the word or words below.
Write the word on the line.

5. bad

_____

6. sketch

_____

7. paid for

_____

8. looked

_____

Add -ly to each word below to make a word from the box.
Write the new word on the line.

| really | finally |

9. final _____   10. real _____

 Notes for Home: Your child spelled words with the vowel sound in *ball* spelled *aw* and *ough* and two frequently used words: *really, finally.* **Home Activity:** Say each spelling word, and then use it in a sentence. Repeat the word, and have your child write it.

Name _____

Write steps in the right order.

Go to the store.
Buy peanut butter, jelly, and bread.

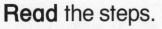

Read the steps.
Write 1, 2, 3, 4 to show the right order.

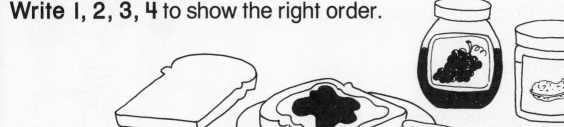

_____

_____ 1. Add jelly on top of the peanut butter.

_____ 2. Set out two slices of toast.

_____ 3. Put the other slice of toast on top of the jelly.

_____ 4. Put peanut butter on one slice.

Write a title that tells what these steps are about.

5. _____

_____

Notes for Home: Your child put steps in a process in order. *Home Activity:* Prepare dinner or
a treat with your child. As you prepare your food, discuss the order in which things need to be
done. Later ask your child to retell you the steps you took in the order you did them.

Name _____

Circle the adverb in each sentence.

1. We go to music class weekly.

2. We will see the music teacher soon.

3. I walk into the classroom quickly.

4. Peter arrives last.

5. The teacher wants us all to sing loudly.

6. We join our voices cheerfully.

7. We go to recess outside.

8. We play games happily.

Pick two of the adverbs circled above.
Write a new sentence using each adverb.

_____

9. _____

_____

10. _____

Notes for Home: Your child identified and wrote adverbs—words that tell how, when, or where something happens. *Home Activity:* Give your child short sentences and ask him or her to add adverbs to them. Discuss how adverbs can make sentences more interesting.

Part 1: Vocabulary

Find the word that best fits in each sentence.
Mark the space for your answer.

1. We went to see Grandpa in the _____ .
   ⬭ team   ⬭ hospital   ⬭ family

2. The sun comes up in the _____ .
   ⬭ paper   ⬭ head   ⬭ morning

3. Mom told me to _____ down.
   ⬭ clean   ⬭ calm   ⬭ fix

4. Sam _____ all his toys together.
   ⬭ giggled   ⬭ gathered   ⬭ exclaimed

5. His shirt is _____ yellow.
   ⬭ another   ⬭ finally   ⬭ really

Part 2: Comprehension

Read each question.
Mark the space for your answer.

6. Why are the children excited on Friday?
   - ⬭ There is no school the next day.
   - ⬭ They are all going on a trip.
   - ⬭ Someone will take Coco home.

7. Coco goes everywhere with his —
   - ⬭ diary.
   - ⬭ rabbit.
   - ⬭ bowl.

8. How did Janine feel when Coco got lost?
   - ⬭ friendly
   - ⬭ sad
   - ⬭ excited

9. Janine guessed where Coco was from the —
   - ⬭ Lost and Found Department.
   - ⬭ frog at the hospital.
   - ⬭ "Toy Drive" sign.

10. Was Janine right to let Teresa keep Coco?
    - ⬭ Yes, because Coco made Teresa feel better.
    - ⬭ No, because Coco belongs to Mrs. Robin.
    - ⬭ Yes, because Coco will get lost again.

STOP

Name _____

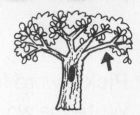

Circle the word for each picture.   <u>kn</u>ee   li<u>mb</u>

1. 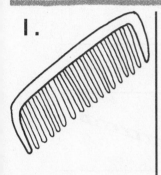	2. 	3. 	4. 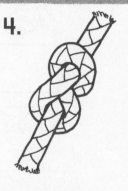
comb cub	nice knife	lamb lab	nut knot

5. 	6. 	7. 	8. 
club climb	kite knight	thumb thump	kitten knit

Find the word that has a silent consonant.

Mark the space to show your answer.

9. ⬭ know
   ⬭ kind
   ⬭ kiss

10. ⬭ plums
    ⬭ plumber
    ⬭ plank

Notes for Home: Your child reviewed words with *kn* and *mb* where one letter in each pair is silent as in <u>kn</u>ee and lim<u>b</u>. **Home Activity:** Make picture cards of words with *kn* and *mb* with your child. Take turns picking cards and writing a sentence about each word pictured.

Name _____

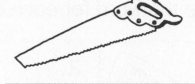

awful   bought   claw   draw   saw   straw

Pick a word from the box to match each picture.
Write the word on the line.

1.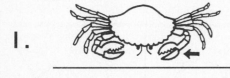
_____
- - - - - - - - - - - - - - - - -
_____

2.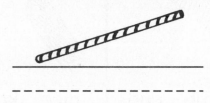
_____
- - - - - - - - - - - - - - - - -
_____

3.
_____
- - - - - - - - - - - - - - - - -
_____

4.
_____
- - - - - - - - - - - - - - - - -
_____

Pick a word from the box that is the opposite of each word below.
Write the word on the line.

_____
- - - - - - - - - - - - - - - - -

5. great _____

_____
- - - - - - - - - - - - - - - - -

6. sold _____

Pick a word from the box to match each clue.
Write the word on the line.

really   finally

7. at last

_____
- - - - - - - - - - - - - - - - -
_____

8. I felt _____ sad.

_____
- - - - - - - - - - - - - - - - -
_____

Notes for Home: Your child spelled words with *aw* and *ough* that have the vowel sound heard
in *straw* and *bought*. **Home Activity:** Hold a spelling bee. Give your child a word, have him or
her repeat the word, and then spell it aloud.

Name _____

The music plays **now.**   The children walk **around.**
The children laughed **loudly.**

An adverb can tell **when, where,** or **how.**
The word **now** tells **when** the music plays.
The word **around** tells **where** the children walk.
The word **loudly** tells **how** the children laugh.

An **adverb** can tell more about a verb.

Circle the adverb that tells about each underlined verb.

1. The children <u>play</u> inside.
2. The chairs <u>stand</u> there.
3. The music <u>stops</u> quickly.
4. The players <u>sit</u> now.
5. Two children <u>stand</u> up.
6. A boy <u>takes</u> a chair carefully.

Underline When if the circled adverb tells when. **Underline Where** if the circled adverb tells where. **Underline How** if the circled adverb tells how.

		When	Where	How
7.	The game ends (soon)	**When**	**Where**	**How**
8.	The children go (outside)	**When**	**Where**	**How**
9.	They walk (slowly)	**When**	**Where**	**How**
10.	(Then) the teacher calls them.	**When**	**Where**	**How**

Notes for Home: Your child identified and wrote adverbs in sentences. *Home Activity:* Have your child draw a picture of himself or herself doing something at school. Then have your child write sentences about the drawing, using at least one adverb.

Complete each sentence with an adverb from one of these lists.

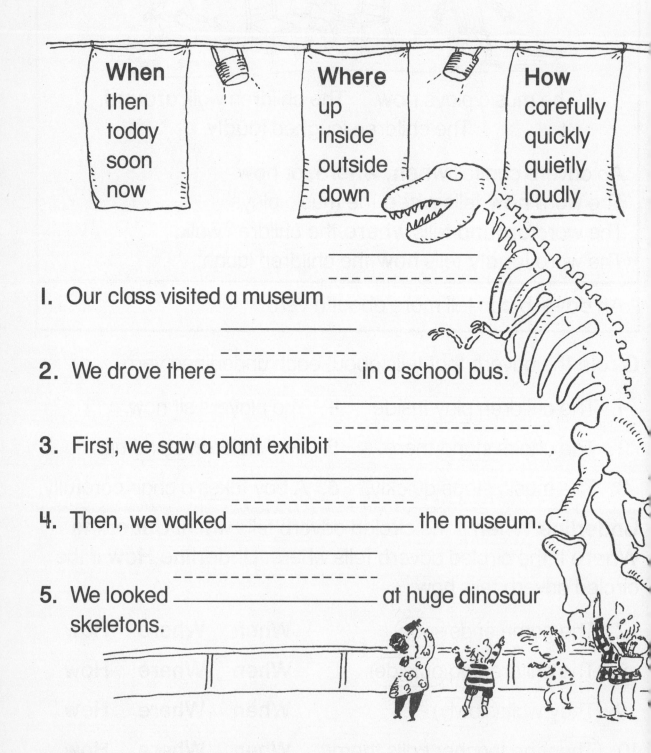

When
then
today
soon
now

Where
up
inside
outside
down

How
carefully
quickly
quietly
loudly

1. Our class visited a museum _____.

2. We drove there _____ in a school bus.

3. First, we saw a plant exhibit _____.

4. Then, we walked _____ the museum.

5. We looked _____ at huge dinosaur skeletons.

Notes for Home: Your child wrote adverbs in sentences. *Home Activity:* Read a favorite story with your child. Have him or her point out three adverbs. Then have him or her write new sentences, using the adverbs.

Name _____

One word in each sentence is **not** correct.

Circle the incorrect word.

Write the word correctly on the line.

Hint: Use words that end in **-er** to compare two things.

Use words that end in **-est** to compare more than two.

1. Use a ball big than a softball.

_____

2. The higher score you can get is ten.

_____

3. Use your fast player to run.

_____

4. Sara is the taller player on our team.

_____

5. Mike is a hardest kicker than Tom.

_____

Notes for Home: Your child corrected comparative adjectives that end in *-er* and superlative adjectives that end in *-est*. **Home Activity:** Look through a picture book with your child. Have him or her make comparisons about the characters using adjectives that end in *-er* or *-est*.

Words I Can Now Read and Write

Astronaut Cousins

We are two friends . . . .
We're cousins too . . . .
We'll touch the moon . . . .
That's what we'll do . . . .

We're astronauts . . . .
Exploring space . . . .
The ride is rough . . . .
Around this place . . . .

We're flying now . . . .
We're traveling far . . . .
We're visiting each . . . .
And every star . . . .

And when we've had . . . .
Enough of space . . . .
We'll double back . . . .
And leave this place . . . .

This rhyme includes words your child is working with in school: words with short *u* spelled *ou* (*cousins*) and words with more than one syllable (*astronauts*). Sing "Cousins in Space" with your child. For each word with more than one syllable, clap out each syllable together.

(fold here)

Name: _____

You are your child's first and best teacher!

Here are ways to help your child practice skills while having fun!

Day 1   Write the following words on slips of paper: *could, count, country, couple, cousin, double, down, dot, through, thought, trouble, truck, you, young.* Have your child identify the words with the short *u* vowel sound heard in *cup.*

Day 2   Have your child write a list of questions to ask an astronaut, using these words: *began, Earth, ever, remember, try.*

Day 3   Read a paragraph from a book or a newspaper together. Have your child explain the most important idea of the paragraph.

Day 4   Challenge your child to summarize the important events of a story or TV show in a few sentences.

Day 5   Read a story or magazine article with your child. Have him or her point out the pronouns *he, she, it, we, they,* and *you.* Identify who or what each pronoun represents.

Read with your child EVERY DAY!

Animal Match

Materials index cards, markers, bag

Game Directions

1. Use index cards to make a set of picture cards with matching word cards as shown.

2. Place the picture cards face down on the table. Place the word cards in a bag.

3. Take turns drawing a word card and flipping over a picture card to try to make a match.

4. Players keep each pair made. If cards don't match, the player turns over the picture card and returns the word card to the bag.

5. When all matches have been made, the player with the most pairs wins!

bulldog

chipmunk

crocodile

kangaroo

lizard

octopus

porcupine

walrus

Pick the word with the **short u** sound you hear in **double**.
Circle the word to finish each sentence.

1. We spent a night in the _____ .

outdoors
country
house

2. My _____ and I saw many stars.

aunt
cousin
hound

3. They seemed close enough to _____ .

count
touch
bounce

4. A _____ of stars were very bright.

couple
group
outline

5. One group of stars looks like a _____ bear.

cute
young
proud

Notes for Home: Your child read words in which the short *u* sound is spelled *ou* as in *double*.
Home Activity: Find words with *ou* as you read together. Have your child say each word aloud
and tell whether it has the same vowel sound as *double*.

Name _____

Circle the word for each picture.

1.

rocket record

2.

pilot plot

3.

battle basket

4.

plant planet

5.

circle circus

6.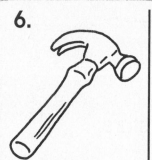

hammer
hamper

7.

little lizard

8.

button
butter

Draw a picture for each word.

9. astronaut

10. elephant

Notes for Home: Your child identified words with two or more syllables by sounding out more familiar word parts, such as *rock • et* for *rocket*. **Home Activity:** As you read with your child, point out words with more than one syllable. Help your child read each word.

Pick a word from the box to finish each sentence.
Write the word on the line.

| began | Earth | ever | remember | try |

1. Nina _____ to build a rocket.

2. I will _____ to fly.

3. _____ to wear a seat belt.

4. Will you _____ come back?

5. I'll come back to _____ soon!

Notes for Home: This week your child is learning to read the words *began, Earth, ever, remember,* and *try.* **Home Activity:** Have your child pretend that he or she is on the moon. Have your child use these words to write a letter home.

Name _____

Read the paragraph.
Write a word or two that tells the topic.
Write a sentence that tells the main idea.
Draw a picture of the main idea.

A United States astronaut was the first person to set foot on the moon. His name was Neil Armstrong. It happened on July 20, 1969. The name of the spaceship was the *Apollo 11*. The world watched on TV as he walked on the moon's surface.

1. Topic: _____

2. Main Idea: _____
   _____
   _____
   _____

3.

Notes for Home: Your child has been learning to identify the main idea of a paragraph. *Home Activity:* Read aloud a paragraph from a nonfiction article with your child. Then have your child tell you the main idea of the paragraph.

Name _____

A **pronoun** is a word that takes the place of a noun or nouns.
The astronaut went to the moon.
<u>He</u> went to the moon.
The rocket landed.
<u>It</u> landed.

Pick a pronoun from the box to take the place of the underlined word or words.
Write the pronoun on the line.

he   she   it   we   they

_____ 1. <u>Eric and his sister</u> came to visit.

_____ 2. <u>My friends and I</u> watched a TV program.

_____ 3. <u>The program</u> was about the first moon walk.

_____ 4. <u>Lisa</u> wants to be an astronaut.

_____ 5. <u>Eric</u> would rather stay on Earth!

Notes for Home: Your child used pronouns to take the place of nouns in sentences. ***Home Activity:*** Find a newspaper or magazine article that your child can read. Underline some of the nouns and have your child replace them with pronouns.

Name _____

Pick a word from the box to finish the sentence.
Write the word on the line.

| began   circled   Earth   ever   remember   rockets   try |

1. Did I _____ tell you about my space trip?

2. Tell me again. I don't _____ it all.

3. My rocket _____ Earth three times.

4. I _____ to get a little scared.

5. I was glad to get back to _____ !

6. I never wanted to _____ flying again!

7. Now I watch _____ launch only on TV.

Notes for Home: Your child used vocabulary words to complete sentences. *Home Activity:* Encourage your child to use some of the vocabulary words to write a description of a trip to space.

Put each group of words in **ABC order**.
Pick a word in ( ) that comes between the two words shown.
Write the word on the line.

(the / toy)

1. tip _____ try

(clap / cent)

2. chill _____ come

(bib / bug)

3. beg _____ black

(wring / why)

4. wet _____ will

(and / air)

5. age _____ all

(got / give)

6. glow _____ grow

(dog / duty)

7. dizzy _____ dry

(sky / snow)

8. sick _____ smile

(ever / eye)

9. erase _____ extra

(brag / bed)

10. bad _____ boy

Notes for Home: Your child alphabetized words by looking at the second letter in words that begin with the same letter. This skill will help your child better use a glossary or dictionary.
Home Activity: Help your child use the telephone book to look up the names of people you know.

str<u>aw</u>   b<u>ough</u>t

Circle the word for each picture.

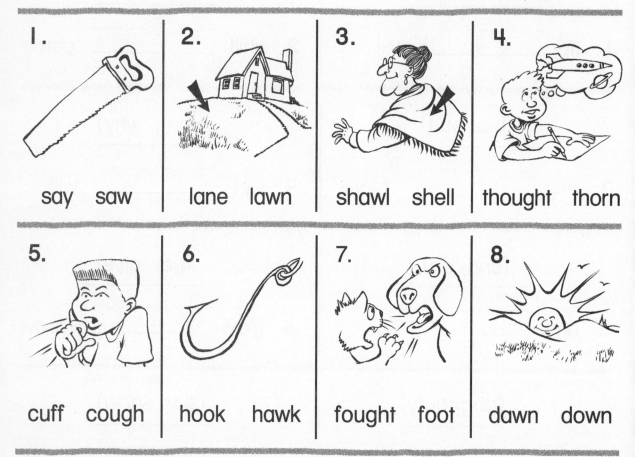

1.
say   saw

2.
lane   lawn

3.
shawl   shell

4.
thought   thorn

5.
cuff   cough

6.
hook   hawk

7.
fought   foot

8.
dawn   down

Find the word that has the same vowel sound as the picture.
Mark the space to show your answer.

9. ⬭ low
    ⬭ law
    ⬭ laugh

10. ⬭ old
    ⬭ ought
    ⬭ own

 Notes for Home: Your child reviewed words spelled with *aw* or *ough* that have the vowel sound heard in *straw* and *bought*. **Home Activity:** Help your child write sentences using words with *aw* and *ough* listed above. Then have your child read the sentences aloud.

Name _____

| camera | carry | follow | lesson | pretty | suddenly |

Write four words from the box that have two syllables.

1. _____

2. _____

3. _____

4. _____

Write two words from the box that have three syllables.

5. _____

6. _____

Pick a word from the box that is the opposite of each word below.
Write the word on the line.

7. ugly _____

8. drop _____

Say the word for each picture.
Write the word from the box that has
the same beginning sound.

| ever | began |

9.

10.

_____

_____

Notes for Home: Your child spelled words that have more than one syllable, such as *suddenly,* and two frequently used words: *ever, began.* **Home Activity:** Help your child use these spelling words to write sentences. Have your child read each sentence aloud.

Name _____

Circle the word or words in the first sentence that the underlined pronoun replaces.

1. We are watching the news. <u>It</u> shows a moon landing.

2. Jack and I just sat down. <u>We</u> haven't watched long.

3. Where are the three pigs? Are <u>they</u> coming?

4. That astronaut is brave. <u>He</u> is very far from home.

5. Bessie doesn't care. <u>She</u> jumped over the moon long ago.

Pick a pronoun from the box to replace each group of words. **Write** the pronoun on the line.

| he | it | she | they | we |

6. you and I
_____

7. the rocket
_____

8. my mom
_____

9. Paul and his dog
_____

10. Jennie's dad _____

Notes for Home: Your child identified words that the pronouns *he, she, it, we,* and *they* replace. *Home Activity:* As you read a book with your child, pause and ask your child to change some of the nouns to pronouns.

Part I: Vocabulary

Find the word that best fits in each sentence.
Mark the space for your answer.

1. Have you _____ looked at the moon?
   ⬭ able   ⬭ ever   ⬭ done

2. Lee will _____ to come to the game.
   ⬭ guess   ⬭ use   ⬭ try

3. The sun _____ to shine.
   ⬭ began   ⬭ gathered   ⬭ circled

4. Three _____ fly into the sky.
   ⬭ paws   ⬭ dinosaurs   ⬭ rockets

5. I can't _____ the cat's name.
   ⬭ remember   ⬭ Earth   ⬭ try

GO ON ➡

Part 2: Comprehension

Read each question.
Mark the space for your answer.

6. Before 1969, no one had ever —
   - ⬭ gone into space.
   - ⬭ walked on the moon.
   - ⬭ made rockets fly.

7. What happened first?
   - ⬭ *Saturn 5* took off.
   - ⬭ Armstrong took pictures on the moon.
   - ⬭ The *Eagle* landed.

8. Collins did not walk on the moon because —
   - ⬭ he was sick.
   - ⬭ he had to fly *Columbia*.
   - ⬭ he did not want to.

9. The writer wanted mostly to tell about —
   - ⬭ the first walk on the moon.
   - ⬭ how to fly rockets.
   - ⬭ what we see on TV.

10. How do you know that men walked on the moon?
    - ⬭ The moon remembers the men.
    - ⬭ They came down in the Pacific Ocean.
    - ⬭ They brought moon rocks back to Earth.

STOP

 **gn**ats

 **Wh**o's there?

 **wr**ist

Circle the word for each picture.

1.	2.	3.	4.
 whole will	 wrench when	 wrapped want	 write white

5.	6.	7.	8.
 sign sing	 design desk	 gown gnaw	 breath wreath

Find the word that has the silent consonant.
Mark the space to show your answer.

9. ⬭ wind
   ⬭ who
   ⬭ wood

10. ⬭ wreck
    ⬭ wet
    ⬭ wig

Notes for Home: Your child reviewed words spelled with *gn, wh,* and *wr.* **Home Activity:** Write some of the following words on index cards and help your child practice reading them: *gnash, gnat, gnaw, gnome, sign, design, whole, who, whose, wholly, wrap, wreath, wrong.*

| camera | carry | follow | lesson | pretty | suddenly |

Pick a word from the box to match each clue.
Write the word on the line.

1. not lead
   _____
   - - - - - - - - - - - - - -
   _____

2. hold
   _____
   - - - - - - - - - - - - - -
   _____

3. something you learn
   _____
   - - - - - - - - - - - - - -
   _____

4. lovely
   _____
   - - - - - - - - - - - - - -
   _____

5. It takes pictures.
   _____
   - - - - - - - - - - - - - -
   _____

6. quickly
   _____
   - - - - - - - - - - - - - -
   _____

Pick a word from the box to match each clue.
Write the word on the line.

| ever | began |

_____
- - - - - - - - - - -

7. It rhymes with *never*. _____

_____
- - - - - - - - - - -

8. It means the same as "started." _____

Notes for Home: Your child spelled words with more than one syllable, such as *suddenly,*
and two frequently used words: *ever, began.* **Home Activity:** Have your child write sentences
using these spelling words and read each sentence aloud, clapping hands for each syllable.

Mrs. Catalano is an art teacher.
She is an art teacher.

The word **she** is a pronoun.
It takes the place of the noun **Mrs. Catalano.**

A **pronoun** is a word that takes the place of a noun or nouns.
The words **he, she, it, we,** and **they** are pronouns.

Draw a line under the pronoun in each sentence.

1. We saw a movie in art class.

2. It was about a man in New Mexico.

3. He made sand paintings for a friend.

4. She loved the colors of the sand.

5. They were beautiful.

6. Our art teacher says we can make sand paintings.

7. She is going to show the class how.

Write the pronoun that can take the place of the noun. Use **he, she, we,** and **they.**

8. James Wolf _____

9. Ed and Flo _____

10. Ms. Silverwater _____

11. Jack and I _____

Notes for Home: Your child identified and wrote pronouns in sentences. *Home Activity:* Say sentences about people your child knows. *(Mr. and Mrs. Jones have a garden.)* Have your child replace the people's names with pronouns. *(They have a garden.)*

Circle the pronoun you can use in place of the word or words in ( ).

1. (Mrs. Choy) saves old newspapers.   He   She

2. (The papers) are in the garage.   They   It

3. (Dennis and I) put the papers in a car.   We   They

4. (Dennis) drives the car.   She   He

5. (The car) is filled with newspapers!   It   We

Write **he, she, it, we,** and **they** in the letter. One of the pronouns will be used twice.

Dear Alex,

    I collect empty cans. _____ have to be cleaned. Then _____ take the cans to a special place. _____ makes the cans useful again. _____ will be used for many things. My brother said _____ will save cans too. Ask your mom if your family can help. I hope _____ says yes.

Your friend,
Eva

Notes for Home: Your child identified and wrote pronouns in sentences. *Home Activity:* Write the pronouns *he, she, we, it,* and *they* on cards. Have your child choose a card and say a sentence, using that pronoun.

All Across the Country

Long ago we chopped down trees.
Built our houses, one, two, three.
Life was simple all around me.
All across the country.

People in the kitchen, do, re, mi.
Cakes on the table, one, two, three.
Sit on the benches, sit with me.
All across the country.

Round up the horses, ride with me.
Pick up the boxes, one, two, three.
Gather up your dresses, dance with me.
All across the country.

This rhyme includes words your child is working with in school: plural words where adding -s or -es adds a syllable (*houses*) and words with the schwa vowel sound spelled *a* and *le* (*a*cross, *people*). Read the rhyme with your child and act it out.

(fold here)

Name: _____

You are your child's first and best teacher!

Here are ways to help your child practice skills while having fun!

Day 1 Ask your child to circle all the words in a newspaper article that end in *le* such as *people*. Help your child read the circled words aloud and listen for the sound *le* represents.

Day 2 Have your child use the words *behind, only, sure, upon,* and *word* to write about a family trip.

Day 3 Encourage your child to draw a character from a favorite story. Help your child write a caption that describes what the character is like.

Day 4 Your child is learning how to give demonstrations. Encourage your child to demonstrate how to make a sandwich or other simple food items, explaining each step aloud in order.

Day 5 Help your child write a series of short steps that explain how to operate a simple household appliance, such as a toaster. Post the information beside the appliance.

Read with your child EVERY DAY!

Three Across

Materials 25 colored paper squares per player (one color per player)

Game Directions

1. Players take turns placing a colored square on a word in a tic tac toe square.

2. To keep the colored square in place, the player must correctly write and say the plural of that word.

3. The first player to line up three squares down, across, or diagonally wins!

cage	house	stage	change	hose
age	wage	dish	race	lunch
fence	beach	piece	prize	place
orange	price	nose	fox	rose
glass	page	nurse	horse	size

Name _____

Amanda likes only things that have
the **schwa sound** in their names.
She doesn't like things that don't have
this sound in their names.

balloon

Circle a word to show what Amanda likes.
Write the word on the line.

apples   berries

1. She likes _____ .

pickles   cabbage

2. She likes _____ .

yellow   purple

3. She likes _____ .

bananas   raisins

4. She likes _____ .

beyond   across

5. She likes to walk _____ the park.

Notes for Home: Your child identified words with the schwa sound which can be spelled with
a or *le* (b<u>a</u>lloon and peop<u>le</u>). **Home Activity:** Have your child read aloud words that end in *le* in
which *le* represents the same vowel sound as in *people*.

Add -s or **-es** to the noun in ( ) to show more than one.
Write the new noun on the line to finish each sentence.

(house)

_____

- - - - - - - - - - - - - - - -

1. The _____ were on the hill.

(bush)

_____

- - - - - - - - - - - - - - - - -

2. Their yards were full of _____ .

(fence)

_____

- - - - - - - - - - - - - - - -

3. Flowers grew along the _____.

(place)

_____

- - - - - - - - - - - - - -

4. In some _____ , there were big trees.

(horse)

_____

- - - - - - - - - - - - - -

5. The _____ pulled a wagon.

Notes for Home: Your child added *-s* and *-es* to nouns to make them plural. *Home Activity:*
Have your child make these words plural: *face, cage, vase, size.* Point out that adding *-s* to
words that end in *e* adds a syllable *(face, faces).*

Name _____

Pick a word from the box to finish each sentence.
Write the word on the line.

| behind | only | sure | upon | word |

_____

1. Young Will sat _____ the wagon seat.

_____

2. He was so happy that he could not say a _____.

_____

3. He had been to town _____ one time before.

_____

4. Pa was not _____ how long they would stay.

_____

5. They had left their cabin far _____ them.

Notes for Home: This week your child is learning to read the words *behind, only, sure, upon,* and *word.* **Home Activity:** Challenge your child to use some of these words to write about some family photographs.

Look at each picture to see what it shows about the person.
Pick a word from the box that tells what each person is like.
Write the word on the line.

fair	funny	greedy	mean
nice	shy	smart	sneaky

1. Amy gets good grades _____

   because she is _____ .

2. Jack is a _____ friend.

3. We let Matt judge the game _____

   because he is _____ .

4. Sally is very _____ .

5. Billy does not always raise his hand _____

   because he can be _____ .

Notes for Home: Your child used word and picture clues to figure out what someone is like.
Home Activity: When you read with your child, pause to ask her or him what a certain
character is like. Then ask why your child thinks so.

Name _____

He, **she**, and **it** are **pronouns**
that name only one.
<u>He</u> is eight years old.
We and **they** are **pronouns**
that name more than one.
<u>They</u> are friends.

Pick a pronoun from the box to take the place of the
underlined word or words.
Write the pronoun on the line.

| he | she | it | we | they |

_____
_____   1. Mary's family moved west in a big wagon.

_____   2. The wagon top was like a round tent.

_____   3. Mary's father drove the wagon all day.

_____   4. Will my family and I ever get there?

_____   5. Mary helped her mother fix meals.

Notes for Home: Your child used singular and plural pronouns to replace subjects in
sentences. **Home Activity:** Ask your child questions about what his or her class did that day.
Encourage your child to answer using the pronouns *he, she, it, we,* and *they.*

Name _____

Pick a word from the box to finish each sentence.
Write the word on the line.

| behind | crops | edge | sure | trade | upon | word |

1. Annie's family came to _____ at the store.

2. They sold some of the _____ they grew.

3. Mr. Clay stood _____ the store counter.

4. Annie was not _____ what to buy.

5. A ribbon hung over the _____ of the counter.

6. A jar of candy sat _____ the counter.

7. She pointed to the jar without saying a _____.

Notes for Home: Your child used new vocabulary words to complete sentences. *Home Activity:* Use these words to pretend you and your child are living out west a century ago.

Name _____

Read each clue.
Look at each picture.
Write the letters to finish each word.
Hint: They all have the same vowel sound as **double**.

d<u>ou</u>ble scoop

---

1. relatives

_____
- - - - - - -
c _____ sins

2. not smooth

_____
- - - - - - -
r _____ gh

---

3. not old

_____
- - - - - - -
y _____ ng

4. not a good thing

_____
- - - - - - -
tr _____ ble

---

5. not a city

_____
- - - - - - -
c _____ ntry

6. not easy

_____
- - - - - - -
t _____ gh

Find the word that has the same vowel sound as **double**.
Mark the space to show your answer.

7. ⬭ couple
   ⬭ cute
   ⬭ cows

8. ⬭ tool
   ⬭ touch
   ⬭ tube

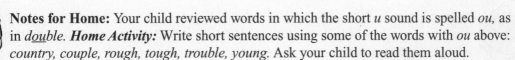

Notes for Home: Your child reviewed words in which the short *u* sound is spelled *ou,* as in *double.* **Home Activity:** Write short sentences using some of the words with *ou* above: *country, couple, rough, tough, trouble, young.* Ask your child to read them aloud.

| blouse | blouses | place | places | race | races |

Read the head at the top of each column.
Write the words from the box that belong in each column.

Names One	**Names More Than One**
1. _____	2. _____
3. _____	4. _____
5. _____	6. _____

Pick a word from the box to match each picture.
Write the word on the line.

7.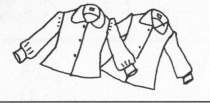

_____

8.

_____

Pick a word from the box to match each clue.
Write the word on the line.

| only | word |

9. a group of letters _____

10. rhymes with *lonely* _____

Notes for Home: Your child spelled pairs of singular and plural words and two frequently used words: *only, word.* **Home Activity:** Help your child use these words to write newspaper ads and announcements.

Name _____

Circle a pronoun to take the place of the underlined words.

1. <u>The children</u> are playing ball.
   He   We   They

2. <u>Tom</u> throws the ball.
   He   We   They

3. <u>Susan</u> catches the ball from Tom.
   He   It   She

4. "<u>Mary and I</u> want the ball!"
   He   We   Her

5. <u>The ball</u> will be thrown to Mary and Nan.
   It   He   They

Circle the pronouns that name one.
Underline the pronouns that name more than one.

6.–10. he   we   they   she   it

Notes for Home: Your child reviewed using pronouns that name only one person, place, or thing and pronouns that name more than one. **Home Activity:** Find a picture that shows activity. Have your child use pronouns to describe what is happening in the picture.

Test-Taking Tips

1. Write your name on the test.

2. Read each question twice.

3. Read all the answer choices for the question.

4. Mark your answer carefully.

5. Check your answer.

Part 1: Vocabulary

Find the word that best fits in each sentence.
Mark the space for your answer.

1. Are you _____ we can go in?
   ⊂⊃ able   ⊂⊃ sure   ⊂⊃ upon

2. What does that _____ mean?
   ⊂⊃ edge   ⊂⊃ city   ⊂⊃ word

3. Jay and I sat _____ Mom and Dad.
   ⊂⊃ across   ⊂⊃ until   ⊂⊃ behind

4. The farmer planted his _____ .
   ⊂⊃ crops   ⊂⊃ feathers   ⊂⊃ paws

5. Meg wanted to _____ a book for my doll.
   ⊂⊃ trade   ⊂⊃ peel   ⊂⊃ follow

GO ON ➡

Part 2: Comprehension

Read each question.
Mark the space for your answer.

6. Laura lived in a little house in the —
   - ⬭ woods.
   - ⬭ town of Pepin.
   - ⬭ city.

7. Pa said they would all go to town as soon as he —
   - ⬭ got cleaned up.
   - ⬭ had enough tools.
   - ⬭ planted the crops.

8. How did Laura and Mary feel about going to town?
   - ⬭ sad
   - ⬭ excited
   - ⬭ terrible

9. What is another good name for this story?
   - ⬭ "A Day by the Lake"
   - ⬭ "The Red Dress"
   - ⬭ "A Special Day"

10. When Laura first saw the town, she was surprised because —
   - ⬭ there were so many houses.
   - ⬭ the town was so small.
   - ⬭ there were no people.

STOP

Name _____

 letter

Circle the word for each picture.

1.

marker   master

2.

hammer   hamster

3.

saddle   sandal

4.

surfing   surprise

5.

singers   sisters

6.

thirsty   thirty

7.

ladder   lady

8.

candle   camel

Find the word that has the same middle consonant sound as the picture.
Mark the space to show your answer.

9. ⬭ carrot
   ⬭ kitten
   ⬭ muffin

10. ⬭ dragon
    ⬭ tuba
    ⬭ buttons

 Notes for Home: Your child reviewed words that have more than one syllable. *Home Activity:* Help your child read ads in newspapers. Sound out each syllable. Circle words that have more than one syllable.

Name _____

| blouse | blouses | place | places | race | races |

Write a word from the box that rhymes with each word below.

1. mouse
   _____
   - - - - - - - - - - - - - -
   _____

2. houses
   _____
   - - - - - - - - - - - - - -
   _____

Change one letter in each word to make a word from the box.
Write the new word on the line.

3. faces
   _____
   - - - - - - - - - - - - - -
   _____

4. rice
   _____
   - - - - - - - - - - - - - -
   _____

5. plates
   _____
   - - - - - - - - - - - - - -
   _____

6. plane
   _____
   - - - - - - - - - - - - - -
   _____

Unscramble the letters to make a word from the box.
Write the word on the line.

| only | word |

7. odwr
   _____
   - - - - - - - - - - - - - -

8. lyon
   _____
   - - - - - - - - - - - - - -

Notes for Home: Your child spelled pairs of singular and plural words and two frequently used words: *only, word.* **Home Activity:** Write a spelling word. Ask your child to use the letters to make as many words as possible *(blouses = blouse, blue, bus, be, us, less).*

Name _____

RETEACHING

He, she, and **it** are pronouns that name only one.
We and **they** are pronouns that name more than one.

He holds the bag.
They clean the yard.

Read the sentences.
Circle the pronoun that can take the place of the underlined word or words.

1. <u>Jason and his friends</u> go to a birthday party. (They/She) bring presents.

2. The birthday party is for <u>Heather</u>. (It/She) is seven years old.

3. <u>The party</u> started at noon. (It/They) will end at three o'clock.

4. <u>Jason</u> loves birthday cake. (We/He) asks if it is a chocolate cake.

5. <u>Heather and I</u> tell Jason that the cake is chocolate. (They/We) laugh when he smiles.

6. We eat the whole <u>cake</u>, and we tell our parents that (she/it) was good.

Notes for Home: Your child matched noun phrases to singular and plural pronouns *(he, she, it, we, they)*. **Home Activity:** Together, make flashcards with sentences about friends, family, and your child. Help your child underline subjects and write pronouns on the other side of the cards.

Name _____

Circle each pronoun that means one person or thing.
Underline each pronoun that means more than one.

1. he   **2.** she   **3.** we   **4.** they   **5.** it

Choose a pronoun from the box to take the place of each
underlined word or group of words.
Write it on the line.

He	She	They	It	We

6. <u>Richard</u> is crying. _____

7. <u>Her bugle</u> is new. _____

8. <u>Sheri and Dan</u> are blowing

up balloons. _____

9. <u>Mom and I</u> made a big sandwich.

_____

10. <u>My sister</u> wakes up early. _____

Notes for Home: Your child identified and used singular and plural pronouns in sentences.
Home Activity: Have your child tell you about a movie or TV show he or she has seen. Help
your child recognize the pronouns he or she uses.

Family Times

A True Boating Family   Riding the Ferry with Captain Cruz

Peggy Sue

My name is Peggy Sue.
I have a boat that's blue.
We'll sail all day, and after that,
We'll have a barbecue.

The water feels so great.
Come over. Don't be late.
Bring your suit and flippers too.
I can hardly wait.

This rhyme includes words your child is working with in school: words with *ue* (*blue*) and words that end in a consonant + *er* (*water*). Together, find the words that rhyme with *Sue*. Look to see how the vowel sound is spelled for these words.

(fold here)

Name: _____

1

You are your child's first and best teacher!

Here are ways to help your child practice skills while having fun!

Day 1 Use the following words with *ue* to create pairs of sentences that rhyme: *argue, avenue, barbecue, blue, clue, continue, due, glue, overdue, rescue, statue, tissue, true, untrue, value.*

Day 2 Your child is learning to read these words: *course, hear, things, which,* and *years*. Write these words on index cards. Have your child pick a word, read it aloud, and use it in a sentence.

Day 3 Take turns with your child pointing out interesting things you see as you walk or drive around your neighborhood. Each person gives one fact and one opinion about each object.

Day 4 Read a pararaph or a page from a nonfiction book with your child. Have your child listen for and identify the most important idea for the paragraph or page.

Day 5 Write the pronouns *I, you, she, he, we, they, me, her, him, us,* and *them* on separate index cards. Have your child choose cards and use the pronouns in sentences.

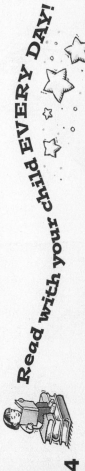

Read with your child EVERY DAY!

4

Kitchen Helpers

Materials crayons or markers, dictionary

Game Directions

1. Look at the kitchen scene. Take turns finding objects with names ending in the same sound you hear in *helper*. Possible answers are given below.

2. Write the names of the objects you find. Help your child use a dictionary to check the spellings of these names as needed.

3. The player who finds the most objects and writes them correctly wins!

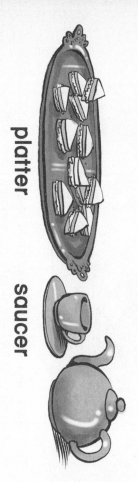

platter   **saucer**

Here are some of the objects you can find:

batter, butter, counter, dishwasher, electric beater, fire extinguisher, hamburger, pepper, pitcher, pot holder, stove burner, thermometer, timer, toaster, water

Name _____

gl<u>ue</u>

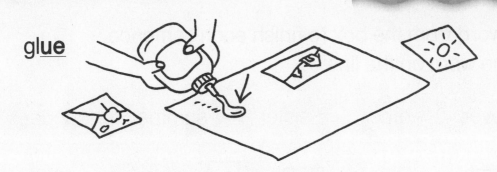

Pick a word from the box to match each clue.
Write the word on the line.

| avenue | blue | glue | rescue | statue | true |

1. save someone

_____

2. a color

_____

3. paste

_____

4. not false

_____

5.

_____

6.

_____

Name _____

Pick a word from the box to finish each sentence.
Write the word on the line.

never	other	sister	summer	under

1. May is visiting New York this _____ .

2. Her _____ Becky is with her.

3. She has _____ been on a ferry before.

4. There are _____ boats on the bay.

5. The ferry goes _____ a bridge.

Notes for Home: Your child read and wrote words ending in *-er* with the same ending sound
as *weather*. **Home Activity:** Help your child write a list of words that end in *-er* that describe
types of people, such as *worker* or *skater*.

Name _____

Pick a word from the box to finish each sentence.
Write the word on the line.

| course | hear | things | which | years |

1. Jed and Matt have been sailing for two _____.

2. They know many _____ about sailing.

3. Their boat stays on its _____ .

4. They _____ cheers from the shore.

5. _____ sailboat do you think will win the race?

Notes for Home: This week your child is learning to read the words *course, hear, things, which,* and *years.* **Home Activity:** Have your child use some of these words in a broadcast about a made-up sports contest.

Write F before each sentence that gives a **fact**.
Write O before each sentence that gives an **opinion**.

1. _____ I have been flying planes for ten years.

2. _____ I flew from New York to Texas today.

3. _____ I have a wonderful job.

4. _____ More people should fly rather than drive.

Write a fact about planes.

5. _____

_____

_____

Notes for Home: Your child practiced distinguishing between facts (statements that can be proven true or false) and opinions (statements that express a feeling or idea). *Home Activity:* As you read with your child, ask him or her to point out statements of fact and opinion.

Name _____

Some pronouns are used as subjects of sentences.
They are: **I, he, she, we, they.**

Some pronouns are used after action verbs.
They are: **me, him, her, us, them.**

Some pronouns can be used anywhere in a sentence.
They are: **you, it.**

Circle a pronoun to take the place of
the underlined word or words.

1. <u>My sisters and I</u> took Mike to the Statue of Liberty.   We
   Us

2. Maria followed <u>Mike and me</u> inside.   we
   us

3. Those stairs lead to the top of <u>the statue.</u>   it
   you

4. <u>Mike</u> didn't want to climb the stairs.   He
   Him

5. Julia and I followed <u>Maria</u> up the stairs.   she
   her

Notes for Home: Your child chose pronouns to use as subjects or after action verbs. *Home Activity:* As you read to your child, point out nouns in sentences. Ask which pronouns he or she would use to replace these nouns.

Name _____

Pick a word from the box to match each clue.
Write the word on the line.

course   deck   dock   hear   steers   things   years

1. the floor of a ship

_____

2. the path of a boat

_____

3. a place to wait for a boat

_____

4. listen

_____

5. many, many months

_____

6. more than one thing

_____

7. drives

_____

Name _____

Say the word for each picture.
Write a or le to finish each word.

People ride across the river.

1.

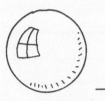

bubb _____

2.

_____ wake

3.

marb _____

4.

app _____

Circle the words that have the same beginning sound as **across**.

5. after
alarm
ant

6. above
art
able

7. ate
arm
ahead

8. about
air
ash

Find the word that has the same ending sound as the picture.
Mark the space to show your answer.

9. ⊖ problem
⊖ purse
⊖ purple

10. ⊖ tumble
⊖ tumbling
⊖ telling

Notes for Home: Your child reviewed words that contain the schwa sound heard in _about_ and _table_. **Home Activity:** Have your child read aloud some billboards and signs to you, pointing out words that contain the schwa sound.

| after | brother | flower | over | sister | summer |

Write four words from the box that begin with a consonant.

1. _____   2. _____

3. _____   4. _____

Write two words from the box that begin with a vowel.

5. _____   6. _____

Write two words from the box that are part of a family.

7. _____   8. _____

Pick a word from the box to finish each sentence.
Write the word on the line.

| year | which |

9. Last _____ we went on a ferry to the city.

10. _____ city did you visit?

Notes for Home: Your child spelled words that end in *-er* and two frequently used words: *year, which.* **Home Activity:** Write these words on slips of paper. Have your child draw two slips and write a sentence trying to use both words.

Circle a pronoun to use in place of the underlined word or words.

1. <u>Kim</u> lives on a boat called a sampan.

She
Her

2. Other families live in boats near <u>Kim's family</u>.

they
them

3. <u>Her mother and father</u> catch fish.

They
Them

4. Kim helps take care of <u>her little brother</u>.

he
him

| I | she | he | we | they | you |
| me | her | him | us | them | it |

Use at least one word from the box.
Write a sentence about something you can ride.

5. _____

Notes for Home: Your child reviewed subject pronouns (*I, she, he, we, they, you, it*) and object pronouns (*me, her, him, us, them, you, it*). **Home Activity:** Write these pronouns on index cards. Take turns picking a word and using it in a sentence.

Test-Taking Tips

1. Write your name on the test.

2. Read each question twice.

3. Read all the answer choices for the question.

4. Mark your answer carefully.

5. Check your answer.

Part I: Vocabulary

Find the word that best fits in each sentence.
Mark the space for your answer.

1. Mr. Brown _____ the boat.
   - ⊂⊃ says
   - ⊂⊃ steers
   - ⊂⊃ rockets

2. Neena's sister is three _____ old.
   - ⊂⊃ years
   - ⊂⊃ feathers
   - ⊂⊃ crops

3. We walked on the _____ of the ship.
   - ⊂⊃ course
   - ⊂⊃ deck
   - ⊂⊃ oven

4. Please put your _____ away.
   - ⊂⊃ things
   - ⊂⊃ paws
   - ⊂⊃ years

5. Bill jumped off the _____ into the water.
   - ⊂⊃ world
   - ⊂⊃ country
   - ⊂⊃ dock

GO ON ➡

Part 2: Comprehension

Read each question.
Mark the space for your answer.

6. This story is mostly about —
   - ⬭ the Statue of Liberty.
   - ⬭ New York City.
   - ⬭ Captain Cruz.

7. Captain Cruz's ferry is for —
   - ⬭ animals.
   - ⬭ people.
   - ⬭ cars.

8. A captain's log is a kind of —
   - ⬭ book.
   - ⬭ tree.
   - ⬭ rope.

9. Captain Cruz is a good captain because —
   - ⬭ a helper sits beside him.
   - ⬭ he likes his job.
   - ⬭ he keeps everyone safe.

10. Which sentence is an opinion?
    - ⬭ "Captain Cruz uses a radio."
    - ⬭ "The captain does his job well."
    - ⬭ "That's Mr. Cruz, my neighbor."

STOP

Name _____

birds

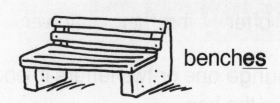 bench**es**

Say the word for each picture.
Add -s or **-es** to finish each word.

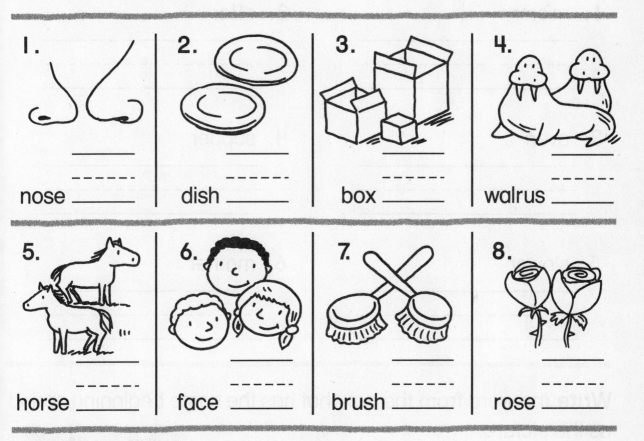

1. _____
nose _____

2. _____
dish _____

3. _____
box _____

4. _____
walrus _____

5. _____
horse _____

6. _____
face _____

7. _____
brush _____

8. _____
rose _____

Find the word that names only one.
Mark the space to show your answer.

9. ⬭ glass
    ⬭ places
    ⬭ porches

10. ⬭ foxes
    ⬭ mess
    ⬭ spaces

 Notes for Home: Your child reviewed adding -s or -es to nouns to show more than one.
Home Activity: Have your child read aloud each word above with and without the
-s or -es ending. Ask your child how many syllables are in each word.

Name _____

after	brother	flower	over	sister	summer

Change one or two letters in each word to make a word from the box.
Write the new word on the line.

1. mister
_____
- - - - - - - - - - - - - - - -
_____

2. offer
_____
- - - - - - - - - - - - - - - -
_____

3. oven
_____
- - - - - - - - - - - - - - - -
_____

4. supper
_____
- - - - - - - - - - - - - - - -
_____

5. slower
_____
- - - - - - - - - - - - - - - -
_____

6. mother
_____
- - - - - - - - - - - - - - - -
_____

Write the word from the box that has the same beginning sound as the picture.

year	which

7.

_____
- - - - - - - - - - - - - - - -

8.

_____
- - - - - - - - - - - - - - - -

Notes for Home: Your child spelled words that end in *-er* and two frequently used words: *year, which.* **Home Activity:** Write each spelling word with its letters scrambled. Ask your child to unscramble and write each word.

Name _____

RETEACHING

The pronouns **I, he, she, we,** and **they** are used as subjects of sentences.

The pronouns **me, him, her, us,** and **them** are used after action verbs.

The pronouns **you** and **it** can be used anywhere in a sentence.

Draw a line from the underlined word or group of words to the pronoun that can take its place.

1. <u>My grandmother and I</u> are sitting on the couch.   him

2. <u>My grandmother</u> is telling me about her friend, Bob.   We

3. Grandmother saw <u>Bob</u> at a party.   them

4. <u>Bob's children</u> were at the party too.   She

5. Grandmother gave <u>Bob's children</u> some cake.   They

Notes for Home: This week your child reviewed pronouns used in subjects and predicates of sentences. *Home Activity:* Ask your child to read a story to you. Have your child keep a tally of the number of pronouns used as subjects and the number of pronouns used in predicates.

Name _____

Find the word that best fits in each sentence.
Mark the space for your answer.

1. _____ love to play music!

   ⬭ She   ⬭ Us   ⬭ We

2. Susie brought drums and played _____ .

   ⬭ they   ⬭ her   ⬭ them

3. Herbie's piano is loud. He plays a special song on _____.

   ⬭ us   ⬭ it   ⬭ she

4. Where did _____ learn to play the guitar?

   ⬭ them   ⬭ him   ⬭ he

5. The audience is clapping for _____!

   ⬭ we   ⬭ I   ⬭ us

6. We are glad _____ came to listen.

   ⬭ they   ⬭ her   ⬭ us

Notes for Home: Your child chose the best subject or object pronoun to fit in a sentence.
Home Activity: Have your child write *I, she, he, we, they, you, me, her, him, us, them,* and *it* on
cards. Pick one of the cards and ask your child a question using the word on the card.

Family Times

My Wonderful Neighborhood

In my wonderful neighborhood under the sea
Live eight beige clams smiling right at me.
There's an octopus going on a shopping spree
In my wonderful neighborhood under the sea.

In my wonderful neighborhood under the sea
There's one pointy starfish floating gracefully.
There's a really big lobster weighing more than me
In my wonderful neighborhood under the sea.

This rhyme includes words your child is working with in school: words with the long *a* sound spelled *ei* as in *eight*, and words that have added endings and suffixes like *smiling* and *wonderful*. Sing the rhyme together. Help your child read and say the words with more than one syllable.

(fold here)

Name: _____

1

You are your child's first and best teacher!

Here are ways to help your child practice skills while having fun!

Day 1 Write each of the following words in a list: *beige, eight, freight, neigh, neighbor, rein, reindeer, sleigh, veil, weigh, weight.* Help your child draw pictures and write captions for them using these words.

Day 2 Encourage your child to use the words *cold, grow, most, move,* and *near* to make up a song or poem about living under the sea.

Day 3 Look through a magazine or newspaper with your child for maps, tables, graphs, and pictures. Discuss what information each graphic source shows.

Day 4 Your child is practicing speaking clearly and politely on the telephone. Act out telephone conversations with your child to practice calling and asking for information, such as how late the library stays open.

Day 5 Find out more about underwater sea life. Help your child take notes on some of the information you find. Encourage your child to use to these notes when telling someone else about this topic.

Read with your child EVERY DAY!

4

Underwater Walk

Materials paper circle, paper clip, pencil, 1 coin, 1 button per player, game board

Game Directions

1. Make a simple spinner as shown.

2. Players take turns tossing a coin and moving one space for heads and two spaces for tails.

3. Players then spin the spinner and add the word ending to the word on the gameboard to try to make a new word, if possible. If a word can't be made, the player goes back to his or her previous position.

4. The first player to get to the end wins!

-ly	-er
-less	-ing
-es	

Start

care
change
cool
dream
free
help
jump
kind
open
pass
push
point
price
quick
round
race
slow
warm
use
touch
spot

You're Safe!

2

Name _____

Pick the word that has the **long a** sound.
Write the word on the line.

fr**ei**ght train

1.

piece
weigh
artichoke

_____

- - - - - - - - - -

2.

talks
neighbors
friends

_____

- - - - - - - - - -

3.

neigh
nag
niece

_____

- - - - - - - - - -

4.

eat
eight
candle

_____

- - - - - - - - - -

5.

veil
head
bride

_____

- - - - - - - - - -

6.

sleigh
field
sled

_____

- - - - - - - - - -

7.

head
animal
reins

_____

- - - - - - - - - -

8.

deer
antlers
reindeer

_____

- - - - - - - - - -

Notes for Home: Your child wrote words in which the long *a* sound is spelled *ei*. **Home Activity:** List these word pairs: *weigh-way, rein-rain,* and *eight-ate.* Have your child read these words and use them in sentences.

Circle a word to finish each sentence.

1. Many big fish like to eat sea _____ .

horses
horsing

2. A sea horse is not a very good _____ .

swimmer
swimming

3. It has small fins so it swims very _____ .

slower
slowly

4. It moves by _____ the waves.

rider
riding

5. It _____ its color to hide.

changing
changes

Notes for Home: Your child read words in which adding endings such as *-ly, -less,* or *-ing* adds syllables *(quick, quickly).* **Home Activity:** Look at the words above. Discuss how the sound and meaning of words change when endings are added *(care, careless, caring).*

Name _____

Pick a word from the box to finish each sentence.
Write the word on the line. Use each word only once.

| cold | grow | most | move | near |

_____
- - - - - - - - - - - -
1. _____ seals live in the sea.

_____
- - - - - - - - - - - -
2. Some spend time on _____ chunks of ice.

_____
- - - - - - - - - - - -
3. Seal pups _____ slowly on land.

_____
- - - - - - - - - - - -
4. They stay _____ their mothers.

_____
- - - - - - - - - - - -
5. They _____ up fast.

Notes for Home: This week your child is learning to read the words *cold, grow, most, move,*
and *near. Home Activity:* Have your child use some of these words to write a conversation
between two animals that live in the sea.

Name _____

Read the sentences. **Look** at the pictures.
Answer the questions.

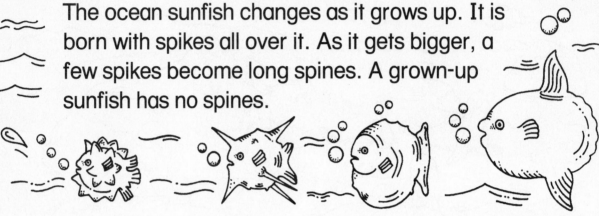

Ocean Sunfish

The ocean sunfish changes as it grows up. It is born with spikes all over it. As it gets bigger, a few spikes become long spines. A grown-up sunfish has no spines.

A. Soon after hatching   **B.** Growing up   **C.** Nearly grown up   **D.** All grown up

1. A baby sunfish has many spikes. What happens to them as the sunfish grows up?

_____

_____

_____

2. Look at picture B.
   How many long spikes does the sunfish have? _____

3. How is the fish in picture D different from the fish in picture C?

_____

_____

_____

_____

Notes for Home: Your child has been learning about looking at graphics, such as diagrams and charts, in order to better understand text. *Home Activity:* Check out library books that use graphics to give information. Discuss with your child the purpose of each graphic.

A **pronoun** takes the place of a noun or nouns.
When you use pronouns, you don't need to use
the same noun over and over.

___

Pick a pronoun from the box to finish the second sentence.
Use each word only once. **Circle** the word or words in the first
sentence that helped you decide which pronoun to use.

| he | it | she | them | they |

1. John took us to a tide pool. There _____ showed
   us a mole crab.

2. This crab has long feelers.

   It uses _____ to catch food.

3. My sister picked up a stick.

   Then _____ poked it in the sand.

4. Suddenly, all we saw was sand.

   The crab was hidden under _____ .

5. My sister and I saw two tiny bumps.

   John told us that _____ were its eyes.

Notes for Home: For each pair of sentences, your child used a pronoun in place of a noun.
Home Activity: Have your child pretend that he or she is visiting the bottom of the sea. Ask
him or her to write you a postcard from there using several pronouns.

Pick a word from the box to match each clue.
Write the word on the line. Use each word once.

beach	cold	floating	flopped
grow	move	near	poke

1.

_____
- - - - - - - - - - - - - - - - -
_____

2.

_____
- - - - - - - - - - - - - - -
_____

3. close by

_____
- - - - - - - - - - - - - - - - -
_____

4. get bigger

_____
- - - - - - - - - - - - - - -
_____

5. jab

_____
- - - - - - - - - - - - - - - - -
_____

6. The fish ____ on the deck

_____
- - - - - - - - - - - - - - -
_____

7. not hot

_____
- - - - - - - - - - - - - - - - -
_____

8. go to a new place

_____
- - - - - - - - - - - - - - -
_____

Notes for Home: Your child used word and picture clues to practice new vocabulary words.
Home Activity: Have your child use some of these words to tell you a story about a morning on a beach.

Name _____

Circle the word that has the same vowel sound as cl**ue**.
Write the word on the line.

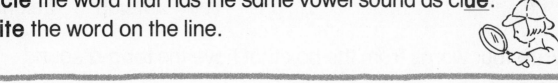

1. glue glee glad
_____
- -
_____

2. avenue about above
_____
- -
_____

3. scrub rescue stuff
_____
- -
_____

4. trust trouble threw
_____
- -
_____

5. true trip trouble
_____
- -
_____

6. blush blue blur
_____
- -
_____

7. bark barbecue butter
_____
- -
_____

8. grape grew grain
_____
- -
_____

Find the picture that has the same vowel sound as **blue**.
Mark the space to show your answer.

9. ⬭   ⬭   ⬭

10. ⬭   ⬭   ⬭

 Notes for Home: Your child reviewed words spelled with *ue* that have the vowel sound heard in *statue*. **Home Activity:** Write sentences using the words *Sue, blue, clue, glue,* and *true*. Help your child read them. Ask your child to draw pictures to match the sentences.

| neighbor | reindeer | sleigh | veil | weigh | weight |

Write four words from the box that have the **long a** sound spelled **eigh**.

1. _____

2. _____

3. _____

4. _____

Write two words from the box that have the **long a** sound spelled **ei**.

5. _____

6. _____

Write the two words from the box that rhyme.

7. _____

8. _____

Read the first letter of each word in each sentence. **Write** the letters on the line to make a word from the box.

grow
near

9. Nine elks are returning. _____

10. Get roses or weeds. _____

Notes for Home: Your child spelled words in which the long *a* sound is spelled *ei* (*veil*) and *eigh* (*weight*) and two frequently used words: *grow, near*. **Home Activity:** Say each spelling word aloud. Have your child repeat the word and spell it.

Name _____

Circle words to finish each sentence.
Write the words on the lines.

She   Her
_____
- - - - - - - - - -
1. _____ sees the seals.

He   Him   he   him
_____   _____
- - - - - - - -   - - - - - - - -
2. _____ gives _____ a book.

They   Them
_____
- - - - - - - -
3. _____ watch one seal eat.

we   us
_____
- - - - - - - - - -
4. "Is the seal looking at _____ ?"

I   me
_____
- - - - - - - - - -
5. "The seal is feeding _____ !"

Notes for Home: Your child practiced using pronouns in sentences. *Home Activity:*
Encourage your child to use pronouns to write about something that happened in school
this week.

Level 2.2

Grammar: Writing with Pronouns 157

Test-Taking Tips

1. Write your name on the test.

2. Read each question twice.

3. Read all the answer choices for the question.

4. Mark your answer carefully.

5. Check your answer.

Part 1: Vocabulary

Find the word that best fits in each sentence.
Mark the space for your answer.

1. Plants need water and sun to _____ .
   ⬭ trade   ⬭ keep   ⬭ grow

2. When you _____ me, it hurts.
   ⬭ poke   ⬭ follow   ⬭ beach

3. Will you sit _____ me today?
   ⬭ near   ⬭ still   ⬭ between

4. A log was _____ in the water.
   ⬭ sealing   ⬭ floating   ⬭ dashing

5. The dog _____ down on the grass.
   ⬭ drew   ⬭ flopped   ⬭ gathered

GO ON ➡

Part 2: Comprehension

Read each question.
Mark the space for your answer.

6. Many of the jellyfish in this story look like —
   - ⬭ wheels.
   - ⬭ ducks.
   - ⬭ parachutes.

7. Most jellyfish use tentacles to —
   - ⬭ catch food.
   - ⬭ swim.
   - ⬭ walk.

8. What will happen if you poke a jellyfish?
   - ⬭ It will melt.
   - ⬭ It will sting you.
   - ⬭ It will eat your finger.

9. The writer wanted to —
   - ⬭ give facts about jellyfish.
   - ⬭ tell how to catch a jellyfish.
   - ⬭ show that jellyfish are not really fish.

10. Which sentence is an opinion?
    - ⬭ Jellyfish eat fish, crabs, and worms.
    - ⬭ Each jellyfish lives about a year.
    - ⬭ Jellyfish are pretty.

STOP

Name _____

Say the word for each picture.
Write the word on the line.
Use the words in the box if you need help.

| baker | camper | catcher |
| marcher | mother | teacher |

sing**er**

1.

_ _ _ _ _ _ _ _ _

2.

_ _ _ _ _ _ _ _ _

3.

_ _ _ _ _ _ _ _ _

4.

_ _ _ _ _ _ _ _ _

5.

_ _ _ _ _ _ _ _ _

6.

_ _ _ _ _ _ _ _ _

Find the word that has the same ending sound as the picture.
Mark the space to show your answer.

7. ⬭ very
⬭ here
⬭ after

8. ⬭ weather
⬭ year
⬭ somewhere

Notes for Home: Your child reviewed words ending in -*er* that have the schwa sound heard in *singer*. **Home Activity:** Many words ending in -*er* name people who do things, such as *singer.* Work with your child to list other words like this.

| neighbor | reindeer | sleigh | veil | weigh | weight |

Write a word from the box that sounds the same as the word or words below.

1. way _____

2. wait _____

Pick a word from the box to match each clue.
Write the word on the line.

3. rain + dear _____

4. like a sled _____

_____

5. It is what a bride wears. _____

_____

6. It is someone who lives near you. _____

Write the word from the box that means the opposite of each word below.

| grow | near |

7. far _____

8. shrink _____

Notes for Home: Your child spelled words in which the long *a* sound is spelled *ei (veil)* and *eigh (weight)* and two frequently used words: *grow, near.* **Home Activity:** Encourage your child to draw a snowy scene and to use the spelling words to write about the picture.

Name _____

RETEACHING

A **pronoun** takes the place of a noun or nouns.
When you use pronouns, you don't need to
use the same noun over and over.

Joe likes **cats**. **He** plays with **them**.

Read each sentence.
Choose a pronoun from the box to finish the second sentence
in each pair. **Write** it on the line.
Circle the word or words in the first sentence in each pair that
helped you decide which pronoun to use.

| He | She | It | them | They |

I. A woman came to visit our class.

_____

_____ was from Guinea.

2. Guinea is a country in West Africa.

_____

_____ is on the coast of the Atlantic Ocean.

3. The woman and her brother told us about their country.

_____

_____ spoke to us in English.

4. They showed us clothes from Guinea.

_____

They even let us try _____ on!

Notes for Home: Your child replaced nouns and noun phrases with pronouns in sentences.
Home Activity: Have your child pretend he or she is visiting another country. Ask him or her
to write a postcard to you from the other country, using several pronouns.

Read each sentence and question.
Answer each question by writing a pronoun from the box on the line. Some words are used more than once.

She	it	them	her	He	They

1. Sally has a messy room. What should Sally do?

   _____   _____

   _____ should clean _____.

2. There are toys everywhere. What should Sally do with the toys?

   _____   _____

   _____ should put _____ away.

3. Sally can't find her homework. What should Sally do?

   _____   _____

   _____ should look for _____.

4. John wants to help Sally. What should John do?

   _____   _____

   _____ should start helping _____.

5. John and Sally finished cleaning. What should John and Sally do?

   _____

   _____ should have lunch!

Notes for Home: Your child used pronouns in sentences. *Home Activity:* Encourage your child to use pronouns to write about a day he or she really enjoyed.

Family Times

Tex and the Big Bad T. Rex

Let's Go Dinosaur Tracking!

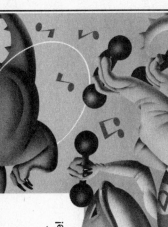

Exercise with Dino!

Exercise with Dino.
He'll show you how.
Express yourself!
And flex right now!

Discover your strength.
Do an extra hop.
Uncurl your tail.
Next you can stop.

Replay the song.
Redo each move.
Exercise with Dino.
Move to the groove!

This rhyme includes words your child is working with in school: words with *ex* (*extra*) and words that begin with the prefixes *un-*, *dis-*, and *re-*. Read "Exercise with Dino!" aloud with your child. Hop each time you say a word with *ex*. Clap for each word with the prefix *un-*, *dis-*, or *re-*.

(fold here)

Name: _____

You are your child's first and best teacher!

Here are ways to help your child practice skills while having fun!

Day 1 Help your child think of words that have the letter combination *ex* in them such as *next* or *Texas*. Write a list of these words.

Day 2 Your child is learning to read the words *along, front, probably, right,* and *someday*. Use these words during a conversation about a future family trip.

Day 3 Read a nonfiction story or news article with your child. As you read, pause to ask your child to tell you the main idea of a paragraph or page.

Day 4 Have your child search a story for word pairs that can be rewritten as contractions, such as *is not (isn't)* or *it is (it's)*. Help your child write these contractions.

Day 5 Your child is learning to use proper grammar when speaking. Help correct any incorrect uses of language you hear by asking: *Does that sound right to you? Is that the correct word to use?*

Read with your child EVERY DAY!

Adding Prefixes

Materials paper circle, paper clip, pencil, 1 button per player, game board

Game Directions

1. Make a simple spinner as shown.

2. Take turns spinning to get a prefix, and then tossing a button on the gameboard. Players try to make a new word, if possible, by adding the prefix to the word landed on.

3. Players earn 1 point for each new word. Use a word only once. Make a list to keep track of words used.

4. The first player to earn 5 points wins!

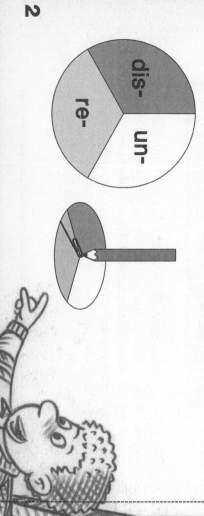

dis-
re-
un-

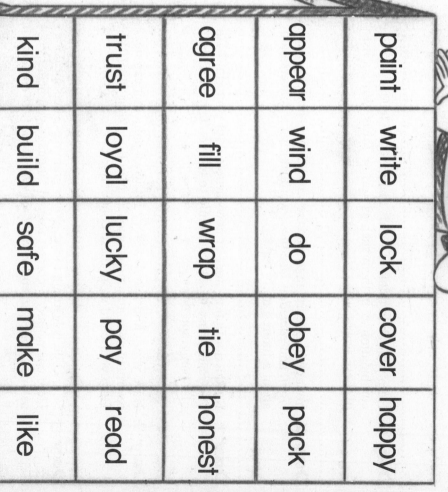

paint	write	lock	cover	happy
appear	wind	do	obey	pack
agree	fill	wrap	tie	honest
trust	loyal	lucky	pay	read
kind	build	safe	make	like

2

3

Pick a word from the box to finish each sentence.
Write the word on the line.

| next | excited | expert | extra | explain |

T**ex**as

1. Dr. Sanchez is an _____ on dinosaurs.

2. Her books _____ how dinosaurs lived.

3. I can't wait for her _____ book about them.

4. I am _____ about going to hear her talk tonight.

5. I have an _____ ticket if you want to come!

Notes for Home: Your child read and wrote words that contain the letter combination *ex*.
Home Activity: Help your child make up facts about someone named Rex, using a word
containing *ex* in each sentence, for example: *Rex is an expert swimmer*.

Name _____

Read each clue.

Add un-, dis-, or **re-** to the word to match each clue.

Hint: Adding **un-** or **dis-** makes a word mean the opposite.

Adding **re-** makes it mean "do again."

happy   **un**happy

---

1. not lucky

   _____

   - - - - - - - -

   _____ lucky

2. paint again

   _____

   - - - - - - - -

   _____ paint

3. not agree

   _____

   - - - - - - - -

   _____ agree

4. opposite of *pack*

   _____

   - - - - - - - -

   _____ pack

5. not locked

   _____

   - - - - - - - -

   _____ locked

6. build again

   _____

   - - - - - - - -

   _____ build

7. not obey

   _____

   - - - - - - - -

   _____ obey

8. not safe

   _____

   - - - - - - - -

   _____ safe

9. read again

   _____

   - - - - - - - -

   _____ read

10. not honest

   _____

   - - - - - - - -

   _____ honest

Notes for Home: Your child practiced figuring out the meanings of words with the prefixes *un-, dis-,* and *re-.* ***Home Activity:*** Look for words like these in ads and signs. Help your child pronounce these words and figure out what they mean.

Name _____

Circle a word to finish each sentence.

1. This dinosaur had very short _____ legs.

right
front

2. It moved _____ on its hind legs.

along
front

3. It was _____ a very scary creature.

probably
someday

4. I knew _____ away I wouldn't want to meet one.

along
right

5. _____ I'd like to dig up dinosaur bones.

Someday
Right

Notes for Home: This week your child is learning to read the words *along, front, probably, right,* and *someday.* **Home Activity:** Have your child use some of these words to write a news announcement about an imaginary and interesting discovery.

Read the paragraph.

Most reptiles lay their eggs and walk away. Scientists thought dinosaurs were like reptiles. Now some scientists think the dinosaur parents were there when the eggs hatched. They may have fed their babies. They may have kept them safe from harm. Perhaps dinosaurs were good parents after all.

1. Write a sentence that tells the main idea of the paragraph.

_____

_____

2. Draw a picture that shows the main idea.

3. Write a title for the paragraph.

_____

Notes for Home: Your child found the most important idea of a paragraph. *Home Activity:* Read aloud paragraphs from a nature magazine or book to your child. Stop to talk about what the most important idea is in each paragraph.

Name _____

A **contraction** is a word made
by putting two words together.
An **apostrophe** ' shows where
letters have been left out.

We **will see** the dinosaurs.
<u>We'll</u> see the dinosaurs.

Put the words together to make a contraction.
Write the contraction on the line.

1. is not

   _____

   _____

2. we are

   _____

   _____

3. he is

   _____

   _____

4. we have

   _____

   _____

5. they are

   _____

   _____

6. do not

   _____

   _____

Pick a word from the box to finish each sentence.
Write the word on the line.

> aren't   haven't

7. There _____ any dinosaurs alive today.

8. They _____ been here for millions of years.

Notes for Home: Your child wrote contractions by joining a pronoun and a verb or a verb
with the word *not*. **Home Activity:** As you read, point out contractions. Have your child write
the two words that were used to make each contraction.

Pick a word from the box to match each clue.
Write the word on the line.

claws	front	giant	helmet
probably	someday	stone	right

1. huge

_____

- - - - - - - - - - - - - - - -

_____

2. a day in the future

_____

- - - - - - - - - - - - - - - -

_____

3. not back

_____

- - - - - - - - - - - - - - - -

_____

4. Do it _____ away!

_____

- - - - - - - - - - - - - - - -

_____

5. a hard hat

_____

- - - - - - - - - - - - - - - -

_____

6. a rock

_____

- - - - - - - - - - - - - - - -

_____

7. a crab's "hands"

_____

- - - - - - - - - - - - - - - -

_____

8. likely

_____

- - - - - - - - - - - - - - - -

_____

 Notes for Home: Your child used word and picture clues to practice new vocabulary words. *Home Activity:* Encourage your child to use these words to tell a fantasy story about a giant dinosaur or dragon with big claws.

Name _____

<u>ei</u>ght

Each word pair goes with the picture.
Circle the word that has the same **long a** sound as **eight**.
Write the word on the line.

1. 	2. 	3. 
weigh apple	neighbor talk	reindeer antler
_____	_____	_____

4. 	5. 	6. 
sleigh dash	hair veil	reins saddle
_____	_____	_____

Find the word that has the same vowel sound as the picture.
Mark the space to show your answer.

7. ⬭ grass
    ⬭ beige
    ⬭ taps

8. ⬭ weight
    ⬭ white
    ⬭ whole

Notes for Home: Your child reviewed words with the long *a* sound spelled *ei* as heard in *eight*. **Home Activity:** Write the words with *ei* listed above on slips of paper. Take turns drawing words and using each word in a sentence.

| undo | unfair | unhappy | unlike | unlucky | untie |

Write four words from the box that have two syllables.

1. _____   2. _____

3. _____   4. _____

Write two words from the box that have three syllables.

5. _____   6. _____

Pick a word from the box to match each clue.
Write the word on the line.

7. not glad

_____

8. not the same

_____

Pick a word from the box to finish each sentence.
Write the word on the line.

| front | probably |

9. Mary will _____ come to the show.

10. We will sit in the _____ row.

Notes for Home: Your child spelled words that begin with the prefix *un-* and two frequently used words: *front, probably.* **Home Activity:** Help your child write a clue for each word with *un-*. Discuss how this prefix changes the meaning of a word.

Take out sentences that don't belong with the other sentences in a paragraph.

Dinosaurs lived a long time ago. They were the largest animals on Earth then. ~~You can see dinosaur bones today.~~ Some dinosaurs were bigger than houses. Anklyosaurus could be up to 56 feet long!

Read the sentences.
Pick three sentences that belong together.
Draw a line through the one that doesn't belong.

1. Ankylosaurus looked a little like a turtle.
2. That is because it had a hard shell like a turtle.
3. Turtles are very slow animals.
4. However, Ankylosaurus was much larger than a turtle.

Write three sentences that belong together about dinosaurs.

_____
- -
5. _____
_____
- -
_____
- -
_____
- -
_____
- -
_____

Notes for Home: Your child identified and wrote sentences that belong together.
Home Activity: Copy a few sentences each from several paragraphs of a story and cut them up. Have your child group the sentences that make sense together.

Use the words in ( ) to make a contraction.
Write the contraction on the line to finish each sentence.

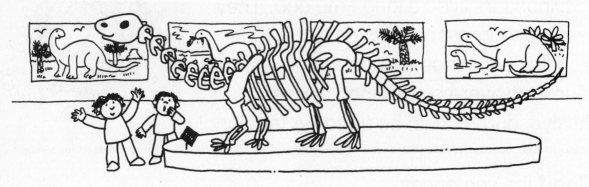

(had not)

_____

- - - - - - - - - - - - - - - - - -

1. They _____ seen a dinosaur before.

(It is)

_____

- - - - - - - - - - - - - - - - - -

2. _____ much bigger than an elephant.

(They are)

_____

- - - - - - - - - - - - - - - - - -

3. _____ glad to see this one.

(would not)

_____

- - - - - - - - - - - - - - - - - -

4. They _____ like to meet a live one.

(They will)

_____

- - - - - - - - - - - - - - - - - -

5. _____ dream of dinosaurs tonight.

Notes for Home: Your child wrote contractions. *Home Activity:* Read with your child and point out pairs of words that can be made into contractions. Have him or her write the contractions and reread the sentences with the contractions in place.

Part 1: Vocabulary

Find the word that best fits in each sentence.
Mark the space for your answer.

1. Jason puts on a _____ when he rides his bike.
   ⬭ surface   ⬭ helmet   ⬭ someday

2. The bear's _____ are sharp.
   ⬭ claws   ⬭ rockets   ⬭ tools

3. The wall was made of _____ .
   ⬭ giant   ⬭ stone   ⬭ beach

4. Mina lost her _____ tooth.
   ⬭ front   ⬭ word   ⬭ poke

5. We will _____ go to the zoo.
   ⬭ since   ⬭ should   ⬭ probably

GO ON ➡

Part 2: Comprehension

Read each question.
Mark the space for your answer.

6. What happened first?
   - ⬯ The tracks turned to stone.
   - ⬯ A dinosaur left some tracks.
   - ⬯ Sand covered the tracks.

7. This story is mostly about —
   - ⬯ finding a real dinosaur.
   - ⬯ Roland Bird.
   - ⬯ looking for dinosaur tracks.

8. You can tell that sauropods were —
   - ⬯ very large.
   - ⬯ three-legged.
   - ⬯ meat eaters.

9. What did you learn about dinosaurs from this story?
   - ⬯ Most dinosaurs were shaped like birds.
   - ⬯ There were many different kinds.
   - ⬯ All dinosaurs were very large.

10. Where is the best place to look for dinosaur tracks?
    - ⬯ in a field of grass
    - ⬯ in a lake
    - ⬯ on flat stone

STOP

Name _____

Circle a word to finish each sentence.

1. It looks around _____ .

   careless   carefully   caring

2. It is a fast _____ .

   running   runny   runner

3. It is _____ .

   helper   helpful   helpless

4. It is _____ .

   sleepless   sleepy   sleeper

Find the words that mean "glad" or "gladly."
Mark the spaces to show your answers.

5. ⬭ sleepy
   ⬭ happily
   ⬭ tired

6. ⬭ cheerful
   ⬭ sadly
   ⬭ slowly

Notes for Home: Your child reviewed words with more than one syllable that end in *-er, -ing, -less, -ful, -ly,* and *-y*. **Home Activity:** Work with your child to list some other words with these endings. Together, write a silly poem about dinosaurs with the words from your list.

Name _____

| undo | unfair | unhappy | unlike | unlucky | untie |

Add un- to each word to make a word from the box.
Write the new word on the line.

1. do

_____

- - - - - - - - - - - - - - - -

_____

2. happy

_____

- - - - - - - - - - - - - - - -

_____

3. tie

_____

- - - - - - - - - - - - - - - -

_____

4. lucky

_____

- - - - - - - - - - - - - - - -

_____

5. like

_____

- - - - - - - - - - - - - - - -

_____

6. fair

_____

- - - - - - - - - - - - - - - -

_____

Pick a word from the box to match each clue.
Write the word on the line.

| front | probably |

_____

- - - - - - - - - - - - - - - -

7. likely _____

_____

- - - - - - - - - - - - - - - -

8. opposite of *back* _____

Notes for Home: Your child spelled words with the prefix *un-* and two frequently used words: *front, probably.* **Home Activity:** Help your child make crossword puzzles that include these spelling words. Work together to think of clues for each word.

Name _____

RETEACHING

Roy **is not** late. Roy **isn't** late.
Isn't is a short way to write **is** and **not**.
An apostrophe **'** takes the place of **o** in **not**.

A contraction is a short way to put two words together. An apostrophe **'** takes the place of one or more letters.

Circle the contraction for the underlined words.

1. The people <u>are not</u> ready.   aren't   didn't

2. They <u>have not</u> found a seat.   haven't   wouldn't

3. The train <u>should not</u> leave.   isn't   shouldn't

4. The train <u>does not</u> go yet.   doesn't   don't

5. The people <u>would not</u> be safe.   couldn't   wouldn't

Circle the words that make up the underlined contraction.

6. <u>She's</u> here to help.   She is   She will

7. Now <u>they'll</u> sit down.   you will   they will

8. Then <u>we'll</u> hear the whistle.   we will   we are

9. At last <u>we're</u> on our way.   they are   we are

Notes for Home: Your child identified contractions correctly in sentences. *Home Activity:* Write contractions, such as *isn't, doesn't,* or *we're,* on cards. Choose a card and have your child use that contraction in a sentence. Then change roles.

Name _____

Write the contraction for each set of words in ( ).

| He's   don't   doesn't   isn't |

1. The kittens (do not) _____ move.

2. Jon (does not) _____ see them.

3. (He is) _____ going by the chair.

4. The chair (is not) _____ empty.

Write the words for the contractions in ( ).

| We are   We will   They will   They are |

5. (They're) _____ jumping out.

6. (We're) _____ laughing at the kittens.

7. (They'll) _____ make us laugh every time.

8. (We'll) _____ play with them again tomorrow.

Notes for Home: Your child wrote contractions in sentences. *Home Activity:* Write a sentence on a piece of paper. (For example: *We are going now.*) Have your child rewrite the sentence, using a contraction. *(We're going now.)*

182 Grammar: Contractions

Name _____

Correct each sentence.
Write it on the line.
Hint: Check that all pronouns are used correctly.

1. Me wrote a report on dinosaurs.

_____

_____

_____

2. Them were big animals.

_____

3. Mrs. Lee said he liked it.

_____

4. Her liked my pictures.

_____

5. My dad was proud of I.

_____

_____

_____

Notes for Home: Your child corrected pronouns in sentences. *Home Activity:* Read a story together. Look for sentences with nouns that can be replaced with pronouns. Have your child read the sentences using the proper pronouns. *(Mike threw the ball. He threw it.)*

Words I Can Now Read and Write

Family Times

The Clubhouse   Lemonade for Sale

Let's Build a Clubhouse

Let's build a clubhouse. What shall we do?
First we need some money,
Then some help from you!
We'll have a bake sale here tonight.
We'll bake some cookies
So they taste just right.
We'll bake a cake and sell each piece.
Please pay Shirley and her little niece.
Half of the money we'll give away.
Half of the money we'll save today.
We'll take a photograph of our bake sale.
We'll hang the photo
On a little nail!

This rhyme includes words your child is working with in school: words with the long *e* sound spelled *ie* and *ey* (*piece, money*) and words with *ph* and *lf* (*photograph, half*). Read the rhyme with your child. Circle all the long *e* words spelled *ie* and *ey*. Underline the words with *ph* and *lf*.

(fold here)

Name: _____

1

You are your child's first and best teacher!

Here are ways to help your child practice skills while having fun!

Day 1   Write a list of words with long *e* spelled *ie* and *ey* such as *chief, cookie, piece, money, monkey,* and *honey.* Use some of these long *e* words to help your child write a story about a monkey.

Day 2   Take turns making up sentences that include these words that your child is learning to read: *above, few, kept, number, sound.*

Day 3   After you read a story with your child, discuss which parts of the story could really happen and which parts are make-believe.

Day 4   Have your child make a poster that advertises a food that he or she likes. Encourage your child to include information that tells his or her opinion about the product.

Day 5   Ask your child what makes a good listener and a good speaker. Then talk with your child about his or her day to practice these listening and speaking skills.

Read with your child EVERY DAY!

4

Climb a Tree

Materials   1 coin, 1 button per player, game board

Game Directions

1. Each player chooses a tree to climb.

2. Players take turns flipping a coin. Move one space for heads and two spaces for tails.

3. As each player lands on a word, he or she reads it aloud and uses it in a sentence. If a player cannot read the word or use it in a sentence correctly, the player moves back to his or her previous position.

4. The first player to reach the top wins!

halfway	laughing	nephew
photos	calf	alphabet
graph	halfway	trophy
rough	graphs	half
alphabet	rough	calf
tough	trophy	laughs
phone	orphan	enough

Name _____

Say the word for each picture.
Write ie or **ey** to finish each word.
Use the words in the box if you need help.

th**ie**f   k**ey**

briefcase	chief	cookie	honey
money	monkey	piece	turkey

1. ch _____ f

2. cook _____

3. p _____ ce

4. hon _____

5. monk _____

6. turk _____

7. mon _____

8. br _____ fcase

Notes for Home: Your child wrote words with the long *e* sound spelled *ie* and *ey* as in *thief* and *key*. **Home Activity:** Work with your child to write a story using as many of the pictured words as possible.

Level 2.2   Phonics: Long *e: ie, ey* **187**

Name _____

Pick the word that has the same consonant sound heard at the end of **graph.**
Write the word on the line to finish each sentence.

gra**ph**

---

enough   some

_____

1. Did we make _____ ?

---

up   halfway

_____

2. It is filled _____ .

---

cough   sneeze

_____

3. Don't _____ , please.

---

trophy   medal

_____

4. We deserve a _____ .

---

smile   laugh

_____

5. Don't _____ , it's true.

 Notes for Home: Your child finished sentences using words with the consonants *gh, ph,* and *lf* that represent the sound /f/. ***Home Activity:*** Make up rhymes with your child using the words with *gh, ph,* and *lf* shown above.

Draw a line to match each word to a clue.

1. above   **a.** something you hear

2. few   **b.** not below

3. kept   **c.** not many

4. number   **d.** tells how many

5. sound   **e.** the opposite of "gave away"

Write a sentence for each word in the box on the lines below.

| above | few | kept | number | sound |

6. _____

7. _____

8. _____

9. _____

10. _____

Notes for Home: This week your child is learning to read the words *above, few, kept, number,* and *sound.* **Home Activity:** Have your child tell you about an experience buying or selling something using as many of the listed words as possible.

Name _____

Look at each picture.
Circle R if the picture shows something that could really happen.
Circle F if the picture shows something that could not really happen.

1. R   F

2. R   F

3. R   F

4. R   F

5. R   F

6. R   F

7. R   F

8. R   F

9. R   F

Draw a picture of something that could happen in a fantasy.
10.

Notes for Home: Your child identified things that could happen in a realistic story and things that could happen in a fantasy. *Home Activity:* Read a story. Ask your child to identify realistic events (real people doing ordinary things) and fantasy events (animals talking).

Name _____

A **sentence** is a group of words that tell a complete idea.

Sentence: Toby likes to drink lemonade.
Not a sentence: A hot and thirsty Toby.

Read the words.
Write an **S** on the line if the words are a complete sentence.
Write an **N** on the line if the words are **not** a complete sentence.

_____ 1. Chris has a plan.

_____ 2. Wants to sell.

_____ 3. I love lemonade and cookies!

_____ 4. More cookies.

Write a sentence to go with the picture above.

5. _____

Notes for Home: Your child identified and wrote complete sentences. *Home Activity:* Ask your child to tell you a story about solving a problem. Encourage him or her to use complete sentences.

Name _____

Pick a word from the box to finish each sentence.
Write the word on the line.

above	few	ice	kept
lemonade	number	sound	

1. Did you hear that _____ ?

2. It came from _____ us.

3. There are a _____ lemons in the tree.

4. Let's count the _____ of lemons.

5. Let's make _____ to drink.

6. Mom _____ the lemons we picked.

7. We need _____ to make it cold.

Notes for Home: Your child completed sentences using words that he or she learned to read this week. **Home Activity:** Work with your child to write a story using as many of these words as possible. Read the story aloud to other family members or friends.

Name _____

Use the graphs to answer the questions.

Cups of Lemonade Sold

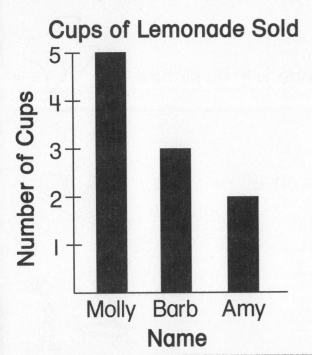

Number of Cups

Molly   Barb   Amy
Name

Cups of Lemonade Sold

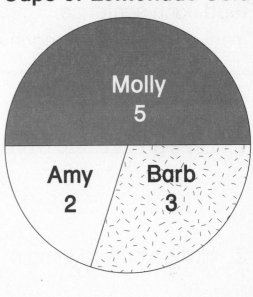

_____

1. What do the graphs show?

_____

- -

_____

_____

- - - - - - - - - - - -

2. Who sold the most cups of lemonade?   _____

_____

- - - - - - - - - - - -

3. Who sold the fewest cups of lemonade?   _____

_____

- - - - - - - - - - - -

4. How many cups were sold all together?   _____

5. Which graph is easier for you to read? Why?

_____

- -

_____

Notes for Home: Your child compared information on a circle graph and on a bar graph.
Home Activity: Together, graph information about your family, such as the number of minutes
it takes to eat dinner each night for a week. Make both a circle and a bar graph.

T**ex**as

Write ex to finish each word.
Read each sentence.
Draw a line to match each sentence with its picture.

1. Let's go _____ plore in this cave!

    a.

2. Hallie wants to jump n _____ t.

    b.

3. Phil is an _____ pert biker.

    c.

4. Alice has an _____ tra cookie.

    d.

Find the word that matches each clue.
Mark the space to show your answer.

5. It's something you do
   to stay healthy.
   - ○ explain
   - ○ exercise
   - ○ explode

6. It's a way out of
   someplace.
   - ○ extra
   - ○ example
   - ○ exit

Notes for Home: Your child reviewed words with the vowel pattern *ex*, as in *Texas*. **Home Activity:** Write a list of words with *ex*, such as *explore, next, expensive,* or *exit*. Help your child read them aloud and use them in sentences.

calf   half   laugh   phone   rough   tough

Write three words from the box spelled with **gh**.

1. _____   2. _____   3. _____

Write the word from the box that rhymes with  .

4. _____

Change one letter in each word to make a word from the box.
Write the new word on the line.

5. halt _____   6. calm _____

Pick a word from the box to finish each sentence.
Write the word on the line.

sound
kept

7. I hear the _____ of popcorn popping.

8. Dean _____ it all for himself.

Notes for Home: Your child spelled words with the consonants *gh*, *ph*, and *lf* and two
frequently used words: *sound, kept.* **Home Activity:** Say each spelling word. Have your child
use it in a sentence. Say the spelling word again, and have your child write it.

Level 2.2

Spelling: Consonants *gh*, *ph*, *lf* **195**

Name _____

Read the sentences Greg and Diane say to each other.
Follow the directions below.

Greg: What do we need to make lemonade?

Diane: We need lemons, sugar, water, and ice.

Diane: Stir it.

Greg: This is the best lemonade I've ever had!

---

1. Draw one line under the command.
2. Draw two lines under the exclamation.
3. Circle the question.
4. Put an X after the statement.
5. Look at the picture. Write a sentence that tells what happens next.

_____

- -

_____

- -

_____

Notes for Home: Your child reviewed sentences. *Home Activity:* Read a story with your child. Ask him or her to identify different types of sentences (questions, statements, commands, and exclamations). Have your child read them aloud with the proper emotion.

Part I: Vocabulary

Find the word that best fits in each sentence.
Mark the space for your answer.

1. Write your name _____ the line.
   - ⬭ ever
   - ⬭ above
   - ⬭ behind

2. The bird made a beautiful _____ .
   - ⬭ sound
   - ⬭ number
   - ⬭ garbage

3. Jill _____ all her toys in a box.
   - ⬭ began
   - ⬭ exclaimed
   - ⬭ kept

4. We have only a _____ cups of milk.
   - ⬭ few
   - ⬭ whole
   - ⬭ enough

5. I like lots of _____ in my water.
   - ⬭ paper
   - ⬭ ice
   - ⬭ room

GO ON ➡

Part 2: Comprehension

Read each question.
Mark the space for your answer.

6. The club members decided to make some money by —
   - ⬭ selling lemonade.
   - ⬭ having a bake sale.
   - ⬭ getting more members.

7. The kids wanted the money to —
   - ⬭ buy lemons.
   - ⬭ set up a corner stand.
   - ⬭ fix their clubhouse.

8. Few people got lemonade on Thursday because —
   - ⬭ the lemonade did not taste good.
   - ⬭ everyone went to watch Jed the juggler.
   - ⬭ Thursday's bar was way down low.

9. Sheri must have asked Jed to —
   - ⬭ do his act next to the lemonade stand.
   - ⬭ leave so they could sell more lemonade.
   - ⬭ never juggle again.

10. The Elm Street kids learned that —
    - ⬭ selling lemonade is no fun.
    - ⬭ they could not fix the clubhouse.
    - ⬭ a job is easier when everyone works together.

STOP

disappear   dislike   remake   repaint   untie   unwrap

Pick a word from the box that is the opposite of each word below.
Write the word on the line.

1. tie

_____

_____

2. wrap

_____

_____

3. like

_____

_____

4. appear

_____

_____

Pick a word from the box that means the same as each group of words.
Write the word on the line.

5. paint again

_____

_____

6. make again

_____

_____

Find the word that matches each clue.
Mark the space to show your answer.

7. not lucky
   - ⬭ unlucky
   - ⬭ lucky
   - ⬭ unkind

8. read again
   - ⬭ understand
   - ⬭ reread
   - ⬭ return

Notes for Home: Your child reviewed words with the prefixes *un-*, *dis-*, and *re-*. **Home Activity:** Work with your child to write a list of words with the prefixes *un-*, *dis-*, and *re-*. Have your child read the words and illustrate their meanings.

Name _____

| calf | half | laugh | phone | rough | tough |

Pick a word from the box to match each picture.
Write the word on the line.

1.

_____
- - - - - - - - - - - - - - - - -
_____

2.

_____
- - - - - - - - - - - - - - - - -
_____

3.

_____
- - - - - - - - - - - - - - - - -
_____

Unscramble the letters to make a word from the box.
Write the word on the line.

4. flha

_____
- - - - - - - - - - - - - -
_____

5. ogruh

_____
- - - - - - - - - - - - - -
_____

6. thugo

_____
- - - - - - - - - - - - - -
_____

Pick a word from the box to match each clue.
Write the word on the line.

| sound | kept |

7. something you hear _____
_____
- - - - - - - - - - - - - - - - -

8. opposite of "gave away" _____
_____
- - - - - - - - - - - - - - - - -

Notes for Home: Your child spelled words with the consonants *gh, ph,* and *lf* and two
frequently used words: *sound, kept.* **Home Activity:** Have your child write sentences using the
spelling words. Challenge your child to use words that rhyme.

RETEACHING

Paints a picture.

This group of words is not a sentence.
It does not tell a complete idea.

Luis paints a picture.

This group of words is a sentence. It tells a complete idea.

Underline each group of words that is a sentence.

1. **a.** Lin draws people.

   b. Draws people.

2. **a.** Need a pencil?

   b. Does he need a pencil?

3. **a.** Nan clay.

   b. Nan works with clay.

4. **a.** She makes a cup.

   b. Makes a cup.

Draw a line to match each group of words with the correct sentence.

5. Bring crayons?

6. Mimi found.

7. I brought.

8. Made a sign.

a. I brought some paper.

b. Did Sam bring crayons?

c. Mimi found the tape.

d. We made a sign.

Notes for Home: Your child identified complete sentences. *Home Activity:* Have your child draw a picture and write an advertisement for a favorite food. Remind your child to use complete sentences.

Underline each group of words that is a sentence.

1. Animals live in the woods.   2. A rabbit hears the call.

3. Some animals may hunt.   4. Does run.

5. They hunt in the dark.   6. Can it get away?

7. Runs at night.   8. In a hole.

9. Howls at the moon.   10. Rabbit is.

11. A rabbit.   12. Will the rabbit sleep?

Now **write** the other groups of words in complete sentences.

13. _____

14. _____

15. _____

16. _____

17. _____

18. _____

Notes for Home: Your child wrote complete sentences. *Home Activity:* Together, write a sentence. Cut the paper between the subject and predicate. *(The rabbit/hopped away.)* Have your child write two new sentences, using the subject in one and the predicate in another.

You are your child's first and best teacher!

Here are ways to help your child practice skills while having fun!

Day 1 Work with your child to write a list of long *e* words using *ei* such as *receive, either, Keith,* and *ceiling.* Read the words to your child and have him or her write them.

Day 2 Ask your child to write or say a funny story that uses any of the following words that your child is learning to read: *eight, road, round, start, young.*

Day 3 As you read together, ask your child to point out unfamiliar words. Encourage your child to use surrounding words and pictures to try to figure out the meaning of an unfamiliar word.

Day 4 Help your child write a letter to a friend or relative. Have your child address an envelope, put the letter in it, and take it to the post office or mailbox.

Day 5 Have your child write a story in which the characters speak. Have him or her use quotations marks as needed to show the speaker's exact words.

(fold here)

Family Times

Start Collecting! It's Fun!

The Puddle Pail

Keith's Leaves

My name is Keith.
I'll play outside today.
I'll collect some leaves
While I skip and play.

The leaves I'll collect
Are either green or brown.
I'll tape them to my ceiling
So they won't fall down.

I'll look at my leaves
While I lie in bed.
I'll put more leaves
On my shelves instead!

This rhyme includes words your child is working with in school: words with the long *e* sound spelled *ei* (*Keith*) and words in which *f* is changed to *v* before adding *-es* (*leaves, shelves*). Read aloud the rhyme with your child. Then write other plurals that change *f* to *v* before adding *-es,* such as *lives, knives,* and *wolves.*

More Than One

Materials 1 coin, 1 button per player, game board

Game Directions

1. Players place buttons at Start.

2. Players take turns flipping a coin and moving 1 space for heads or 2 spaces for tails.

3. Each time a player lands on a word, he or she changes that word to show more than one. If the player misspells the word, the player goes back to the previous position.

4. The first player to reach the end wins!

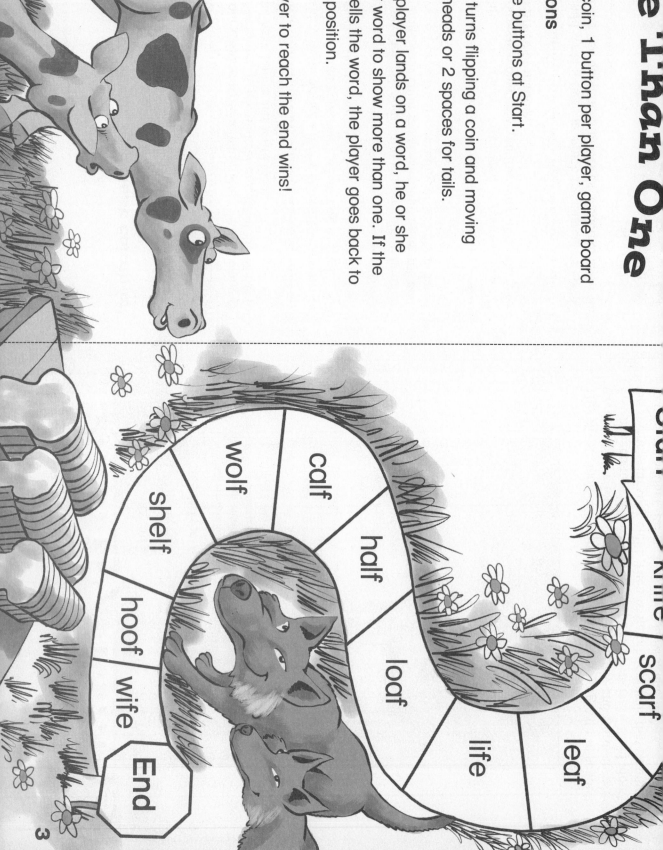

scarf

leaf

life

loaf

half

calf

wolf

shelf

hoof | wife | End

2

3

Name _____

Start Collecting! It's Fun!
The Puddle Pail

Pick a word from the box to finish each sentence.
Write the word on the line.

either   neither   receive   ceiling

1. Did you _____ the two toy bugs I sent?

2. _____ one has come yet.

3. They may come _____ Friday or Saturday.

4. You can hang them from your _____ .

Notes for Home: Your child identified words with the long *e* sound spelled *ei* as in *ceiling*.
Home Activity: Work with your child to write sentences using the listed words.

Name _____

Write the word for each picture.
Use the word in ( ) to help you.

leaf   lea**ves**

1.

(calf)

_____

- - - - - - - - - - - - - - - -

2.

(knife)

_____

- - - - - - - - - - - - - - - -

3.

(loaf)

_____

- - - - - - - - - - - - - - - -

4.

(shelf)

_____

- - - - - - - - - - - - - - - -

Draw a picture of the word below.

5. wolves

Notes for Home: Your child wrote plural words in which *f* is changed to *v* before adding
-es. **Home Activity:** Ask your child to write a sentence using each of the plural words above.

Name _____

Read each sentence.
Circle the picture that shows the meaning
of the underlined word.

1. Al has a very <u>young</u> puppy.

2. Al and his puppy walk across the <u>road</u> to go to the park.

3. Al wants to <u>start</u> a rock collection.

4. Al found <u>eight</u> rocks.

5. This rock is very <u>round</u> and smooth.

 Notes for Home: This week your child is learning to read the words *eight, road, round, start,* and *young.* **Home Activity:** Write these words on slips of paper and have your child practice reading them aloud and using them in sentences.

Name _____

Start Collecting! It's Fun!
The Puddle Pail

Read each sentence.
Use the other words in the sentence and the pictures to help you figure out the meaning of the underlined word.
Circle the meaning of the word.

1. Carrie added a British <u>pound</u> to her collection.
   a. a kind of money or coin
   b. a scale

2. She likes to collect <u>currency</u>.
   a. type of food
   b. money

3. She <u>stores</u> her collection in a box.
   a. keeps
   b. shops

4. Carrie is <u>eager</u> to get more coins.
   a. not careful
   b. looking forward to

5. She <u>adores</u> collecting coins!
   a. decorates
   b. loves

 Notes for Home: Your child used context clues—pictures or words that surround an unfamiliar word—to figure out a word's meaning. **Home Activity:** Read a story to your child. Ask him or her to use context clues to figure out the meanings of unfamiliar words.

Name _____

Quotation marks  " " show the beginning and
the end of what someone says.

Tim said, "Do you like my shells?"
"Yes, I do," Greta answered.

Put a ✓ on the line if the sentence does not need quotation marks.
Put an X on the line if the sentence needs quotation marks.
Then add quotation marks to the sentence.

_____ 1. Gus asked Nan to look at his baseball cards.

_____ 2. Nan said, You have a lot of cards.

_____ 3. Gus said, I've collected over 50 cards.

_____ 4. Nan asked her mom if she could collect cards too.

_____ 5. Her mom said, I'll help you get started.

Notes for Home: Your child identified sentences that use quotation marks. *Home Activity:*
Write a simple conversation between two characters or family members. Have your child help
you put the quotation marks where they belong.

Name _____

Start Collecting! It's Fun!
The Puddle Pail

Pick a word from the box to match each clue.
Write the word on the line.

| castle | crocodile | eight | puddle |
| road | round | shadows | young |

1.

_____

- - - - - - - - - - - -

_____

2.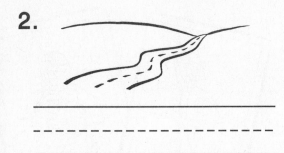

_____

- - - - - - - - - - - -

_____

3.

_____

- - - - - - - - - - - -

_____

4.

_____

- - - - - - - - - - - -

_____

5. They go everywhere you go!

_____

- - - - - - - - - - - -

_____

6. seven, _____, nine, ten

_____

- - - - - - - - - - - -

_____

7. not old, but _____

_____

- - - - - - - - - - - -

_____

8. A square is not, but a circle is.

_____

- - - - - - - - - - - -

_____

 Notes for Home: Your child matched clues with vocabulary words that he or she learned to read this week. *Home Activity:* Work with your child to write a story using as many of these words as possible.

Name _____

monk**ey**   cook**ie**s

Circle the word for each picture.

1.	2.	3.	4.
piece peas	moan money	turkey turtle	honey hotter

5.	6.	7.	8.
keep key	donkey done	cheek chief	three thief

Find the word that has the same **long e** sound as the picture.
Mark the space to show your answer.

9. ⬭ veil
   ⬭ vase
   ⬭ valley

10. ⬭ felt
    ⬭ field
    ⬭ fried

Notes for Home: Your child reviewed words with long *e* spelled *ie* and *ey* as in *cookies* and *monkey*. **Home Activity:** Write a list of long *e* words spelled *ie* and *ey*. Have your child tell you a story using as many of the words as possible.

Name _____

Start Collecting! It's Fun!
The Puddle Pail

calves	halves	lives	leaves	shelves	wolves

Write the word from the box that names more than one for each word below.

1. shelf _____

2. half _____

3. calf _____

4. leaf _____

5. life _____

6. wolf _____

Pick a word from the box to match each picture.
Write the word on the line.

7. _____

8. _____

Pick a word from the box to match each clue.
Write the word on the line.

young	road

9. not old

_____

10. rhymes with *toad*

_____

Notes for Home: Your child spelled plural words that change *f* to *v* before adding *-es (calves)*, as well as two frequently used words: *young, road*. **Home Activity:** Write each spelling word on separate slips of paper. Take turns picking two words and using them both in a sentence.

Name _____

Read each sentence.

Add quotation marks if the sentence needs them.

Write an **X** after the sentence if quotation marks are not needed.

1. Cal wants to collect rocks.

2. He asks, Mom, can I have a bucket for my rocks?

3. His mom gives him a big bucket.

4. She says, Look in the backyard for rocks.

Add words to finish this sentence.

Write the complete sentence below.

Use quotation marks as needed.

5. Cal says, _____.

_____

- -

_____

_____

- -

_____

Notes for Home: Your child identified sentences that require quotation marks and added them. **Home Activity:** Read a simple story with your child. Have him or her point out which sentences use quotation marks.

Test-Taking Tips

1. Write your name on the test.

2. Read each question twice.

3. Read all the answer choices for the question.

4. Mark your answer carefully.

5. Check your answer.

Name _____

Start Collecting! It's Fun!
The Puddle Pail

Part I: Vocabulary

Find the word that best fits in each sentence.
Mark the space for your answer.

1. Hank made a picture with _____ stars.
   - ⬭ quite
   - ⬭ between
   - ⬭ eight

2. The _____ chick followed its mother.
   - ⬭ young
   - ⬭ whole
   - ⬭ near

3. The queen lived in a _____ .
   - ⬭ castle
   - ⬭ crocodile
   - ⬭ puddle

4. Which _____ goes to the lake?
   - ⬭ round
   - ⬭ road
   - ⬭ edge

5. The cat hides in the _____ .
   - ⬭ paws
   - ⬭ shadows
   - ⬭ attention

GO ON ➡

Part 2: Comprehension

Read each question.
Mark the space for your answer.

6. Sol and Ernst first go to —
   - ⬭ a castle.
   - ⬭ the beach.
   - ⬭ the moon.

7. What does Ernst collect?
   - ⬭ puddles
   - ⬭ clouds
   - ⬭ feathers

8. You can tell from this story that starfishes are —
   - ⬭ cookies.
   - ⬭ animals.
   - ⬭ people.

9. How is Sol different from Ernst?
   - ⬭ Sol likes to eat blackberries.
   - ⬭ Sol is small and blue.
   - ⬭ Sol collects things he can keep.

10. The water in Ernst's pail is most like a —
    - ⬭ mirror.
    - ⬭ cloud.
    - ⬭ painting.

STOP

Say the word for each picture.
Write gh, ph, or **lf** to finish each word.
Use the words in the box if you need help.

calf	cough	half
laugh	photos	trophy

ph_one

1.

tro _____ y

2.

cou _____

3.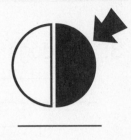

ha _____

4.

ca _____

5.

_____ otos

6.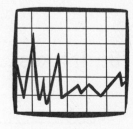

lau _____

Pick the word that has the same ending sound as the picture.
Mark the space to show your answer.

7. ⬭ rough
    ⬭ rugs
    ⬭ rush

8. ⬭ thought
    ⬭ tough
    ⬭ tugs

Notes for Home: Your child reviewed words with the sound /f/ spelled *gh, ph,* and *lf (laugh, graph,* and *half)*. **Home Activity:** Make a set of cards. Write words with the /f/ sound on half the cards. Illustrate the words on the other half. Have your child match the pairs pof cards.

Phonics: Consonants *gh, ph, lf* Review **217**

Name _____

Start Collecting! It's Fun!
The Puddle Pail

| calves | halves | lives | leaves | shelves | wolves |

Pick a word from the box to match each clue.
Write the word on the line.

1. grows on trees
_____
- - - - - - - - - - - - - - - -
_____

2. more than one life
_____
- - - - - - - - - - - - - - - -
_____

3. like dogs
_____
- - - - - - - - - - - - - - - -
_____

4. baby cows
_____
- - - - - - - - - - - - - - - -
_____

5. where you find library books
_____
- - - - - - - - - - - - - - - -
_____

6. I half + I half = 2 _____
_____
- - - - - - - - - - - - - - - -
_____

Pick a word from the box to finish each sentence.
Write the word on the line.

| young | road |

_____
- - - - - - - - - - - - - - - -

7. The bus drives down the _____ .

_____
- - - - - - - - - - - - - - - -

8. It takes _____ children to school.

_____
- - - - - - - - - - - - - - - -

Notes for Home: Your child spelled plural words that change *f* to *v* before adding *-es* and two frequently used words: *young, road*. **Home Activity:** Help your child write sentences that use the spelling words. Together draw pictures to illustrate each sentence.

RETEACHING

Quotation marks show the beginning and ending of what someone says.

"How much is this?" asked Nancy.

The saleswoman said, "It is one dollar."

Finish each sentence.
Remember to put quotation marks around what someone says.

1. The baker said, _____
_____
_____

2. _____
_____
_____ asked Billy.

3. My friend said, _____
_____
_____

4. _____
_____
_____ yelled the boy to his dog.

Notes for Home: Your child used quotation marks to show a speaker's exact words in sentences. **Home Activity:** Have your child tell you about a conversation he or she had. Write it, leaving out the quotation marks. Have your child insert quotation marks.

Add quotation marks if the sentence needs them.
Write an **X** next to the sentences that don't need quotation marks.

1. Where should we go to dinner tonight? asked Mom.

2. The children looked at each other with big smiles.

3. Let's go to the pizza place! they yelled.

Read the sentences.
Cross out the quotation marks that do not belong.

"Did you make this sandcastle?" asked my friend. X

4.–10.

"Do you want to make a treehouse?"
Joey asked his friends.
"Yes! Great idea!" his friends
answered."
"Joey said, "I'll get the hammer and"
nails."
"What should we get?" asked" his friends.
"Get some wood," said Joey. Joey
found the hammer and nails, and his
friends found some wood. "Joey and
his friends built a great treehouse."

Notes for Home: Your child made decisions about where quotation marks belong in sentences. **Home Activity:** Have your child look through a newspaper and find sentences with quotation marks.

220 Grammar: Quotation Marks

Family Times

Stone Soup

Stone Soup: A Folktale

The Country Fair

Let's go to the country fair.
We'll join the dairy contest.
A judge compares and then declares
Which cheese wedge tastes the very best.

Let's go to the country fair.
We saved up our bus fare.
We'll travel far and cross a bridge.
We'll bring our Swiss cheese to share.

This rhyme includes words your child is working with in school: words with *air* and *are* (*fair, fare*) and words with *dge* (*judge*). Sing "The Country Fair" with your child. Together, find all the words with *air*, *are*, and *dge* in the rhyme.

(fold here)

Name: _____

You are your child's first and best teacher!

Here are ways to help your child practice skills while having fun!

Day 1 Write *chair* and *spare* on two sheets of paper. Work with your child to write other words with *air* and *are* that rhyme with *chair* and *spare*.

Day 2 Ask your child to write or say sentences that use any of the following words that your child is learning to read: *add, any, both, making, mean.*

Day 3 After you read a story with your child, ask your child to tell you what happened in the beginning, middle, and end of the story.

Day 4 Have your child tell you about a movie, play, or TV show he or she has seen. Encourage your child to tell about the most important events in the movie, play, or TV show.

Day 5 Write a scene for a play about cooking food. Get family members to act out the different parts of the scene.

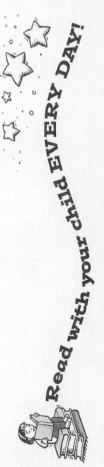

Read with your child EVERY DAY!

Cover It Up!

Materials 16 slips of paper, bag, 16 colored paper squares per player, game board

Game Directions

1. Write the 16 words shown below on slips of paper. Put the slips in a bag.

2. Each player cuts out small paper squares and colors them. Each player should use a different color for his or her set of squares.

3. Players take turns picking a slip of paper, reading the word aloud, and putting a colored paper square over the word on the gameboard.

4. The first player to cover 4 words in a row across, down, or diagonally wins!

Words

fair, hair, pair, prepare, stare, hare, dare, mare, airplane, hardware, care, fare, snare, chair, stair, spare

fair	hair	pair	prepare
stare	hare	dare	mare
airplane	hardware	care	fare
snare	chair	stair	spare

Say the word for each picture.
Write air or **are** to finish each word.

st**are**

1. h _____

2. p _____

3. sh _____

4. h _____

5. st _____ s

6. m _____

7. ch _____

8. squ _____

Draw a picture for each word.

9. airplane

10. fair

Notes for Home: Your child identified words where the letter *r* changes the vowel sound of the word as in *chair* and *stare*. **Home Activity:** Work with your child to write silly sentences that rhyme using as many of the pictured words as possible.

Name _____

Pick a word from the box to match each picture.
Write the word on the line.

badge	bridge	fudge	hedge	judge
ledge	pledge	smudge	wedge	

1.

_____

2.

_____

3.

_____

4.

_____

5.

_____

6.

_____

7.

_____

8.

_____

9.

_____

Write a sentence using one of the words from the box.

_____

10. _____

 Notes for Home: Your child matched words with *dge* to pictures. **Home Activity:** Ask your child to read aloud the words in the box. Work together to write sentences that use these words.

Pick a word from the box to finish each sentence.
Write the word on the line.

| add | any | both | making | mean |

_____
- - - - - - - - - - - - - - - - -
1. What are you _____ ?

- - - - - - - - - - - - - - - - -
2. Do you need _____ help?

_____
- - - - - - - - - - - - - - - - -
3. Please _____ the carrots.

_____
- - - - - - - - - - - - - - - - -
4. I think it needs _____ salt and pepper.

- - - - - - - - - - - - - - - - -
5. What do you _____ ? I think it's too salty.

Notes for Home: This week your child is learning to read the words *add, any, both, making,* and *mean.* **Home Activity:** Prepare a food item together. Before you start, write a list of the steps, using as many of these words as possible.

Name _____

Put the sentences in order to make a story.
Write 1, 2, 3, 4 on the lines to show the right order.

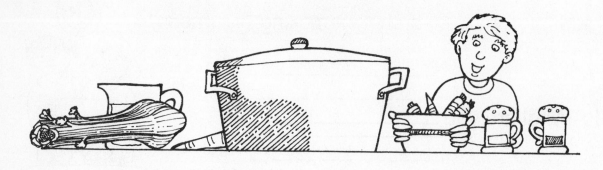

_____

1. Danny wanted to make some soup.

_____

2. Danny put the soup on the stove and cleaned up his mess.

_____

3. He chopped up the vegetables and put them in the pot.

_____

4. Danny got out a big pot, a spoon, and vegetables.

Draw a picture that shows something that happened in the middle of the story.

5.

Notes for Home: Your child identified the order of story events. *Home Activity:* Cut some short comic strips into separate panels. Ask your child to put them in their correct order. Ask your child to use the words *beginning, middle,* and *end* to describe what happens.

Here are some places where **commas** are used:

6 Morrow Court, Apt. 2B ← **in addresses**
Salem, MA 01944

May 29, 2000 ← **in dates**

Dear Harry, ← **to start a letter**
How are you?
↙ **to separate three or more things**
Liz, Jan, and Phil are going to the game next Saturday. Do
you want to go with me?

Your friend, ← **to end a letter**
Jimmy

1.–8. Add eight commas to this letter.

19 East Lake Dr.
Gladstone MI 49837

June 5 2000

Dear Uncle Sid

Sarah and I made soup for lunch. Sarah put carrots peas
and mushrooms into a pot of water. I added salt pepper and
garlic.

Love
Jake

Notes for Home: Your child placed commas in a letter. *Home Activity:* Together, write a postcard to a friend. Help your child place the commas in addresses, in dates, after the opening and closing, and when listing more than two items.

Name _____

Pick a word from the box to match each clue.
Write the word on the line.

| add | both | contest | delicious |
| judges | making | mean | stranger |

1. something you enter to win a prize

   _____

2. We are _____ pies.

   _____

3. two together

   _____

4. people who choose the winner

   _____

5. a person you don't know

   _____

6. Did you _____ to call my cooking bad?

   _____

7. tastes great

   _____

8. join one thing to another

   _____

Notes for Home: Your child matched vocabulary words to clues. *Home Activity:* Write each word on an index card. Take turns drawing a card, saying the word aloud, and using it in a sentence.

Pick a **long e** word from the box to finish each sentence.
Write the word on the line.

ceiling   either   Neil   receive

_____

1. My friend _____ collects kites.

_____

2. He hangs them from the _____ .

_____

3. Did he _____ the kite his uncle sent?

_____

4. He should get it _____ today or tomorrow.

Find the word that has the same **long e** sound as **receive**.
Mark the space to show your answer.

5. ⬭ seize   6. ⬭ deck
   ⬭ size   ⬭ dent
   ⬭ sister   ⬭ deceive

Notes for Home: Your child reviewed words with the long *e* sound spelled with *ei,* as in *ceiling.* **Home Activity:** Write a list of words with the long *e* sound spelled *ei* from this page. Have your child read them aloud to you.

| airplane | care | chair | hair | pair | share |

Write four words from the box spelled with **air**.

1. _____

2. _____

3. _____

4. _____

Write two words from the box spelled with **are**.

5. _____

6. _____

Pick a word from the box to match each clue.
Write the word on the line.

making
mean

7. _____

8. Does this trophy _____ I won?

Notes for Home: Your child spelled words with *air* and *are,* such as *hair* and *share,* and two
frequently used words: *making, mean.* **Home Activity:** Write each spelling word, leaving
some spaces blank. (h_ _r; *hair*). Have your child fill in the missing letters.

Circle the commas.

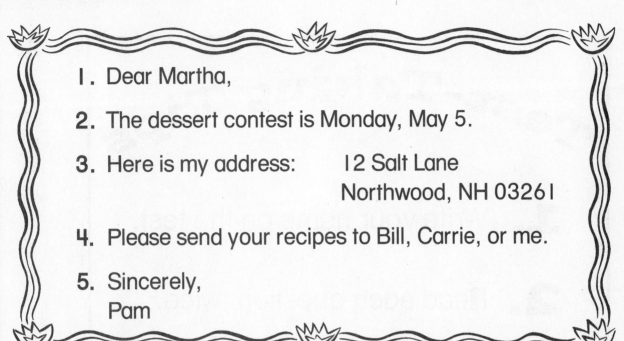

1. Dear Martha,

2. The dessert contest is Monday, May 5.

3. Here is my address: 12 Salt Lane
                           Northwood, NH 03261

4. Please send your recipes to Bill, Carrie, or me.

5. Sincerely,
   Pam

Write the commas where they belong.

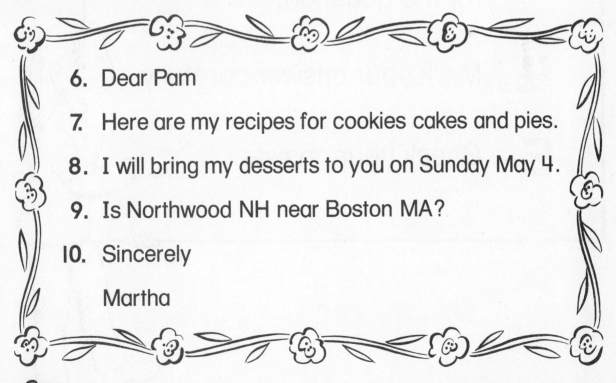

6. Dear Pam

7. Here are my recipes for cookies cakes and pies.

8. I will bring my desserts to you on Sunday May 4.

9. Is Northwood NH near Boston MA?

10. Sincerely

    Martha

Notes for Home: Your child identified and placed commas. *Home Activity:* Together, write postcards to a real or imaginary pen pal. Have your child point out where commas should be placed.

Test-Taking Tips

1. Write your name on the test.

2. Read each question twice.

3. Read all the answer choices for the question.

4. Mark your answer carefully.

5. Check your answer.

Part 1: Vocabulary

Find the word that best fits in each sentence.
Mark the space for your answer.

1. Holly loves _____ cookies.
   ⬭ making   ⬭ sealing   ⬭ dashing

2. Julio won the baking _____ .
   ⬭ contest   ⬭ stranger   ⬭ deck

3. They _____ like to paint.
   ⬭ mean   ⬭ both   ⬭ add

4. The _____ say my soup is the best.
   ⬭ Earth   ⬭ spiders   ⬭ judges

5. What a _____ cake!
   ⬭ few   ⬭ delicious   ⬭ young

GO ON ➤

Part 2: Comprehension

Read each question.
Mark the space for your answer.

6. The person who wins the contest gets a —
   ⬭ bowl of soup.
   ⬭ gold soup ladle.
   ⬭ black pot.

7. Who are the judges in the contest?
   ⬭ Minnie Stronie and Ann Chovie
   ⬭ Vida Minn and Ida Know
   ⬭ Brock Lee and Sal Lamie

8. The judges had second helpings of Ida Know's soup because they —
   ⬭ really liked it.
   ⬭ were very hungry.
   ⬭ did not know what was in it.

9. Which sentence tells about Bill Lownie?
   ⬭ He likes to eat soup.
   ⬭ He does not know how to cook.
   ⬭ He likes to play tricks.

10. Which could **not** really happen?
    ⬭ having a soup contest
    ⬭ making good soup from only a stone
    ⬭ living in a town called Bellie Acres

STOP

leaf

leaves

Draw a picture for each word.

1. wolf | 2. shelf

3. calves | 4. wolves

5. shelves | 6. calf

Find the word that matches each picture.
Mark the space to show your answer.

7. ⬭ scars
   ⬭ scarf
   ⬭ scarves

8. ⬭ loaf
   ⬭ loans
   ⬭ loaves

 Notes for Home: Your child reviewed words that change *f* to *v* and add *-es* to mean more than one. ***Home Activity:*** Write a list of singular words such as *half, calf, knife, loaf, shelf,* and *wolf.* Have your child write the plural spelling for each word.

airplane	care	chair	hair	pair	share

Change one letter of each word to make a word from the box.
Write the word on the line.

1. chain

   _____

2. pail

   _____

3. shore

   _____

4. cart

   _____

Pick a word from the box to match each clue.
Write the word on the line.

5. something a pilot flies

   _____

6. grows on your head

   _____

Pick a word from the box to finish each rhyme.
Write the word on the line.

making
mean

   _____

7. What do you _____?
   That frog isn't green!

   _____

8. Is it a pie you are _____?
   Or a cake you are baking?

Notes for Home: Your child spelled words with *air* and *are*, such as *hair* and *share*, and two
frequently used words: *making, mean*. **Home Activity:** Mix up the letters of each spelling
word. Have your child unscramble and spell each word correctly.

Commas are used in addresses:
6000 Michigan Avenue, Apt. 3
Chicago, IL 60615

Commas are used in dates: March 15, 2001

Commas are used to start letters: Dear Marge,

Commas are used to separate three or more things:
I need to buy rice, sugar, and milk.

Commas are used to end a letter: Your friend,
Jimmy

Add commas where they belong in this letter.

1.–10.

Jake Fountain
321 Miller Court Apt. 6A
Boulder CO 83009

July 6 2001

Dear Dad
Summer camp is great! Today we went hiking
swimming and biking. Tomorrow we will cook
hamburgers hot dogs fries and sweet corn.

Love
Tabitha

Notes for Home: Your child inserted commas into the following parts of a letter: the address,
the date, the greeting, items in a series, and the closing. **Home Activity:** Have your child write
a letter to you about something funny that happened at school.

Read this letter.

44 Dixie Lane
New Orleans, LA 70003
June 3, 2000

Dear Friend,

Hi. I just moved into this neighborhood. I come from
Lincoln, Nebraska. I have a cat, a dog, and a bird. I was
wondering if you would like to come over for lunch on
Saturday, June 10.

Sincerely,
Mindy

Write a letter in response to the letter above.
Remember to use commas.

_____

_____

_____

_____

_____

_____

_____

Notes for Home: Your child read and wrote letters with commas. *Home Activity:* Write a
letter to your child, and have him or her circle the commas and then write back to you.

Family Times

A Good Idea

Annie's Gifts

The School Chorus

I like singing in the chorus
And when there's a school play.
We will sing a chord or two
And practice every Friday.

I will use a microphone
Singing with my classmates.
We will wear our uniforms.
Our chorus sounds just first-rate!

Later on we'll have some treats
Like bagels and some cocoa.
Before we eat the band will play
And I will play the oboe.

I will use a microphone . . .

This rhyme includes words your child is working with in school: words with long vowels at the end of syllables (*microphone, uniform*) and the consonants *ch* and *sch* (*chorus, school*). Sing "The School Chorus" with your child. Take turns singing a line and then having the other person repeat the same line.

(fold here)

Name: _____

1

You are your child's first and best teacher!

Here are ways to help your child practice skills while having fun!

Day 1 Write the words *anchor, chorus, ache,* and *stomach*. Have your child read each word aloud and listen for the sound /k/ that the letters *ch* represent. Have your child compare this sound to the sound *ch* stands for in *chair, lunch,* and *chicken*.

Day 2 Write simple sentences that use any of the following words that your child is learning to read: *also, group, soon, though, tried.* Have your child read each sentence aloud.

Day 3 After reading a story, ask your child questions about its theme, such as: *What lessons did the characters learn? Are these lessons something you can use in your life?*

Day 4 Ask your child to write about a book he or she has read. Encourage your child to include what he or she likes about the book and why it would be interesting to other people.

Day 5 Look through some favorite stories with your child. Point out commas in sentences and discuss why commas are used.

Read with your child EVERY DAY!

4

Read for Points

Materials   index cards, markers, timer

Game Directions

1. Write the words shown on page 3 on index cards.

2. Divide the cards among 2 or 4 players.

3. Players take turns choosing a card from another player's hand. If the first player is able to read the word and use it in a sentence, he or she earns 1 point. If not, the player returns the card to the original player's hand.

4. Play until all cards have been used. The player with the most points at the end wins! If the score is tied, take 1 minute to write as many two-syllable words as possible. Then the player with most words wins!

paper	program	nobody	grocery
music	uniform	tuna	baby
spider	tiger	radio	dragon
zebra	repair	rewind	nowhere

Name _____

A Good Idea
Annie's Gifts

Say the word for each picture.
Write a, e, i, o, or **u** on the line to finish the word.

tom<u>a</u>t<u>o</u>

1.

r ____ dio

2.

z ____ bra

3.

comp ____ ter

4.

m ____ sic

5.

p ____ lot

6.

b ____ by

7.

t ____ ger

8.

m ____ tor

Notes for Home: Your child completed words with long vowel sounds at the end of syllables as in *to•ma•to*. **Home Activity:** Write these words: *navy, lazy, zebra, tiny, lion, total, October, tuba*. Help your child say each word and identify the long vowel sounds.

Name _____

Circle the word for each picture.

<u>ch</u>oir's <u>sch</u>edule

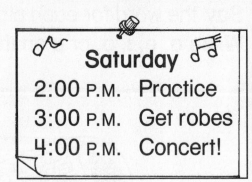

Saturday
2:00 P.M. Practice
3:00 P.M. Get robes
4:00 P.M. Concert!

1.

chorus   chore

2.

schooner picture

sooner   schooner

3.

school   stool

4.

keeps   chemist

5.

ankle   anchor

6.

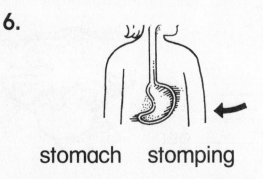

stomach   stomping

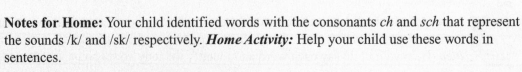

Notes for Home: Your child identified words with the consonants *ch* and *sch* that represent the sounds /k/ and /sk/ respectively. *Home Activity:* Help your child use these words in sentences.

Pick a word from the box to finish each sentence.
Write the word on the line.

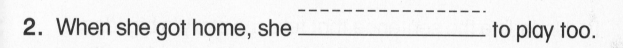

also   group   soon   though   tried

1. Lil saw this _____ play.

2. When she got home, she _____ to play too.

3. Her little brother Kevin _____ tried to play.

4. Even _____ he is little, Kevin is a good partner.

5. They both will take piano lessons _____ .

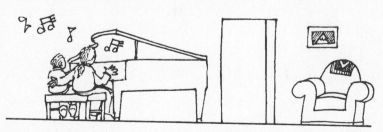

Read the story.
Follow the directions below.

Max wanted to be in a club. He tried out for the school play. But he didn't get a part. Max thought about joining the school chorus. But he sounds like a frog when he sings.

Max was sad. His mom told him to keep trying because everyone is good at something.

One day, Max saw the soccer club playing soccer. He liked sports. Maybe he would like soccer. Max joined the game. He was surprised when he scored a goal. The other players asked Max to play with them every afternoon. Max was happy to say "Yes!"

1. Underline the sentence that tells the story's big idea.
2. Write a sentence that tells what you learned from the story.

_____

- -

_____

_____

- -

_____

Draw two pictures. One should show how Max felt at the beginning of the story, and one should show how he felt at the end.

3.   4.

Notes for Home: Your child identified the theme of a story. *Home Activity:* Read a story to your child. Discuss the theme. Ask your child to tell you what the big idea is in the story and to share anything he or she learned from the story.

Commas are placed between the date and the year.
They also go between the day of the week and the date.

Hannah was born on May 5, 1991.
She will have a party on Saturday, May 3.

Commas are also used to join two complete sentences with a connecting word like *and*.

Harry likes to play the drums, and he likes to sing.

Read each sentence.
Add commas where they are missing.

1. The play is on June 26 2000.

2. Tryouts will begin Sunday April 5.

3. They will start to practice on Tuesday April 7.

4. Everyone got a part so all the children were happy.

5. The play was great and everyone wants to do it again!

Notes for Home: Your child added commas to dates and compound sentences. *Home Activity:* Read a story with your child. Ask your child to point out the commas in the sentences. Talk about why these commas are used where they are.

Name _____

Draw a line to match each word on the left to a clue on the right.

| also | group | instrument | radio |
| soon | squeaked | though | tried |

1. also   **a.** a mouse might have done this

2. group   **b.**

3. instrument   **c.** too

4. radio   **d.** made an effort

5. soon   **e.**

6. squeaked   **f.**

7. though   **g.** in a short while

8. tried   **h.** She spoke up, even _____ she was shy.

Notes for Home: Your child matched the words above with word and picture clues. **Home Activity:** Work with your child to tell a story using as many of these words as possible. Take turns, each person adding one sentence to the story at a time.

Name _____

h**are**      ch**air**

Say the word for each picture.
Write air or **are** to finish each word.

1.

p _____

2.

st _____ s

3.

c _____

4.

st _____

5.

squ _____

6.

f _____

7.

h _____

8.

_____ plane

Find the word that has the same vowel sound as **chair**.
Mark the space to show your answer.

9. ⬭ dare
   ⬭ dark
   ⬭ drain

10. ⬭ sprain
    ⬭ spark
    ⬭ spare

Notes for Home: Your child reviewed words with *air* and *are* where the letter *r* changes the
vowel sounds, such as *hare* and *chair*. **Home Activity:** Challenge your child to make up
sentences that rhyme using the words on this page. *(There's a hare on the chair!)*

Level 2.2   **Phonics:** *r*-Controlled Vowels: *air, are* Review **247**

| ache | chord | chorus | echo | school | stomach |

Unscramble the letters to make a word from the box.
Write the word on the line.

1. msocaht

_____

2. rucosh

_____

3. haec

_____

4. coeh

_____

Write the word from the box that rhymes with each word below.

_____   _____

5. cool _____   6. board _____

Pick a word from the box to finish each sentence.
Write the word on the line.

though
group

_____

7. Jill plays flute for a small _____ of people.

_____

8. Even _____ it is late, Jill keeps playing.

Notes for Home: Your child spelled words with the sounds /k/ spelled *ch* as in *chorus* and /sk/
spelled *sch* as in *school* and two frequently used words: *though, group*. **Home Activity:** Say
each spelling word. Have your child use it in a sentence. Then have your child write each word.

Read each sentence.
Circle the comma in each sentence.

1. Jill likes to play the drums, and Ben likes to sing.

2. Phil likes to draw, but Tammy does not.

3. Molly plays soccer, and Tommy cheers for her.

4. Sam wanted to be in the play, but he missed the tryouts.

5. Karen joined the math club, and she won a trophy.

Read each sentence.
Add a comma where it belongs in each sentence.

6. Liz takes flute lessons but she doesn't enjoy them.

7. Her mom wants her to practice but Liz likes to play outdoors.

8. Liz drew a picture of herself playing baseball and she gave it to her mom.

9. Her mom had an idea and she took Liz to baseball tryouts.

10. Liz joined the baseball team and she is much happier.

Notes for Home: Your child identified and placed commas in compound sentences—two complete sentences joined by a comma and a connecting word like *and* or *but*. **Home Activity:** Read a simple news article with your child. Look for compound sentences.

Test-Taking Tips

1. Write your name on the test.

2. Read each question twice.

3. Read all the answer choices for the question.

4. Mark your answer carefully.

5. Check your answer.

Part 1: Vocabulary

Find the word that best fits in each sentence.
Mark the space for your answer.

1. Ed went to school, and I went _____ .
   ⬭ friend   ⬭ also   ⬭ thumb

2. Anya _____ to read her brother's book.
   ⬭ tried   ⬭ squeaked   ⬭ exclaimed

3. A _____ of children marched down the street.
   ⬭ spray   ⬭ group   ⬭ patch

4. Jack eats peas even _____ he doesn't really like them.
   ⬭ until   ⬭ both   ⬭ though

5. Please turn off the _____ .
   ⬭ garbage   ⬭ homework   ⬭ radio

GO ON

Part 2: Comprehension

Read each question.
Mark the space for your answer.

6. Who played in the school band?
   - ⬭ Patty
   - ⬭ Lee
   - ⬭ Annie

7. What did Annie try to play last?
   - ⬭ drums
   - ⬭ recorder
   - ⬭ piano

8. How did Annie feel after she sang for the guests?
   - ⬭ sad
   - ⬭ excited
   - ⬭ happy

9. What did Annie learn in this story?
   - ⬭ Music is the best thing in the world.
   - ⬭ Most people don't try hard enough.
   - ⬭ Everyone has special gifts.

10. Which one did **not** really happen in the story?
    - ⬭ Frogs jumped in the house.
    - ⬭ Daddy and Momma danced at night.
    - ⬭ Annie drew some pictures.

STOP

Name _____

Circle the word for each picture.

ba**dge**

1.

ledge   leave

2

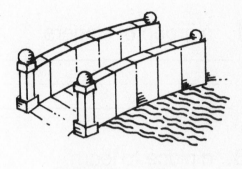

bridge   bring

3.

fudge   funnel

4.

jug   judge

Find the word that has the same ending sound as **badge**.
Mark the space to show your answer.

5. ⬭ edge
    ⬭ egg
    ⬭ end

6. ⬭ plug
    ⬭ plaid
    ⬭ pledge

Notes for Home: Your child reviewed the sound /j/ spelled *dge* as in *badge*. **Home Activity:** Challenge your child to use the words with *dge* listed above in sentences. Work together to illustrate each sentence.

| ache | chord | chorus | echo | school | stomach |

Pick a word from the box to match each clue.
Write the word on the line.

1. a group of singers
_____
- - - - - - - - - - - - - - - - - -
_____

2. where your food goes
_____
- - - - - - - - - - - - - - - - - -
_____

3. a place to learn
_____
- - - - - - - - - - - - - - - - - -
_____

4. a hurt
_____
- - - - - - - - - - - - - - - - - -
_____

5. rhymes with *sword*
_____
- - - - - - - - - - - - - - - - - -
_____

6. a sound you hear again
_____
- - - - - - - - - - - - - - - - - -
_____

Pick a word from the box to finish each sentence.
Write the word on the line.

though
group

_____
- - - - - - - - - - - - - - - -
7. _____ Tim likes tennis, he likes baseball more.

_____
- - - - - - - - - - - - - - - -
8. Tim likes to play with a _____ of people.

Notes for Home: Your child spelled words with the consonant sound /k/ spelled *ch* and two frequently used words: *though, group.* **Home Activity:** Have your child write the spelling words on paper. Cut and mix the letters. Have your child use the letters to rebuild the words.

A **comma** is placed between the date and the year.

A **comma** is also placed between the day of the week and the date.

Priscilla will be seven years old on May 5, 2003.
We're going to Miami on Sunday, April 19.

Commas are also used to join two complete sentences with a connecting word, such as *and*.

I like to swim, and my brother likes to hike.

1.–4. Circle the commas in this paragraph.

Max's sister is the smartest girl in the school. She is graduating on June 22, 2002. She will read a speech to her classmates, and they will all sing a song. Max can bring one friend to her party on Monday, June 23. Max is going to buy his sister a book, and he is going to give her a card.

Add commas where they belong.

5. Call me on Monday March 11.

6. I am going to summer camp on Tuesday July 22 and he is going on vacation.

Notes for Home: Your child identified and placed commas in dates and in sentences with connecting words. **Home Activity:** Have your child show you his or her work on this page. Ask your child to explain why the commas are used where they are.

Read each sentence.

Add a comma where it belongs in each sentence.

1. Alisa wrote a story and she drew a picture.

2. Mom ran a race and we watched.

3. The students like to play outside but today it is raining.

4. My birthday is in March and I am having a party.

5. We lost our cat but she came home on her own.

Write three sentences about a family dinner.

Use and or **but** with a comma in each sentence.

6. _____

_____

_____

7. _____

_____

_____

8. _____

_____

Notes for Home: Your child placed commas in sentences and wrote sentences using commas.
Home Activity: Read a story with your child. Ask him or her to point out the commas and to explain why they are there.

Family Times

Wicker School Takes Action

City Green

Have You Heard?

Have you heard about our great plan?
We'll help our town and learn.
We'll wake up at an early hour.
Pride is what we'll earn.

It's our vacation. We have time.
We'll take some action now.
It is tradition to help out.
Just watch. We'll show you how.

We'll search our streets and look for trash
On our spring vacation.
We'll set in motion our great plans.
We'll have a celebration.

This rhyme includes words your child is working with in school: words with *ear* and *our* in which the letter *r* changes the vowel sound (*early, hour*) and words with the syllable pattern *-tion* (*action*). Read aloud "Have You Heard?" with your child. Clap every time you say a word that ends in *-tion*.

(fold here)

Name: _____

You are your child's first and best teacher!

Here are ways to help your child practice skills while having fun!

Day 1 Your child is working with the syllable pattern *-tion* as in *nation, motion,* and *action.* Look through a newspaper together and circle words with *-tion.*

Day 2 Ask your child to write sentences that rhyme and include these words: *already, buy, nothing, piece,* and *used.*

Day 3 Watch a TV show with your child. Have your child make judgments about characters' actions. Ask questions such as: *Was that a smart thing to do? Is that what you would do?*

Day 4 Look at some letters to the editor in a newspaper. Ask your child to write a letter trying to persuade readers about the need to help improve the neighborhood.

Day 5 Talk with your child about how he or she would present information to a group of younger children, to a group of children his or her own age, and to a group of adults. Discuss how you might change how you speak depending on your audience.

Read with your child EVERY DAY!

Finish the Word!

Materials 1 coin, 1 button per player, game board

Game Directions

1. Players place their buttons on Start.

2. Players take turns flipping a coin and moving one space for heads or two spaces for tails.

3. Players add *ear* or *our* to the letters in each space on the gameboard to finish the words. A player then uses the word in a sentence. If a player cannot finish the word or use it correctly in a sentence, the player moves back to his or her previous position.

4. The first player to reach the end wins!

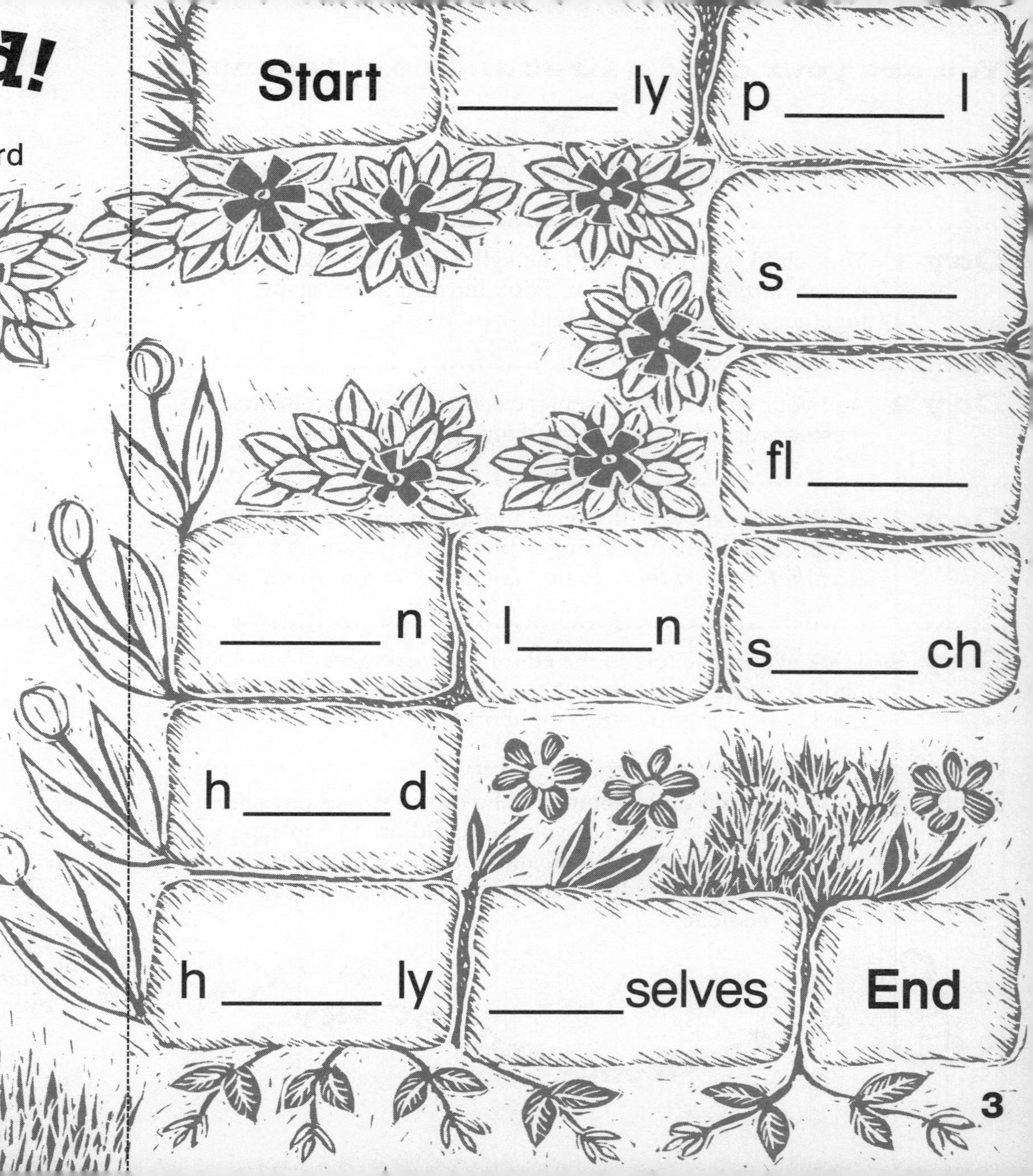

2

Start

_____ ly

p _____ l

s _____

fl _____

s _____ ch

h _____ n

n _____ n

h _____ d

h _____ ly

_____ selves

End

3

Read the word at the top of each column.
Write the words from the box that have the same vowel sound.

flour   Earth   heard   pearls   sour

early	**hour**

1. _____

2. _____

3. _____

4. _____

5. _____

Pick a word from the box to match each clue.
Write the word on the line.

6.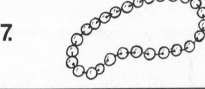

_____

7.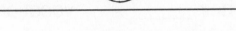

_____

8. It sounds the same
   as *flower*.

_____

9. not sweet, but _____

_____

10. _____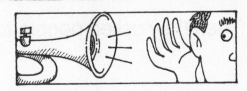

 Notes for Home: Your child read and wrote words where the letter *r* changes the vowel sound
as in *(heard, sour)*. **Home Activity:** Ask your child to write and then read a sentence using
each of the following words: *earn, search, hour, sour.*

Circle a word to finish each sentence.

1. The stream near the school was full of _____.

   pollution
   pollute

2. The children wanted to take _____ to clean it up.

   acting
   action

3. They held a clean-up day during their _____.

   vacation
   vacate

4. They spent the day _____ garbage.

   collecting
   collection

5. Then they asked people to sign a _____ .

   petting
   petition

Notes for Home: Your child read words that include the syllable *-tion* as in *lotion*. **Home Activity:** Write or say words with *-tion* (attention, solution, prediction, fiction, creation). Give your child clues about the word to help him or her guess the meaning.

Read each sentence.
Circle the picture that shows the meaning for each underlined word.

1. Beth picked an empty <u>piece</u> of the garden to use.

2. Dave went to <u>buy</u> some seeds.

3. Beth and Dave <u>used</u> tools to dig a hole in the soil.

4. At first, <u>nothing</u> grew.

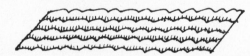   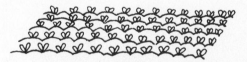

5. Now, only a week later, the plants have <u>already</u> sprouted.

   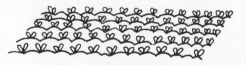

Notes for Home: This week your child is learning to read the words *already, buy, nothing, piece,* and *used.* **Home Activity:** Have your child write or tell a story about working together using these words.

Read each sentence.
Write H if the person is doing something helpful.
Write N if the person is doing something that is **not** helpful.

_____ 1. Tommy threw his wrapper on the ground.

_____ 2. Sue collected money to buy a new slide.

_____ 3. Tal used the money to buy himself a snack.

_____ 4. Jason fixed the broken swing.

Draw a picture to show something helpful that one of the children did.

5.

Notes for Home: Your child made judgments about actions that are helpful and those that are not. *Home Activity:* As you read, ask your child whether the characters are acting in a good way or a bad way. Ask your child why he or she thinks a particular action is good or bad.

Circle the sentences that tell about the same idea.
Put these sentences in order to make a paragraph.
Write numbers in front of these sentences to show the order.

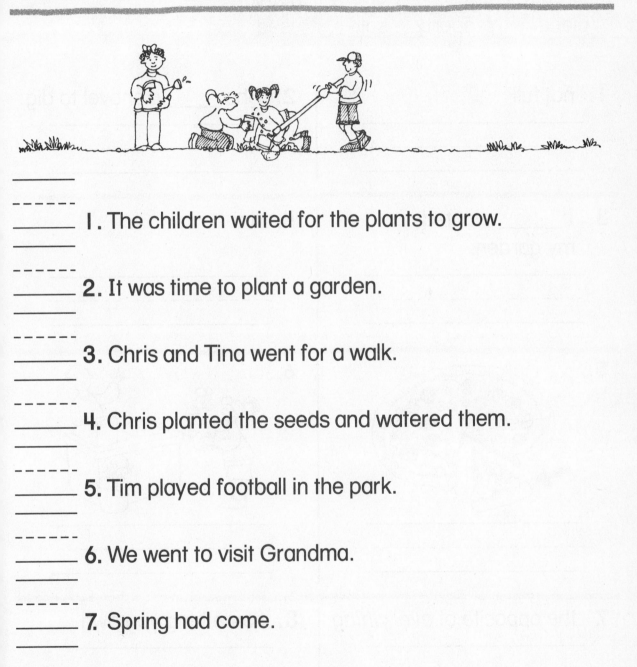

_____ **1.** The children waited for the plants to grow.

_____ **2.** It was time to plant a garden.

_____ **3.** Chris and Tina went for a walk.

_____ **4.** Chris planted the seeds and watered them.

_____ **5.** Tim played football in the park.

_____ **6.** We went to visit Grandma.

_____ **7.** Spring had come.

_____ **8.** Everyone had a job to do.

Notes for Home: Your child identified sentences that can be grouped into a paragraph.
Home Activity: Have your child write sentences about a time he or she did something as part
of the neighborhood or community. Help your child put the sentences cito paragraphs.

Pick a word from the box to match each clue.
Write the word on the line.

| already | buy | empty | nothing |
| piece | property | soil | used |

1. not full

   _____

   _ _ _ _ _ _ _ _ _ _ _ _ _

   _____

2. She _____ a shovel to dig.

   _____

   _ _ _ _ _ _ _ _ _ _ _ _ _

   _____

3. I _____ planted my garden.

   _____

   _ _ _ _ _ _ _ _ _ _ _ _ _

   _____

4. dirt

   _____

   _ _ _ _ _ _ _ _ _ _ _ _ _

   _____

5.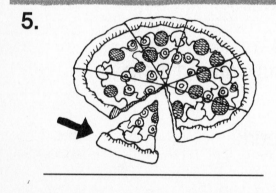

   _____

   _ _ _ _ _ _ _ _ _ _ _ _ _

6.

   _____

   _ _ _ _ _ _ _ _ _ _ _ _ _

7. the opposite of *everything*

   _____

   _ _ _ _ _ _ _ _ _ _ _ _ _

   _____

8. something you own

   _____

   _ _ _ _ _ _ _ _ _ _ _ _ _

   _____

 Notes for Home: Your child completed sentences using words that he or she learned to read this week. *Home Activity:* Play act that you and your child are planting a garden. Try to use as many words from the list above as you can.

Name _____

Say the word for the picture.
Write a, e, i, o, or u to finish each word.

tiger

1. p _____ pers

2. b _____ cycle

3. p _____ ny

4. pot _____ toes

5. l _____ on

6. _____ pron

7. r _____ ler

8. z _____ bra

Find the missing long vowel sound in each word.
Mark the space to show your answer.

9. phot __

◯ a   ◯ u   ◯ o

10. tr __ angle

◯ a   ◯ i   ◯ e

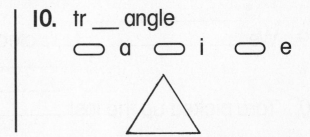

Notes for Home: Your child reviewed words with long vowels at the end of syllables as in *tiger*. **Home Activity:** Work with your child to make picture cards with word labels of the words on this page. Have your child pick a card, read the word aloud, and use it in a sentence.

earn	flour	heard	hour	learn	sour

Write three words from the box spelled with **ear**.

1. _____ 2. _____ 3. _____

Write three words from the box spelled with **our**.

4. _____ 5. _____ 6. _____

Write two words from the box that rhyme with **burn**.

7. _____ 8. _____

Pick a word from the box to finish each sentence.
Write the word on the line.

piece
already

9. We _____ cleaned up the playground.

10. Tara picked up the last _____ of trash.

Notes for Home: Your child spelled words with the *r*-controlled vowels *ear* and *our* in which the letter *r* changes the sound of the vowel, as well as two frequently used words: *piece, already*. **Home Activity:** Help your child use these words to write a short story.

Leave out details that do **not** support the main idea.

Main Idea: We need to clean the park.
John will pick up trash.
~~Pat will go for a bike ride~~.

Read the sentence that tells the main idea.
Cross out the sentence that does **not** support the main idea.

1. **Main Idea:** Our city needs a skateboard park.
   Many people enjoy using skateboards.
   Skateboards don't cost very much.
   It isn't safe to skateboard in the streets.

2. **Main Idea:** Do something besides watching TV.
   There are too many ads on TV.
   You can make something with your hands.
   You can play make-believe with a friend.

3. **Main Idea:** Dogs are smart animals.
   Dogs can understand commands.
   Some dogs have long hair.
   A dog remembers what you teach it.

Write a sentence to go with this main idea:

4. A cow does not make a very good pet.

_____

- -

_____

Notes for Home: Your child identified sentences that did not belong with the main idea of a
paragraph. *Home Activity:* Have your child give you a main idea. Make up sentences that go
with it and one that does not. Ask your child which sentence does not belong. Switch roles.

Read the paragraph.
Underline a sentence if it belongs in the paragraph.
Draw a line through it if it does **not** belong in the paragraph.

1. Jess wants to plant a garden.
2. Jess picks a spot for the garden.
3. She dusts the shelves.
4. She digs in the dirt.
5. She plants the seeds.
6. Jess brushes her hair.
7. She waters her seeds.
8. Jess loves to read books.

Add two sentences of your own to finish the paragraph.

9. _____
_____
_____

10. _____
_____
_____

Notes for Home: Your child identified sentences that can be grouped into a paragraph.
Home Activity: Help your child write a story. Work together to group the sentences together into paragraphs.

Name _____

Part 1: Vocabulary

Find the word that best fits in each sentence.
Mark the space for your answer.

1. I need a _____ of tape.
   ⬯ word   ⬯ piece   ⬯ number

2. The cookie jar is _____ again.
   ⬯ empty   ⬯ nothing   ⬯ calm

3. Are you done _____?
   ⬯ between   ⬯ never   ⬯ already

4. The Changs bought a _____ car.
   ⬯ used   ⬯ round   ⬯ pleased

5. We planted the seeds in the _____.
   ⬯ tool   ⬯ wheel   ⬯ soil

GO ON

Part 2: Comprehension

Read each question.
Mark the space for your answer.

6. The building was torn down because it was —
   - ⬭ ugly.
   - ⬭ new.
   - ⬭ unsafe.

7. How did Old Man Hammer feel when he looked at the empty lot?
   - ⬭ pleased
   - ⬭ upset
   - ⬭ excited

8. What did the neighbors do first?
   - ⬭ They paid one dollar to rent the lot.
   - ⬭ They planted seeds.
   - ⬭ They cleaned up the junk.

9. The neighbors work together to —
   - ⬭ knock down the building.
   - ⬭ make something good.
   - ⬭ buy the empty lot.

10. Who worked the most to make the garden?
    - ⬭ Old Man Hammer
    - ⬭ Marcy
    - ⬭ Mr. Bennett

STOP

Name _____

Say the word for each picture.
Write **ch** or **sch** to finish each word.

an**ch**or

1.

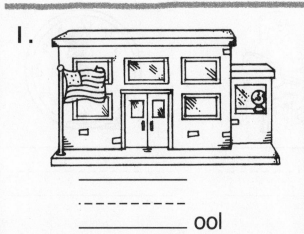

_____
- - - - - - - - - -
_____ ool

2.

_____
- - - - - - - - - -
_____ orus

3.

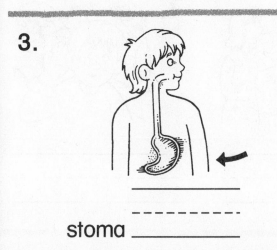

_____
- - - - - - - - - -
stoma _____

4.

_____
- - - - - - - - - -
e _____ o

Find the word where **ch** has the same sound heard in **anchor**.
Mark the space to show your answer.

5. ⊙ lunch
   ⊙ chair
   ⊙ ache

6. ⊙ character
   ⊙ branches
   ⊙ chin

Notes for Home: Your child reviewed the consonant sounds /k/ spelled *ch* (*chorus*) and /sk/ spelled *sch* (*school*). ***Home Activity:*** Write each word from this page on an index card. Place them around a room. When your child finds a card, have him or her read the word to you.

earn	flour	heard	hour	learn	sour

Write a word from the box to match each picture.

1.

_____

2.

_____

3.

_____

4.

_____

5.

_____

6.

_____

Pick a word from the box to match each clue.
Write the word on the line.

piece	already

7. rhymes with *steady*

_____

8. a part of something

_____

Notes for Home: Your child spelled words with *r*-controlled vowels *ear* and *our* where the letter *r* changes the vowel sound and two frequently used words: *piece, already*. **Home Activity:** Help your child write and illustrate a short story that uses the spelling words.

RETEACHING

Circle the sentences that tell about the same idea. **Draw** a line through the sentence that does not tell about the same idea.

I like to play with my friends.   We play games and sports.

Dogs can be small or big.

A **paragraph** is a group of sentences that tell about the same idea. The sentences are in an order that makes sense.

Circle the sentences that tell about the same idea.
Put these sentences in order to make a paragraph.
Write numbers in front of these sentences to show order.

_____ 1. Other people keep stamps that are their favorite colors.

_____ 2. Many people collect stamps.

_____ 3. My brother likes to buy baseball cards.

_____ 4. Some people like stamps that show places.

_____ 5. Whatever their reasons are, people who collect stamps enjoy their hobby.

Notes for Home: Your child identified sentences that can be grouped into a paragraph. ***Home Activity:*** Look at a favorite story with your child. Have your child choose an interesting sentence or idea from the story, and help him or her write a paragraph about that sentence or idea.

Grammar: The Paragraph **273**

Draw a box around the group of sentences that is in paragraph order. Write another sentence that fits in the paragraph.

1. Doug took the toy away from Rollo. Doug's dog Rollo broke a new toy car. Rollo put his head down on his paws.

2. Willa's mom got a new car. It was bright blue. Mom took Willa for a ride. Willa waved to the neighbors as they drove along.

_____

_____

_____

_____

_____

Number each sentence in paragraph order. **Draw** a line through the sentence that doesn't belong in the paragraph.

_____ Roxanne was waiting for her little sister Sue.

_____ Finally Roxanne saw her sister walking outside.

_____ Roxanne and her sister like to go swimming.

_____ First she saw her sister go into the library.

_____ Next Sue returned a book.

_____ Then the girls rode home on their bikes.

Notes for Home: Your child identified a paragraph and rearranged sentences in paragraph order. *Home Activity:* Talk with your child about what he or she did today. Then help your child write a paragraph to describe his or her day.

Name _____

Correct each sentence.

Write it on the line.

Hint: Use capital letters and the correct end marks.

1. i help mrs. woo

_____

- -

_____

2. how do you help her

_____

- -

_____

3. we pick up trash in oak park

_____

- -

_____

- -

_____

4. a clean park is nice

_____

- -

_____

5. flowers grow there in may

_____

- -

_____

Notes for Home: Your child capitalized the beginning of sentences and proper nouns and wrote end marks for sentences. **Home Activity:** Write sentences for your child to check. Have him or her tell you if the sentences are written correctly.

Name _____

Words I Can Now Read and Write

_____   _____
- - - - - - - - - - - - -   - - - - - - - - - - - - -

_____   _____
- - - - - - - - - - - - -   - - - - - - - - - - - - -

_____   _____
- - - - - - - - - - - - -   - - - - - - - - - - - - -

_____   _____
- - - - - - - - - - - - -   - - - - - - - - - - - - -

_____
- - - - - - - - - - - - -

_____
- - - - - - - - - - - - -

Reading Log

Date	What is the title?	Who is the author?	What did you think of it?

Directions: Use the tables below to find the percentage score for the total number correct out of the total number of items. The last entry in each table shows the total number of items.

Number Correct	1	2
Percentage Score	50%	100%

Number Correct	1	2	3
Percentage Score	33%	66%	100%

Number Correct	1	2	3	4
Percentage Score	25%	50%	75%	100%

Number Correct	1	2	3	4	5
Percentage Score	20%	40%	60%	80%	100%

Number Correct	1	2	3	4	5	6
Percentage Score	17%	33%	50%	66%	83%	100%

Number Correct	1	2	3	4	5	6	7
Percentage Score	14%	29%	43%	57%	71%	86%	100%

Number Correct	1	2	3	4	5	6	7	8
Percentage Score	13%	25%	38%	50%	63%	75%	88%	100%

Number Correct	1	2	3	4	5	6	7	8	9
Percentage Score	11%	22%	33%	44%	56%	67%	78%	89%	100%

Number Correct	1	2	3	4	5	6	7	8	9	10
Percentage Score	10%	20%	30%	40%	50%	60%	70%	80%	90%	100%

Number Correct	1	2	3	4	5	6	7	8	9	10	11	12	13	14	15
Percentage Score	7%	13%	20%	27%	33%	40%	47%	53%	60%	67%	73%	80%	87%	93%	100%

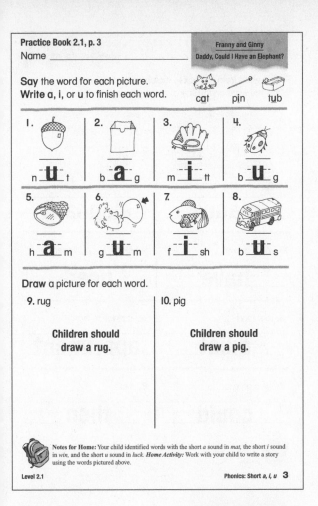

Say the word for each picture.
Write a, i, or u to finish each word.

cat   pin   tub

1. n_u_t

2. b_a_g

3. m_i_tt

4. b_u_g

5. h_a_m

6. g_u_m

7. f_i_sh

8. b_u_s

Draw a picture for each word.

9. rug

**Children should
draw a rug.**

10. pig

**Children should
draw a pig.**

Notes for Home: Your child identified words with the short *a* sound in *mat*, the short *i* sound in *win*, and the short *u* sound in *luck*. **Home Activity:** Work with your child to write a story using the words pictured above.

Level 2.1   Phonics: Short *a, i, u* **3**

Circle a word to finish each sentence.
Write the word on the line.

star

1. He _grabs_ his things.   (grabs) grins

2. Al's dad _drives_ .   (drives) drips

3. Al makes a big _splash_ .   spring (splash)

4. Al's _grin_ is big.   (grin) glad

5. Al likes to _swim_ .   (swim) smell

Notes for Home: Your child wrote words with *l, r,* and *s* blends. **Home Activity:** Look through a children's dictionary with your child to see how many words begin with the following blends: *bl, cl, fl, gl, pl, sl, br, cr, dr, fr, gr, pr, tr, sc, sk, sm, sn, sp, st, sw,* and *str.*

4 Phonics: *l, r,* and *s* Blends   Level 2.1

Pick a word from the box to finish each sentence.
Write the word on the line.

could   have   need   then   was

1. Bess _was_ sad.

2. "I _need_ a pet," she said.

3. "I _could_ get a hippo."

4. "You can _have_ a cat," her dad said.

5. _Then_ Bess was happy.

Notes for Home: This week your child is learning to read the words *could, have, need, then,* and *was.* **Home Activity:** Write these words on slips of paper. Take turns picking a word and using it in a sentence.

Level 2.1   High-Frequency Words **5**

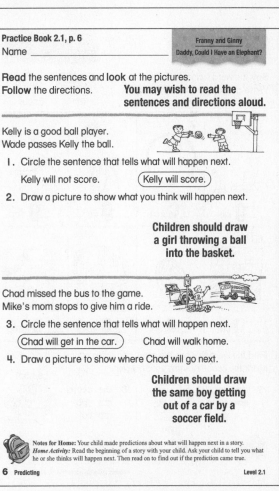

Read the sentences and look at the pictures.
Follow the directions.   **You may wish to read the
sentences and directions aloud.**

Kelly is a good ball player.
Wade passes Kelly the ball.

1. Circle the sentence that tells what will happen next.

   Kelly will not score.   (Kelly will score.)

2. Draw a picture to show what you think will happen next.

   **Children should draw
   a girl throwing a ball
   into the basket.**

Chad missed the bus to the game.
Mike's mom stops to give him a ride.

3. Circle the sentence that tells what will happen next.

   (Chad will get in the car.)   Chad will walk home.

4. Draw a picture to show where Chad will go next.

   **Children should draw
   the same boy getting
   out of a car by a
   soccer field.**

Notes for Home: Your child made predictions about what will happen next in a story. **Home Activity:** Read the beginning of a story with your child. Ask your child to tell you what he or she thinks will happen next. Then read on to find out if the prediction came true.

6 Predicting   Level 2.1

Answers **279**

Practice Book 2.1, p. 7

A **sentence** is a group of words that tells a complete idea.

This is a sentence: Jon likes to play ball.
This is not a sentence: To play.

Read each group of words.
Write S if the words make a complete sentence.
Write N if the words do **not** make a complete sentence.

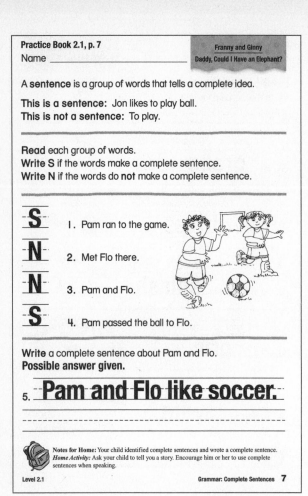

S 1. Pam ran to the game.

N 2. Met Flo there.

N 3. Pam and Flo.

S 4. Pam passed the ball to Flo.

Write a complete sentence about Pam and Flo.
Possible answer given.

5. **Pam and Flo like soccer.**

Notes for Home: Your child identified complete sentences and wrote a complete sentence. **Home Activity:** Ask your child to tell you a story. Encourage him or her to use complete sentences when speaking.

Level 2.1 — Grammar: Complete Sentences **7**

Practice Book 2.1, p. 8

Pick a word from the box to match each clue.
Write the word on the line.

| apartment | could | elephant | have |
| need | pianos | quiet | then |

1. 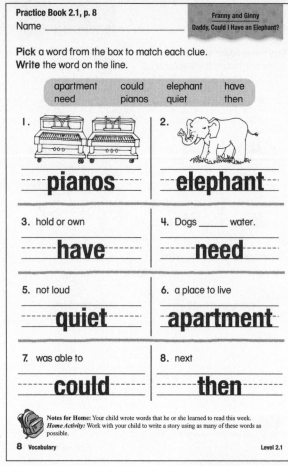 **pianos**

2. **elephant**

3. hold or own — **have**

4. Dogs _____ water. — **need**

5. not loud — **quiet**

6. a place to live — **apartment**

7. was able to — **could**

8. next — **then**

Notes for Home: Your child wrote words that he or she learned to read this week. **Home Activity:** Work with your child to write a story using as many of these words as possible.

8 Vocabulary — Level 2.1

Practice Book 2.1, p. 9

Say the word for each picture.
Write g or **c** to finish each word.

gerbil   circus

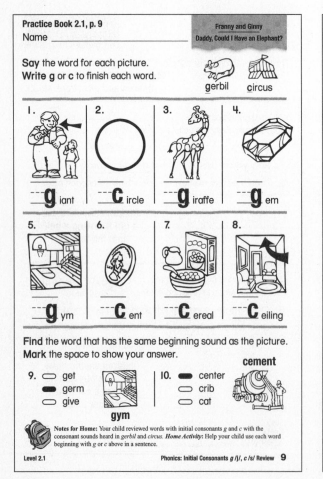

1. **g** iant
2. **c** ircle
3. **g** iraffe
4. **g** em
5. **g** ym
6. **c** ent
7. **c** ereal
8. **c** eiling

Find the word that has the same beginning sound as the picture.
Mark the space to show your answer.

cement

9. ○ get
   ● germ
   ○ give
   gym

10. ● center
    ○ crib
    ○ cat

Notes for Home: Your child reviewed words with initial consonants g and c with the consonant sounds heard in gerbil and circus. **Home Activity:** Help your child use each word beginning with g or c above in a sentence.

Level 2.1 — Phonics: Initial Consonants g /j/, c /s/ Review **9**

Practice Book 2.1, p. 10

| bat | that | fit | this | cub | mug |

Write the word from the box that rhymes with each word below.

1. rug — **mug**
2. tub — **cub**
3. hit — **fit**
4. hiss — **this**

Write two words from the box that rhyme with **cat**.

5. **bat**
6. **that**

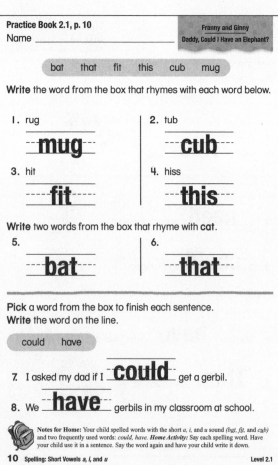

Pick a word from the box to finish each sentence.
Write the word on the line.

could   have

7. I asked my dad if I **could** get a gerbil.

8. We **have** gerbils in my classroom at school.

Notes for Home: Your child spelled words with the short a, i, and u sound (bat, fit, and cub) and two frequently used words: could, have. **Home Activity:** Say each spelling word. Have your child use it in a sentence. Say the word again and have your child write it down.

10 Spelling: Short Vowels a, i, and u — Level 2.1

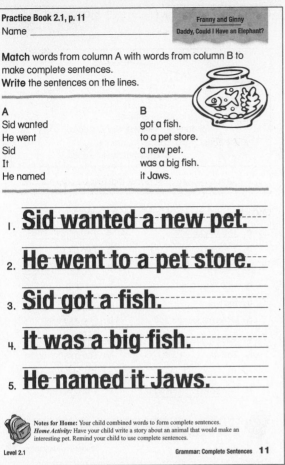

Match words from column A with words from column B to
make complete sentences.
Write the sentences on the lines.

A	B
Sid wanted	got a fish.
He went	to a pet store.
Sid	a new pet.
It	was a big fish.
He named	it Jaws.

1. **Sid wanted a new pet.**

2. **He went to a pet store.**

3. **Sid got a fish.**

4. **It was a big fish.**

5. **He named it Jaws.**

Notes for Home: Your child combined words to form complete sentences.
Home Activity: Have your child write a story about an animal that would make an
interesting pet. Remind your child to use complete sentences.

Level 2.1   Grammar: Complete Sentences **11**

Part I: Vocabulary

Find the word that best fits in each sentence.
Mark the space for your answer.

1. Sam saw the _____ at the zoo.
   ○ trap   ○ must   ● elephant

2. Lin will _____ some pie.
   ○ could   ○ slip   ● have

3. Will you please be _____ ?
   ○ apartment ○ are   ● quiet

4. Dan and Ben are good _____ .
   ○ pianos   ● company   ○ running

5. Do I _____ a hat?
   ○ hear   ○ then   ● need

GO ON ▶

Level 2.1   Selection Test: Vocabulary **13**

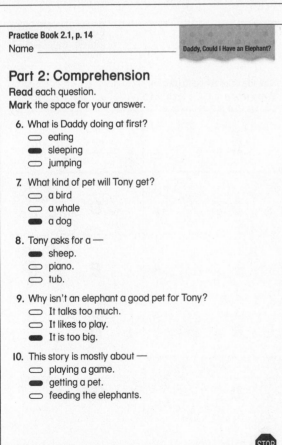

Part 2: Comprehension

Read each question.
Mark the space for your answer.

6. What is Daddy doing at first?
   ○ eating
   ● sleeping
   ○ jumping

7. What kind of pet will Tony get?
   ○ a bird
   ○ a whale
   ● a dog

8. Tony asks for a —
   ● sheep.
   ○ piano.
   ○ tub.

9. Why isn't an elephant a good pet for Tony?
   ○ It talks too much.
   ○ It likes to play.
   ● It is too big.

10. This story is mostly about —
    ○ playing a game.
    ● getting a pet.
    ○ feeding the elephants.

STOP

14 Selection Test: Comprehension   Level 2.1

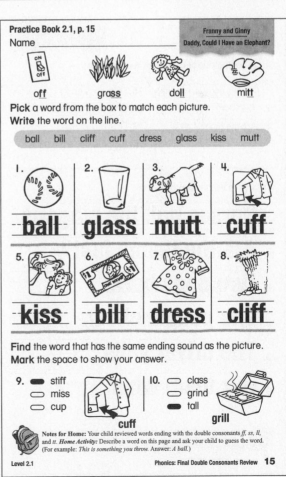

off   grass   doll   mitt

Pick a word from the box to match each picture.
Write the word on the line.

ball	bill	cliff	cuff	dress	glass	kiss	mutt

1. **ball**   2. **glass**   3. **mutt**   4. **cuff**

5. **kiss**   6. **bill**   7. **dress**   8. **cliff**

Find the word that has the same ending sound as the picture.
Mark the space to show your answer.

9. ● stiff
   ○ miss
   ○ cup
   cuff

10. ○ class
    ○ grind
    ● tall
    grill

Notes for Home: Your child reviewed words ending with the double consonants *ff, ss, ll,*
and *tt*. **Home Activity:** Describe a word on this page and ask your child to guess the word.
(For example: *This is something you throw.* Answer: *A ball.*)

Level 2.1   Phonics: Final Double Consonants Review **15**

Name _____

Franny and Ginny
Daddy, Could I Have an Elephant?

| bat | that | fit | this | cub | mug |

Pick a word from the box to finish each sentence.
Write the word on the line.

1. Get the ball and __bat__ .

2. Does the mitt __fit__ your hand?

Pick a word from the box to finish each rhyme.
Write the word on the line.

3. Did you see __that__ ?
   It was a black cat.

4. Did you see a __cub__ ?
   It was in the tub.

5. What is __this__ ?
   It is just a kiss.

6. Look in the __mug__ .
   I see a bug.

Write the word from the box that fits in each puzzle.

7. | c | o | u | l | d |

   | could | have |

8. | h | a | v | e |

Notes for Home: Your child spelled words with short vowels *a, i,* and *u* and two frequently used words: *could, have.* **Home Activity:** Together, make up a story using the spelling words. Write it but leave blanks for the spelling words. Ask your child to fill in the blanks.

16 Spelling: Short Vowels *a, i,* and *u*   Level 2.1

Name _____

Franny and Ginny
Daddy, Could I Have an Elephant?

RETEACHING

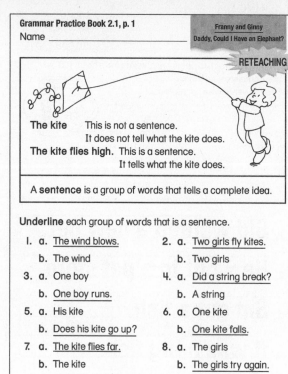

The kite   This is not a sentence.
               It does not tell what the kite does.
The kite flies high. This is a sentence.
               It tells what the kite does.

A **sentence** is a group of words that tells a complete idea.

Underline each group of words that is a sentence.

1. a. <u>The wind blows.</u>
   b. The wind

2. a. <u>Two girls fly kites.</u>
   b. Two girls

3. a. One boy
   b. <u>One boy runs.</u>

4. a. <u>Did a string break?</u>
   b. A string

5. a. His kite
   b. <u>Does his kite go up?</u>

6. a. One kite
   b. <u>One kite falls.</u>

7. a. <u>The kite flies far.</u>
   b. The kite

8. a. The girls
   b. <u>The girls try again.</u>

9. a. The boy
   b. <u>The boy holds on tight.</u>

10. a. <u>The children have fun.</u>
    b. The children

Notes for Home: Your child identified complete sentences. **Home Activity:** Say a sentence to your child, such as *Bob went to the park.* Ask your child whether it is a sentence or not. Do the same with an incomplete sentence, such as *The tree.*

Grammar: Complete Sentences **17**

Name _____

Franny and Ginny
Daddy, Could I Have an Elephant?

Circle each group of words that is a sentence.

1. (Horses pull the wagons.)
2. The race
3. (Are the teams fast?)
4. One wagon

5. (Two dogs bark.)
6. (The people cheer.)
7. (The driver yells.)
8. (Our team wins.)

Write each sentence you circled.

9. **Horses pull the wagons.**

10. **Are the teams fast?**

11. **Two dogs bark.**

12. **The people cheer.**

13. **The driver yells.**

14. **Our team wins.**

Notes for Home: Your child identified and wrote complete sentences. **Home Activity:** Write several sentences on strips of paper with your child. Cut the sentences in half, mix the papers, and have your child recombine them into sentences.

18 Grammar: Complete Sentences

Name _____

Wobbly People/Block House
Poppleton and the Grapefruit

Say the word for each picture.
Write e or o to finish each word.

b e d   s o ck

1. h __e__ n

2. n __e__ t

3. d __o__ g

4. bl __o__ ck

5. t __e__ nt

6. m __e__ n

7. d __e__ sk

8. m __o__ p

9. fr __o__ g

10. p __o__ t

Notes for Home: Your child wrote words with the short *e* sound in *bed* and the short *o* sound in *sock.* **Home Activity:** Work with your child to write a story using the words pictured above.

Level 2.1   Phonics: Short *e, o* **21**

Say the word for each picture.
Write the letters from the box to finish each word.

| ld | nd | sk | st | mp | nt |

ant

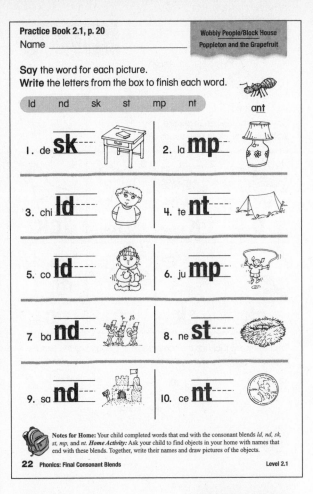

1. de **sk**

2. la **mp**

3. chi **ld**

4. te **nt**

5. co **ld**

6. ju **mp**

7. ba **nd**

8. ne **st**

9. sa **nd**

10. ce **nt**

Notes for Home: Your child completed words that end with the consonant blends *ld, nd, sk, st, mp,* and *nt*. **Home Activity:** Ask your child to find objects in your home with names that end with these blends. Together, write their names and draw pictures of the objects.

22 Phonics: Final Consonant Blends

Level 2.1

Pick a word from the box to finish each sentence.
Write the word on the line.

| live | made | people | taste | your |

1. I **live** by a baker.

2. **People** go to his shop.

3. They **taste** his rolls.

4. He **made** rolls for us.

5. Here is **your** roll.

Notes for Home: This week your child is learning to read the words *live, made, people, taste,* and *your*. **Home Activity:** Write these words on slips of paper and have your child practice reading them aloud to you.

Level 2.1

High-Frequency Words 23

Practice Book 2.1, p. 22
Name _____
You may wish to read the story and directions aloud.

Wobbly People/Block House
Poppleton and the Grapefruit

Read the story.
Follow the directions.
Answer the question.

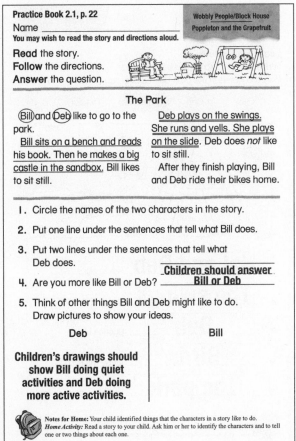

The Park

(Bill) and (Deb) like to go to the park.

Bill sits on a bench and reads his book. Then he makes a big castle in the sandbox. Bill likes to sit still.

Deb plays on the swings. She runs and yells. She plays on the slide. Deb does *not* like to sit still.

After they finish playing, Bill and Deb ride their bikes home.

1. Circle the names of the two characters in the story.

2. Put one line under the sentences that tell what Bill does.

3. Put two lines under the sentences that tell what Deb does.

4. Are you more like Bill or Deb? __Children should answer Bill or Deb__

5. Think of other things Bill and Deb might like to do. Draw pictures to show your ideas.

| Deb | Bill |

Children's drawings should show Bill doing quiet activities and Deb doing more active activities.

Notes for Home: Your child identified things that the characters in a story like to do. **Home Activity:** Read a story to your child. Ask him or her to identify the characters and to tell one or two things about each one.

24 Character

Level 2.1

The **subject** tells who or what does something.
The subject of this sentence is **man**.

The **man** fixed our door

Underline the subject in each sentence.
Draw a line from each sentence to the picture it matches.

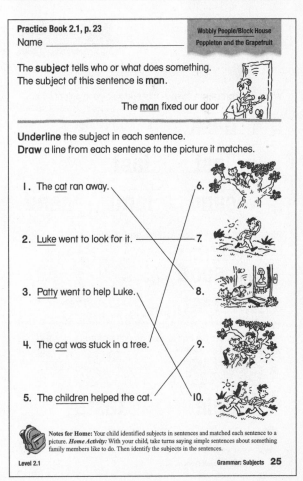

1. The cat ran away.

2. Luke went to look for it.

3. Patty went to help Luke.

4. The cat was stuck in a tree.

5. The children helped the cat.

6.

7.

8.

9.

10.

Notes for Home: Your child identified subjects in sentences and matched each sentence to a picture. **Home Activity:** With your child, take turns saying simple sentences about something family members like to do. Then identify the subjects in the sentences.

Level 2.1

Grammar: Subjects 25

Answers **283**

Pick a word from the box to match each clue.
Write the word on the line.

| hundred | knocked | outside |
| sick | taste | tears |

1. eat a little bit

taste

2. not inside

outside

3.

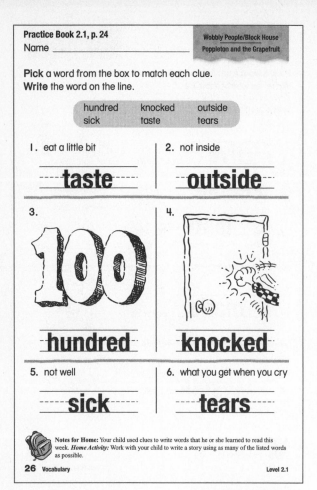

hundred

4.

knocked

5. not well

sick

6. what you get when you cry

tears

Notes for Home: Your child used clues to write words that he or she learned to read this week. Home Activity: Work with your child to write a story using as many of the listed words as possible.

cone   kite   clock

Say the word for each picture.
Write c, k, or ck to finish each word.

| 1. **c** orn | 2. **k** itchen | 3. **k** id | 4. so **ck** |
| 5. bla **ck** | 6. du **ck** | 7. **c** ab | 8. **c** ast |

Find the word that has the same beginning sound as the picture.
Mark the space to show your answer.

9. ● kit
   ○ circus
   ○ tar

10. ○ cent
    ○ bar
    ● came

car

Notes for Home: Your child reviewed words with the consonants c, k, and ck, such as cone, kite, and clock. Home Activity: Have your child use words with the consonants shown above in a sentence.

| sand | land | send | desk | lost | last |

Write the words from the box that end with each pair of letters.

sk 1. **desk**

st 2. **lost**   3. **last**

nd 4. **sand**   5. **land**   6. **send**

Pick a word from the box to finish each sentence.
Write the word on the line.

7. Did you **send** Ned a letter?

8. I sent it **last** week.

Pick a word from the box to match each picture.
Write the word on the line.

taste
people

9.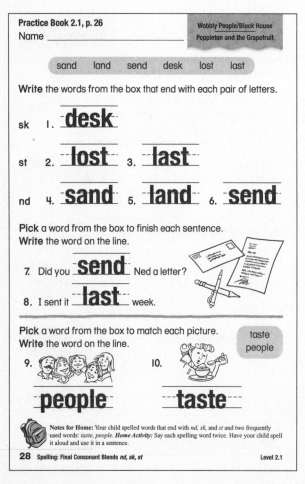

people

10.

taste

Notes for Home: Your child spelled words that end with nd, sk, and st and two frequently used words: taste, people. Home Activity: Say each spelling word twice. Have your child spell it aloud and use it in a sentence.

Look at the picture.
Write a subject to finish each sentence.
Use the words in the box. Use each group of words only once.

| The swings | Deb | Hal and Deb | The park | Birds |

1. **Hal and Deb** like to play.

2. **The swings** go up and down.

3. **Deb** pushes Hal.

4. **Birds** fly by the swings.

5. **The park** is a fun place to play.

Notes for Home: Your child wrote subjects to complete sentences. Home Activity: Read a simple story with your child. Have him or her identify the subject in each sentence. Remind your child that the subject tells who or what does something.

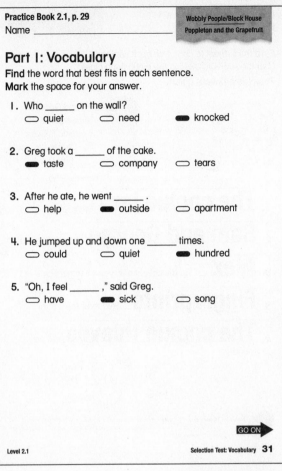

Part I: Vocabulary

Find the word that best fits in each sentence.
Mark the space for your answer.

I. Who _____ on the wall?
   ○ quiet   ○ need   ● knocked

2. Greg took a _____ of the cake.
   ● taste   ○ company   ○ tears

3. After he ate, he went _____ .
   ○ help   ● outside   ○ apartment

4. He jumped up and down one _____ times.
   ○ could   ○ quiet   ● hundred

5. "Oh, I feel _____ ," said Greg.
   ○ have   ● sick   ○ song

GO ON ➜

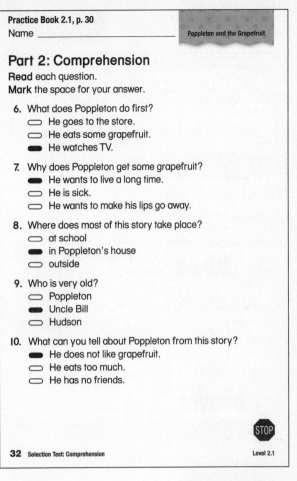

Part 2: Comprehension

Read each question.
Mark the space for your answer.

6. What does Poppleton do first?
   ○ He goes to the store.
   ○ He eats some grapefruit.
   ● He watches TV.

7. Why does Poppleton get some grapefruit?
   ● He wants to live a long time.
   ○ He is sick.
   ○ He wants to make his lips go away.

8. Where does most of this story take place?
   ○ at school
   ● in Poppleton's house
   ○ outside

9. Who is very old?
   ○ Poppleton
   ● Uncle Bill
   ○ Hudson

10. What can you tell about Poppleton from this story?
   ● He does not like grapefruit.
   ○ He eats too much.
   ○ He has no friends.

STOP

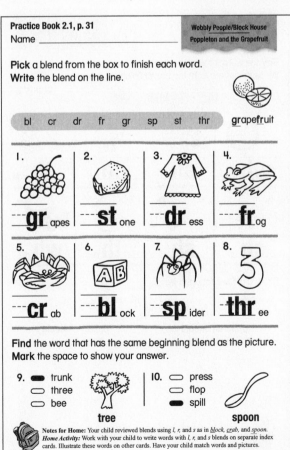

Pick a blend from the box to finish each word.
Write the blend on the line.

grapefruit

| bl | cr | dr | fr | gr | sp | st | thr |

I. **gr** apes   2. **st** one   3. **dr** ess   4. **fr** og

5. **cr** ab   6. **bl** ock   7. **sp** ider   8. **thr** ee

Find the word that has the same beginning blend as the picture.
Mark the space to show your answer.

9. ● trunk   10. ○ press
   ○ three   ○ flop
   ○ bee   ● spill
   tree   **spoon**

Notes for Home: Your child reviewed blends using *l*, *r*, and *s* as in *block*, *crab*, and *spoon*.
Home Activity: Work with your child to write words with *l*, *r*, and *s* blends on separate index cards. Illustrate these words on other cards. Have your child match words and pictures.

| sand | land | send | desk | lost | last |

Write the word from the box that means the opposite of each word below.

I. first	2. found	3. get
last	**lost**	**send**

Write two words from the box that rhyme with **hand**.

4. **sand**   5. **land**

Write a word from the box to match the picture.

6. **desk**

Pick a word from the box to finish each sentence.
Write the word on the line.

taste
people

7. I like the **taste** of grapefruit.

8. Some **people** eat it every day.

Notes for Home: Your child spelled words that end with *nd*, *sk*, and *st* and two frequently used words: *taste*, *people*. **Home Activity:** Work with your child to write a short story that uses the spelling words. Encourage your child to use as many of the words as possible.

Answers **285**

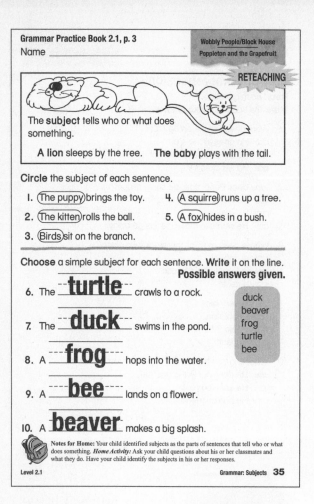

RETEACHING

The **subject** tells who or what does something.

A lion sleeps by the tree.   **The baby** plays with the tail.

Circle the subject of each sentence.

1. (The puppy) brings the toy.
2. (The kitten) rolls the ball.
3. (Birds) sit on the branch.
4. (A squirrel) runs up a tree.
5. (A fox) hides in a bush.

Choose a simple subject for each sentence. **Write** it on the line.
Possible answers given.

6. The **turtle** crawls to a rock.
7. The **duck** swims in the pond.
8. A **frog** hops into the water.
9. A **bee** lands on a flower.
10. A **beaver** makes a big splash.

duck
beaver
frog
turtle
bee

Notes for Home: Your child identified subjects as the parts of sentences that tell who or what does something. **Home Activity:** Ask your child questions about his or her classmates and what they do. Have your child identify the subjects in his or her responses.

Find the subject to complete each sentence.
Use the subjects listed in the magnifying glass.
Possible answers given.

Sam and George
Fingerprints
The cookie thieves
The cookie jar
Alex

1. **The cookie jar** is missing!
2. **Sam and George** are missing too.
3. **Alex** will collect everyone's fingerprints.
4. **Fingerprints** are never the same.
5. **The cookie thieves** will be found!

Notes for Home: Your child added subjects to sentences. **Home Activity:** Help your child write sentences about family members. Remind your child that the subject of a sentence tells who or what does something.

🔲 gate

Say the word for each picture.
Circle the words that have the same long vowel sound.

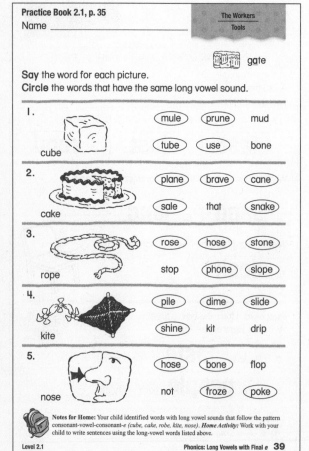

1. cube
   (mule) (prune) mud
   (tube) (use) bone

2. cake
   (plane) (brave) (cane)
   (sale) that (snake)

3. rope
   (rose) (hose) (stone)
   stop (phone) (slope)

4. kite
   (pile) (dime) (slide)
   (shine) kit drip

5. nose
   (hose) (bone) flop
   not (froze) (poke)

Notes for Home: Your child identified words with long vowel sounds that follow the pattern consonant-vowel-consonant-e (cube, cake, robe, kite, nose). **Home Activity:** Work with your child to write sentences using the long-vowel words listed above.

Say the word for each picture.
Write the letters from the box to finish each word.

cherry

ch   sh   th   wh

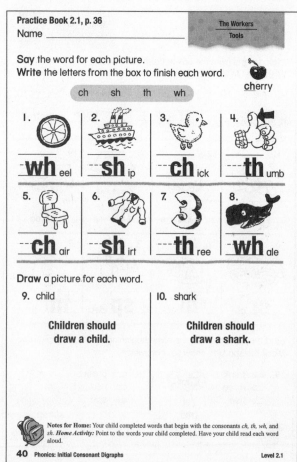

1. **wh** eel
2. **sh** ip
3. **ch** ick
4. **th** umb
5. **ch** air
6. **sh** irt
7. **th** ree
8. **wh** ale

Draw a picture for each word.

9. child

Children should draw a child.

10. shark

Children should draw a shark.

Notes for Home: Your child completed words that begin with the consonants ch, th, wh, and sh. **Home Activity:** Point to the words your child completed. Have your child read each word aloud.

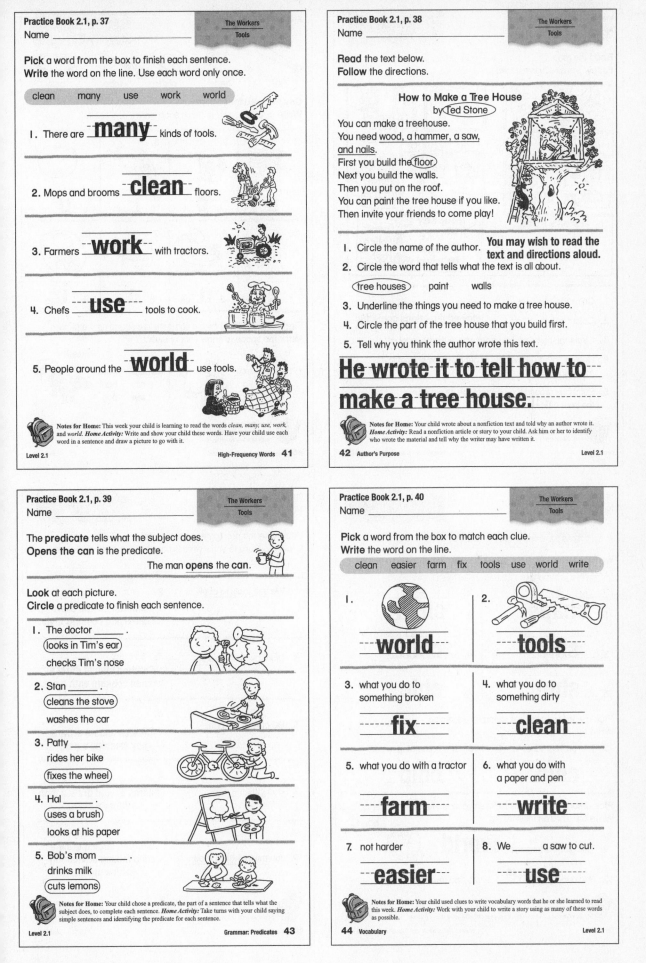

Practice Book 2.1, p. 37
Name _____

The Workers / Tools

Pick a word from the box to finish each sentence.
Write the word on the line. Use each word only once.

> clean   many   use   work   world

1. There are **many** kinds of tools.

2. Mops and brooms **clean** floors.

3. Farmers **work** with tractors.

4. Chefs **use** tools to cook.

5. People around the **world** use tools.

Notes for Home: This week your child is learning to read the words *clean, many, use, work,* and *world*. **Home Activity:** Write and show your child these words. Have your child use each word in a sentence and draw a picture to go with it.

Level 2.1   High-Frequency Words **41**

Practice Book 2.1, p. 38
Name _____

The Workers / Tools

Read the text below.
Follow the directions.

How to Make a Tree House
by (Ted Stone)

You can make a treehouse.
You need wood, a hammer, a saw, and nails.
First you build the (floor)
Next you build the walls.
Then you put on the roof.
You can paint the tree house if you like.
Then invite your friends to come play!

1. Circle the name of the author.   **You may wish to read the text and directions aloud.**

2. Circle the word that tells what the text is all about.

   (tree houses)   paint   walls

3. Underline the things you need to make a tree house.

4. Circle the part of the tree house that you build first.

5. Tell why you think the author wrote this text.

He wrote it to tell how to make a tree house.

Notes for Home: Your child wrote about a nonfiction text and told why an author wrote it. **Home Activity:** Read a nonfiction article or story to your child. Ask him or her to identify who wrote the material and tell why the writer may have written it.

42 Author's Purpose   Level 2.1

Practice Book 2.1, p. 39
Name _____

The Workers / Tools

The **predicate** tells what the subject does.
Opens the can is the predicate.

The man **opens** the **can**.

Look at each picture.
Circle a predicate to finish each sentence.

1. The doctor _____ .
   (looks in Tim's ear)
   checks Tim's nose

2. Stan _____ .
   (cleans the stove)
   washes the car

3. Patty _____ .
   rides her bike
   (fixes the wheel)

4. Hal _____ .
   (uses a brush)
   looks at his paper

5. Bob's mom _____ .
   drinks milk
   (cuts lemons)

Notes for Home: Your child chose a predicate, the part of a sentence that tells what the subject does, to complete each sentence. **Home Activity:** Take turns with your child saying simple sentences and identifying the predicate for each sentence.

Level 2.1   Grammar: Predicates **43**

Practice Book 2.1, p. 40
Name _____

The Workers / Tools

Pick a word from the box to match each clue.
Write the word on the line.

> clean   easier   farm   fix   tools   use   world   write

1. **world**

2. **tools**

3. what you do to something broken
   fix

4. what you do to something dirty
   clean

5. what you do with a tractor
   farm

6. what you do with a paper and pen
   write

7. not harder
   easier

8. We _____ a saw to cut.
   use

Notes for Home: Your child used clues to write vocabulary words that he or she learned to read this week. **Home Activity:** Work with your child to write a story using as many of these words as possible.

44 Vocabulary   Level 2.1

Answers **287**

Read the map.
Follow the directions below.

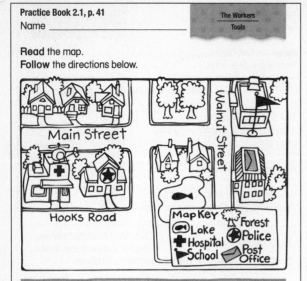

1. Color the lake blue.

2. Color the school red.

3. Circle the name of the street where the hospital is.

4. Draw a path to show how to get from the school to the hospital.

5. Put a box around the name of the street where the post office is.

Check that children have followed directions correctly.

 Notes for Home: Your child practiced reading a simple map. *Home Activity:* Draw a simple map of your neighborhood. Take your child on a walk. Have him or her identify places on the map. Encourage your child to add to the map.

Level 2.1   Research and Study Skills: Map **45**

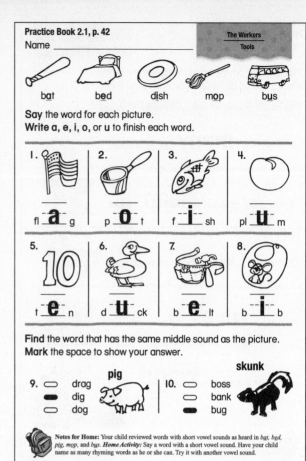

bat   bed   dish   mop   bus

Say the word for each picture.
Write a, e, i, o, or u to finish each word.

1. fl **a** g
2. p **o** t
3. f **i** sh
4. pl **u** m
5. t **e** n
6. d **u** ck
7. b **e** lt
8. b **i** b

Find the word that has the same middle sound as the picture.
Mark the space to show your answer.

pig

9. ○ drag
   ● dig
   ○ dog

skunk

10. ○ boss
    ○ bank
    ● bug

 Notes for Home: Your child reviewed words with short vowel sounds as heard in *bat, bed, pig, mop,* and *bus.* *Home Activity:* Say a word with a short vowel sound. Have your child name as many rhyming words as he or she can. Try it with another vowel sound.

46 Phonics: Short Vowels Review   Level 2.1

---

child   chin   chip   shape   ship   shut

Write the words from the box that begin with the letters at the top of each column.

sh
1. **shape**
3. **ship**
5. **shut**

ch
2. **child**
4. **chin**
6. **chip**

Pick a word from the box to match each clue.
Write the word on the line.

7. It is on your face.
   chin

8. It is something to eat.
   chip

Pick a word from the box to finish each sentence.
Write the word on the line.

use
world

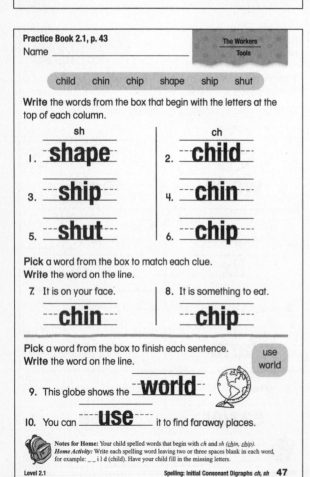

9. This globe shows the **world**.

10. You can **use** it to find faraway places.

 Notes for Home: Your child spelled words that begin with *ch* and *sh* (*chin, ship*). *Home Activity:* Write each spelling word leaving two or three spaces blank in each word, for example: _ _ i l d (child). Have your child fill in the missing letters.

Level 2.1   Spelling: Initial Consonant Digraphs *ch, sh* **47**

Underline the predicate in each sentence.
Draw a picture to show what is happening in each sentence.

1. We <u>use tools to cook.</u>

2. **Children should draw people using cooking tools.**

3. Mom <u>cooks with a pot.</u>

4. **Children should draw a woman cooking with a pot.**

5. Bill <u>cleans the pan.</u>

6. **Children should draw a boy cleaning a pan.**

7. Dad <u>cuts the cake.</u>

8. **Children should draw a man cutting a cake.**

9. Jan <u>mixes with a spoon.</u>

10. **Children should draw a child mixing something with a spoon.**

 Notes for Home: Your child identified the predicate, or action part, in sentences and drew pictures to show each action. *Home Activity:* Read a simple story with your child. Have him or her identify the predicates in several sentences.

48 Grammar: Predicates   Level 2.1

Part I: Vocabulary

Find the word that best fits in each sentence.
Mark the space for your answer.

1. They will _____ the boat with water.
   ○ write   ● clean   ○ fix

2. My job is _____ than yours.
   ○ good   ○ again   ● easier

3. They _____ on flat land.
   ● farm   ○ tools   ○ need

4. May I _____ your bike?
   ○ read   ● use   ○ call

5. We live in a big _____ .
   ● world   ○ boy   ○ school

GO ON

Part 2: Comprehension

Read each question.
Mark the space for your answer.

6. Which people use tools to dig?
   ○ teachers
   ○ cooks
   ● farmers

7. From this story, you can tell that —
   ○ only grown-ups use tools.
   ○ tools cost a lot money.
   ● tools have many uses.

8. The author wrote this story to —
   ○ make fun of people.
   ● tell about tools.
   ○ teach you to work faster.

9. Which sentence tells what the story is mostly about?
   ● "Tools help us in many ways."
   ○ "We can even eat with tools!"
   ○ "People use tools to make things."

10. People can use tools when they —
    ○ read books.
    ○ walk.
    ● fix cars.

STOP

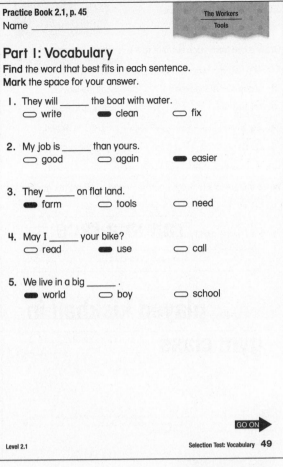

wi**nd**   wor**ld**   he**lp**   te**nt**

Circle the word for each picture.

1. (child) chair
2. (bend) bed
3. call (cold)
4. (gulp) gum
5. play (plant)
6. bad (band)
7. (ant) at
8. cell (cent)

Find the word that has the same ending sound as the picture.
Mark the space to show your answer.

9. ○ ham   ○ hint   ● blind   **hand**

10. ○ tall   ○ flap   ● told   **fold**

Notes for Home: Your child reviewed words that end with *ld, lp, nd,* and *nt.* **Home Activity:** Write a word that ends with each of the blends. Have your child build new words by changing the beginning letters, *cold* becomes *mold,* for example.

---

child   chin   chip   shape   ship   shut

Pick a word from the box to match each picture.
Write the word on the line.

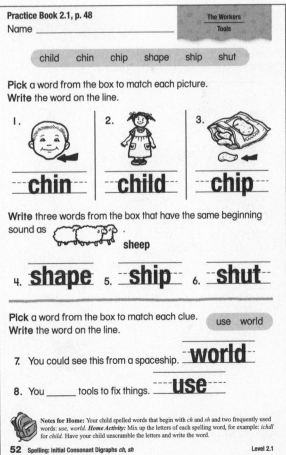

1. chin
2. child
3. chip

Write three words from the box that have the same beginning sound as **sheep**.

4. **shape**   5. **ship**   6. **shut**

Pick a word from the box to match each clue.
Write the word on the line.   use   world

7. You could see this from a spaceship.   **world**

8. You _____ tools to fix things.   **use**

Notes for Home: Your child spelled words that begin with *ch* and *sh* and two frequently used words: *use, world.* **Home Activity:** Mix up the letters of each spelling word, for example: *ichdl* for *child.* Have your child unscramble the letters and write the word.

Answers   **289**

Name _____

The Workers
Tools

RETEACHING

The **predicate** tells what the subject is or does.

The girls **feed the fish.**

The fish **eat the food.**

Circle the predicate in each sentence.

1. Yesterday Sam (called a friend)   4. The friend (went home)

2. His friend (came over)   5. Sam (ate dinner)

3. They (played three games)

Choose a predicate from the box for each sentence.
Write it on the line.

> go to the lake.
> swims with us.
> fly in the sky.
> is warm and still.

6. We **go to the lake.**

7. The water **is warm and still.**

8. Mom **swims with us.**

9. The birds **fly in the sky.**

 Notes for Home: Your child identified and wrote predicates in sentences. **Home Activity:** Write two sentences. Have your child underline the predicate in each sentence. Then have your child write two new sentences, using the same predicates.

Grammar: Predicates **53**

Name _____

The Workers
Tools

Draw a line from each subject to the predicate that matches it.
Possible answers given.

1. The fall ————————— is a pretty time of year.

2. Many colorful leaves   rakes the leaves.

3. My brother   hide nuts in trees.

4. Sarah and I   jump in the leaves.

5. Some squirrels   are on the ground.

Write a predicate to finish each sentence.   **Possible answers given.**

6. My friends and I **ran in a race**

7. At school we **played kickball in gym class**

Notes for Home: Your child identified and wrote predicates in sentences. **Home Activity:** Write three sentences, and cut the paper between the subject and predicate. Have your child put the sentences back together correctly.

54 Grammar: Predicates

Practice Book 2.1, p. 51

Name _____

The Green Leaf Club News
Three Little Bikers

These bees only fly past words with the **long e** sound.
Draw a line to show the path from the bees to the tree.

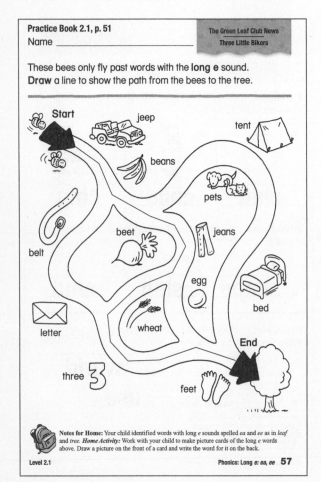

Start
jeep
tent
beans
pets
jeans
belt
beet
egg
bed
letter
wheat
End
three
feet

Notes for Home: Your child identified words with long e sounds spelled ea and ee as in leaf and tree. **Home Activity:** Work with your child to make picture cards of the long e words above. Draw a picture on the front of a card and write the word for it on the back.

Level 2.1   Phonics: Long e: ea, ee **57**

Practice Book 2.1, p. 52

Name _____

The Green Leaf Club News
Three Little Bikers

Circle a word to finish each sentence.
Write the word on the line.

wrench

(wash)   watch   wish

1. Jon will **wash** his bike.

lunch   bunch   (bench)

2. He sits on a **bench** to eat.

what   (watch)   wash

3. He likes to **watch** the birds.

pad   (path)   pat

4. He rides on the **path**

long   (song)   son

5. He sings a **song**

Notes for Home: Your child completed sentences by choosing words that end with th, ch, ng, sh, or tch. **Home Activity:** Read a simple story with your child. As you find words with these endings, ask your child to read the words aloud.

58 Phonics: Final Consonant Digraphs   Level 2.1

Name _____

Pick a word from the box to finish each sentence.
Write the word on the line.

| should | their | through | very | would |

1. Jill and Bill ride **their** bikes.

2. They ride **through** the park.

3. They know they **should** always wear helmets.

4. They are **very** safe riders.

5. They **would** like to ride every day.

Notes for Home: This week your child is learning to read the words *should, their, through, very,* and *would.* **Home Activity:** Help your child write a story using as many of the words as possible. Draw pictures to illustrate the story.

Level 2.1 — High-Frequency Words **59**

Name _____

Read each story.
Underline the sentence that tells where the story takes place.
Draw a picture that shows where the story takes place.

1. <u>Last week Anne rode her bike to the animal park.</u> She saw seals and birds. Then she ate a snack.

2. Children should draw a picture of a girl at an animal park.

3. <u>Cal and Ben slept in their backyard.</u> They had a tent. Their mom made them some popcorn and gave them flashlights.

4. Children should draw a picture of two boys sleeping in a tent outside.

Write the name of a story you have read.
Draw a picture that shows where the story takes place. It can be a real place or make-believe. It can take place now or long ago.

5. **Title of Book**

Children should draw a picture that shows the setting of a book they have read.

Notes for Home: Your child identified the setting of a story. **Home Activity:** Read a story to your child. Ask questions such as: *Is this a real or make-believe place? Is it long ago or now?* Have your child tell you where and when the story takes place.

60 Setting — Level 2.1

Name _____

A **statement** is a sentence that tells something.
It begins with a capital letter.
It ends with a ▪.   **It is fun to ride bikes.**

A **question** is a sentence that asks something.
It begins with a capital letter.
It ends with a ▪.   **Is it fun to ride bikes?**

Read each sentence.
Write the correct end mark on the line to finish each sentence.

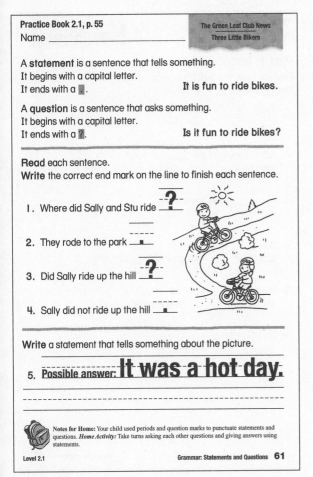

1. Where did Sally and Stu ride **?**

2. They rode to the park **.**

3. Did Sally ride up the hill **?**

4. Sally did not ride up the hill **.**

Write a statement that tells something about the picture.

5. Possible answer: **It was a hot day.**

Notes for Home: Your child used periods and question marks to punctuate statements and questions. **Home Activity:** Take turns asking each other questions and giving answers using statements.

Level 2.1 — Grammar: Statements and Questions **61**

Name _____

Pick a word from the box to match each clue.
Write the word on the line.

| climb | everywhere | giggled | should | spray | through |

1. go from one side to another — **through**

2. laughed — **giggled**

3. in all places — **everywhere**

4. You _____ ask your mom. — **should**

5.  **climb**

6. **spray**

Notes for Home: Your child used clues to write vocabulary words that he or she learned this week. **Home Activity:** Work with your child to write a story using as many of these words as possible.

62 Vocabulary — Level 2.1

Answers **291**

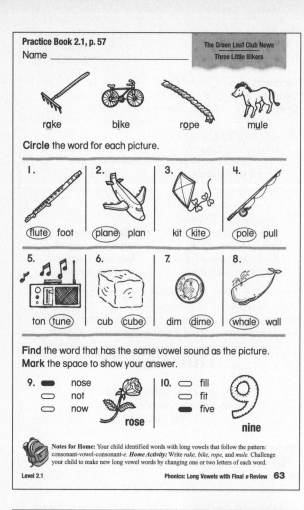

rake   bike   rope   mule

Circle the word for each picture.

1.	2.	3.	4.
(flute) foot	(plane) plan	kit (kite)	(pole) pull

5.	6.	7.	8.
ton (tune)	cub (cube)	dim (dime)	(whale) wall

Find the word that has the same vowel sound as the picture.
Mark the space to show your answer.

9. ● nose
   ○ not
   ○ now
   rose

10. ○ fill
    ○ fit
    ● five
    nine

Notes for Home: Your child identified words with long vowels that follow the pattern: consonant-vowel-consonant-*e*. Home Activity: Write *rake, bike, rope,* and *mule*. Challenge your child to make new long vowel words by changing one or two letters of each word.

Level 2.1   Phonics: Long Vowels with Final *e* Review **63**

---

leaf   meal   team   deep   free   seen

Write three words from the box with **ee**.

1. **deep**   2. **free**   3. **seen**

Write three words from the box with **ea**.

4. **leaf**   5. **meal**   6. **team**

Pick a word from the box to match each clue.
Write the word on the line.

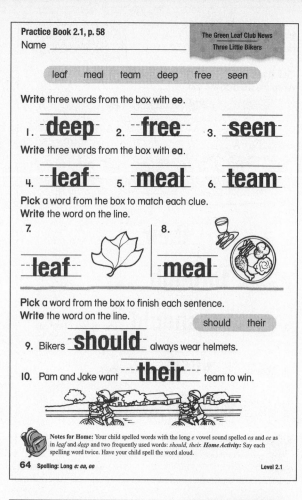

7. **leaf**   8. **meal**

Pick a word from the box to finish each sentence.
Write the word on the line.

should   their

9. Bikers **should** always wear helmets.

10. Pam and Jake want **their** team to win.

Notes for Home: Your child spelled words with the long *e* vowel sound spelled *ea* and *ee* as in *leaf* and *deep* and two frequently used words: *should, their*. Home Activity: Say each spelling word twice. Have your child spell the word aloud.

64 Spelling: Long *e: ea, ee*   Level 2.1

Look at the picture. **Read** each question.
Write a statement to answer each question.

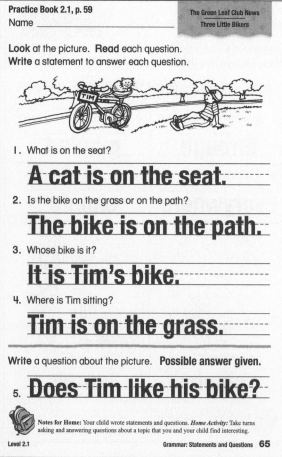

1. What is on the seat?

A cat is on the seat.

2. Is the bike on the grass or on the path?

The bike is on the path.

3. Whose bike is it?

It is Tim's bike.

4. Where is Tim sitting?

Tim is on the grass.

Write a question about the picture. **Possible answer given.**

Does Tim like his bike?

Notes for Home: Your child wrote statements and questions. Home Activity: Take turns asking and answering questions about a topic that you and your child find interesting.

Level 2.1   Grammar: Statements and Questions **65**

Part 1: Vocabulary

Find the word that best fits in each sentence.
Mark the space for your answer.

1. I can _____ to the top.
   ○ fix   ● climb   ○ clean

2. Jim got wet from the _____ of water.
   ● spray   ○ world   ○ spider

3. Ali _____ at the funny story.
   ○ drew   ○ took   ● giggled

4. You _____ eat your lunch.
   ○ about   ● should   ○ long

5. We rode _____ the grass.
   ● through   ○ everywhere   ○ after

GO ON ➡

Level 2.1   Selection Test: Vocabulary **67**

Part 2: Comprehension

Read each question.
Mark the space for your answer.

6. You can tell at the beginning of the story that —
   - ● it was a nice day.
   - ○ a storm was coming.
   - ○ it was almost night.

7. What made the bikers' shirts puff out like sails?
   - ○ the flags
   - ● the wind
   - ○ their packs

8. The tracks in the grass were made by —
   - ● the bikes' tires.
   - ○ three little snakes.
   - ○ the bikers' feet.

9. Where did the bikers spend most of their time?
   - ○ in a puddle
   - ● on the hill
   - ○ in a gully

10. What helps the bikers when they ride at night?
    - ○ having a flag that flaps
    - ○ bringing a lunch
    - ● turning on their headlights

STOP

---

white   shirt   thorn   chest

Say the word for each picture.
Write wh, sh, th, or ch to finish each word.

1. **sh**eep	2. **sh**orts	3. **wh**eel	4. **ch**erry
5. **th**umb	6. **ch**imp	7. **sh**ovel	8. **wh**ale

Find the word that has the same beginning sound as the picture.
Mark the space to show your answer.

9. ○ cheek
   ● shine
   ○ flip
   ship

10. ● chain
    ○ plane
    ○ green
    ✓ **check**

Notes for Home: Your child reviewed words that begin with *wh, sh, th,* and *ch* as in *whale, shirt, thorn,* and *chest.* **Home Activity:** Ask your child to read aloud the words above that begin with these letter pairs. Together, write a story using some of these words.

---

leaf	meal	team	deep	free	seen

Pick a word from the box to match each picture.
Write the word on the line.

1. **team**
2. **meal**
3. **leaf**

Pick a word from the box to finish each rhyme.
Write the word on the line.

4. Please **free** my kite from the tree.

5. Have you ever **seen** a frog that's not green?

6. You don't hear a peep from the fish in the **deep**.

Write the word from the box that fits in each puzzle.

should   their

7. | t | h | e | i | r |

8. | s | h | o | u | l | d |

Notes for Home: Your child spelled words with long *e* spelled *ee* and *ea* and two frequently used words: *should, their.* **Home Activity:** Read the spelling words to your child. Have him or her write each word down and then use it in a sentence about himself or herself.

RETEACHING

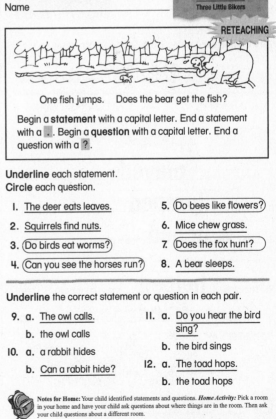

One fish jumps.   Does the bear get the fish?

Begin a **statement** with a capital letter. End a statement with a ▓ . Begin a **question** with a capital letter. End a question with a ? .

Underline each statement.
Circle each question.

1. The deer eats leaves.
2. Squirrels find nuts.
3. Do birds eat worms?
4. Can you see the horses run?
5. Do bees like flowers?
6. Mice chew grass.
7. Does the fox hunt?
8. A bear sleeps.

Underline the correct statement or question in each pair.

9. a. The owl calls.
   b. the owl calls

10. a. a rabbit hides
    b. Can a rabbit hide?

11. a. Do you hear the bird sing?
    b. the bird sings

12. a. The toad hops.
    b. the toad hops

Notes for Home: Your child identified statements and questions. **Home Activity:** Pick a room in your home and have your child ask questions about where things are in the room. Then ask your child questions about a different room.

Answers **293**

Write these sentences correctly.
Use a period or a question mark at the end.

is there a gorilla in my room

Is there a gorilla in my room?

i saw a shadow on the wall

I saw a shadow on the wall.

it was near my bed

It was near my bed.

was it big

Was it big?

it was bigger than my dad

It was bigger than my dad.

Notes for Home: Your child wrote statements and questions. *Home Activity:* Play a round robin question game with your child and others. Write a simple question and hand it to the next person. He or she will answer the question and write a new question.

72 Grammar: Statements and Questions

Underline the word in each sentence that has the **long e** sound.
Write the word on the line.

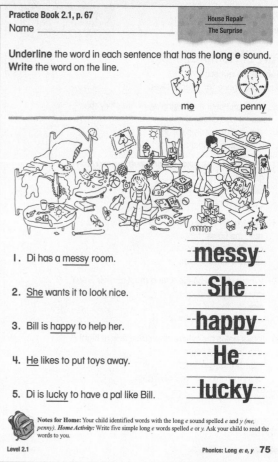

me   penny

1. Di has a <u>messy</u> room.

2. <u>She</u> wants it to look nice.

3. Bill is <u>happy</u> to help her.

4. <u>He</u> likes to put toys away.

5. Di is <u>lucky</u> to have a pal like Bill.

messy
She
happy
He
lucky

Notes for Home: Your child identified words with the long e sound spelled e and y (me, penny). *Home Activity:* Write five simple long e words spelled e or y. Ask your child to read the words to you.

Level 2.1   Phonics: Long e: e, y   **75**

Add -ed to the word in ( ).
Write the new word on the line to finish each sentence.

push + ed = push**ed**

1. Vera and Gail **played** in the leaves.   (play)

2. Then they **jumped** in the pile.   (jump)

3. Dad **watched** them play.   (watch)

4. The girls **helped** make a new pile.   (help)

5. The leaves **filled** up two bags!   (fill)

Notes for Home: Your child formed and used words that end with -ed as in *picked*. *Home Activity:* Write words that end with -ed. Have your child say each word aloud and use it in a sentence about someone in his or her family.

76 Phonics: Inflected Ending -ed   Level 2.1

Pick a word from the box to finish each sentence.
Write the word on the line.

| house | never | off | these | took |

1. **These** leaves are a mess!

2. Greg **never** wants to rake.

3. Becky **took** the rake.

4. Greg gets a bag from the **house**.

5. Now all the leaves are **off** the ground!

Notes for Home: This week your child is learning to read the words *house, never, off, these,* and *took. Home Activity:* Have your child use these words to write or say a story about helping someone.

Level 2.1   High-Frequency Words   **77**

---

294   Answers

Look at the picture.
Circle the word that best finishes each sentence.
Write the word on the line.

1. The girl is (sad) happy
   sad

2. She wants her book (mom)
   mom

3. The boy wants to make her sad (happy)
   happy

4. He gives her a pencil (toy)
   toy

Write a sentence about how you think the girl feels now.

5. **Children's sentence should conclude that the girl feels**

   better or happy now.

Notes for Home: Your child used text and illustrations to draw conclusions about a story.
Home Activity: As you read a story to your child, stop often to ask your child to think about
what is happening or why a character is doing something.

A sentence that tells you to do something is a **command**.
In every command the subject is *you*, but *you* is not shown.
This is a command: **Pick up the socks.**

A sentence that shows surprise or strong feelings is an **exclamation**.
Put an exclamation mark **!** at the end of an exclamation.
This is an exclamation: **That is a big dog!**

Read each sentence.
Write C on the line if the sentence is a command.
Write E on the line if the sentence is an exclamation.

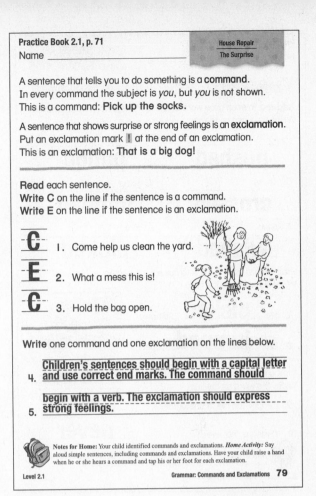

C 1. Come help us clean the yard.

E 2. What a mess this is!

C 3. Hold the bag open.

Write one command and one exclamation on the lines below.

4. **Children's sentences should begin with a capital letter**
   and use correct end marks. The command should

5. **begin with a verb. The exclamation should express**
   strong feelings.

Notes for Home: Your child identified commands and exclamations. *Home Activity:* Say
aloud simple sentences, including commands and exclamations. Have your child raise a hand
when he or she hears a command and tap his or her foot for each exclamation.

Pick a word from the box to match each clue.
Write the word on the line.

| guess | house | never | pile |
| pleased | surprised | tomorrow | |

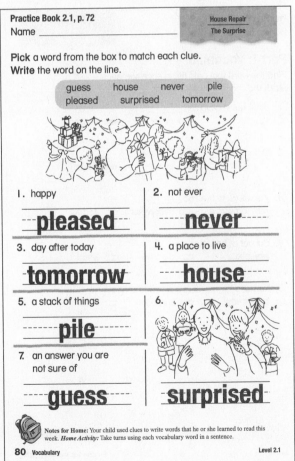

1. happy
   pleased

2. not ever
   never

3. day after today
   tomorrow

4. a place to live
   house

5. a stack of things
   pile

6. **surprised**

7. an answer you are not sure of
   guess

Notes for Home: Your child used clues to write words that he or she learned to read this
week. *Home Activity:* Take turns using each vocabulary word in a sentence.

Circle the word for each picture.   leaf   teeth

1. (beach) bench
2. bead (bed)
3. suds (seeds)
4. sell (seal)
5. (sheep) ship
6. buns (beans)
7. (tree) trip
8. best (bees)

Find the word that has the same middle sound as the picture.
Mark the space to show your answer.

9. ◯ best
   ◯ bake
   ● bean
   beak

10. ◯ fed
    ● feed
    ◯ felt
    feet

Notes for Home: Your child reviewed words with long *e* spelled *ea* and *ee* as in *leaf* and
teeth. Home Activity: Write *leaf* and *teeth*. Have your child build new long *e* words by
changing some of the consonants, for example, *leaf* becomes *lean* or *leap*.

wished   crossed   jumped   picked   pulled   pushed

Add -ed to each base word below to make a word from the box.
Write the word on the line.

1. push

pushed

2. pull

pulled

3. cross

crossed

4. jump

jumped

5. wish

wished

6. pick

picked

Pick a word from the box to finish each sentence.
Write the word on the line.

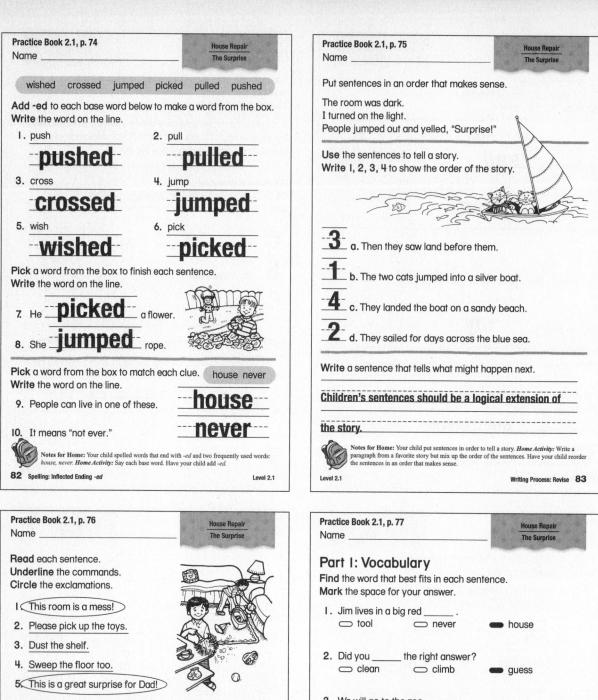

7. He **picked** a flower.

8. She **jumped** rope.

Pick a word from the box to match each clue.
Write the word on the line.

house   never

9. People can live in one of these.

house

10. It means "not ever."

never

Notes for Home: Your child spelled words that end with *-ed* and two frequently used words: *house, never.* **Home Activity:** Say each base word. Have your child add *-ed.*

82   Spelling: Inflected Ending *-ed*

Level 2.1

Put sentences in an order that makes sense.

The room was dark.
I turned on the light.
People jumped out and yelled, "Surprise!"

Use the sentences to tell a story.
Write 1, 2, 3, 4 to show the order of the story.

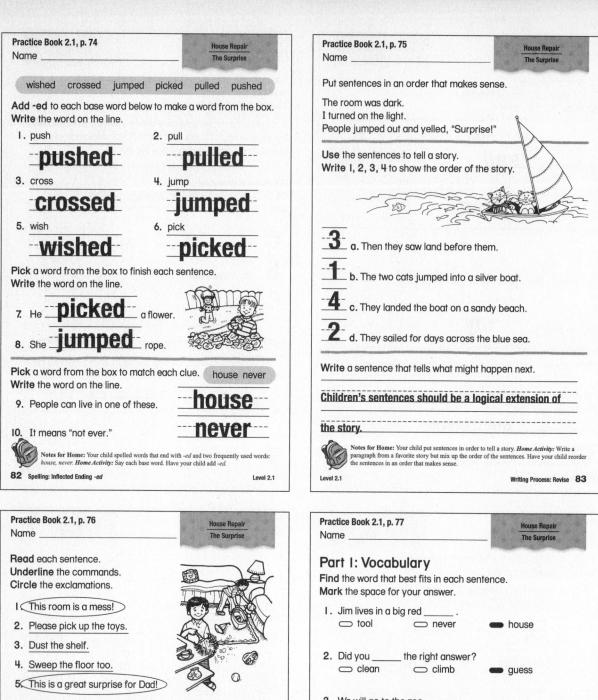

3 a. Then they saw land before them.

1 b. The two cats jumped into a silver boat.

4 c. They landed the boat on a sandy beach.

2 d. They sailed for days across the blue sea.

Write a sentence that tells what might happen next.

_____

Children's sentences should be a logical extension of

the story.

Notes for Home: Your child put sentences in order to tell a story. **Home Activity:** Write a paragraph from a favorite story but mix up the order of the sentences. Have your child reorder the sentences in an order that makes sense.

Level 2.1

Writing Process: Revise   83

Read each sentence.
Underline the commands.
Circle the exclamations.

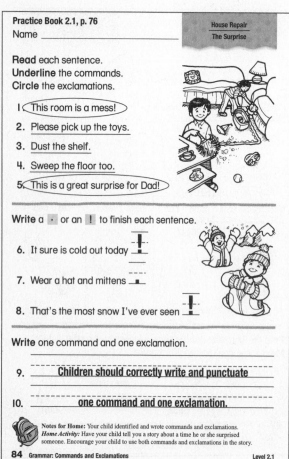

1. (This room is a mess!)

2. Please pick up the toys.

3. Dust the shelf.

4. Sweep the floor too.

5. (This is a great surprise for Dad!)

Write a **.** or an **!** to finish each sentence.

6. It sure is cold out today **!**

7. Wear a hat and mittens **.**

8. That's the most snow I've ever seen **!**

Write one command and one exclamation.

9. **Children should correctly write and punctuate**

10. **one command and one exclamation.**

Notes for Home: Your child identified and wrote commands and exclamations. **Home Activity:** Have your child tell you a story about a time he or she surprised someone. Encourage your child to use both commands and exclamations in the story.

84   Grammar: Commands and Exclamations

Level 2.1

Part I: Vocabulary

Find the word that best fits in each sentence.
Mark the space for your answer.

1. Jim lives in a big red _____ .
   ○ tool   ○ never   ● house

2. Did you _____ the right answer?
   ○ clean   ○ climb   ● guess

3. We will go to the zoo _____ .
   ● tomorrow   ○ everywhere   ○ perfect

4. Sal put all her toys in a _____ .
   ● pile   ○ pleased   ○ world

5. Leo was _____ to see a cow in school.
   ○ pretty   ● surprised   ○ done

GO ON ▶

Level 2.1

Selection Test: Vocabulary   85

---

296   Answers

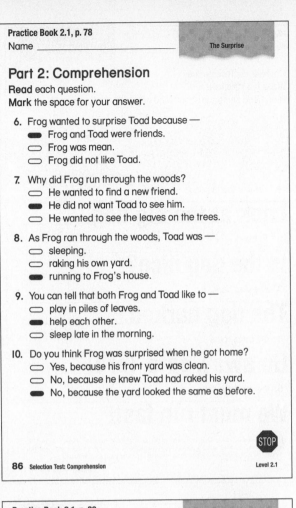

Part 2: Comprehension

Read each question.
Mark the space for your answer.

6. Frog wanted to surprise Toad because —
   - ● Frog and Toad were friends.
   - ○ Frog was mean.
   - ○ Frog did not like Toad.

7. Why did Frog run through the woods?
   - ○ He wanted to find a new friend.
   - ● He did not want Toad to see him.
   - ○ He wanted to see the leaves on the trees.

8. As Frog ran through the woods, Toad was —
   - ○ sleeping.
   - ○ raking his own yard.
   - ● running to Frog's house.

9. You can tell that both Frog and Toad like to —
   - ○ play in piles of leaves.
   - ● help each other.
   - ○ sleep late in the morning.

10. Do you think Frog was surprised when he got home?
    - ○ Yes, because his front yard was clean.
    - ○ No, because he knew Toad had raked his yard.
    - ● No, because the yard looked the same as before.

STOP

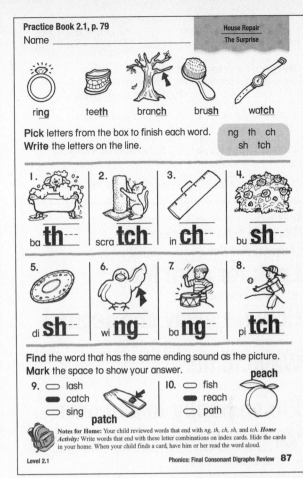

ring teeth branch brush watch

Pick letters from the box to finish each word.
Write the letters on the line.

ng th ch
sh tch

1. ba **th**
2. scra **tch**
3. in **ch**
4. bu **sh**
5. di **sh**
6. wi **ng**
7. ba **ng**
8. pi **tch**

Find the word that has the same ending sound as the picture.
Mark the space to show your answer.

9. ○ lash
   ● catch
   ○ sing

   patch

10. ○ fish
    ● reach
    ○ path

    peach

Notes for Home: Your child reviewed words that end with *ng, th, ch, sh,* and *tch.* **Home Activity:** Write words that end with these letter combinations on index cards. Hide the cards in your home. When your child finds a card, have him or her read the word aloud.

wished crossed jumped picked pulled pushed

Write a word from the box to match each picture.

1. **jumped**
2. **picked**
3. **pulled**

Pick a word from the box to match each clue.
Write the word on the line.

4. Jo did this when she saw a star. **wished**

5. You did this to get across the street. **crossed**

6. Bob's dad did this to Bob's swing. **pushed**

Pick a word from the box to finish each sentence.
Write the word on the line.

house
never

7. Vera and her dad live in a big **house** .

8. She **never** stays home alone.

Notes for Home: Your child spelled words that end with *-ed* and two frequently used words: *house, never.* **Home Activity:** Play charades with your child. One person acts out a spelling word while the other tries to guess and spell it.

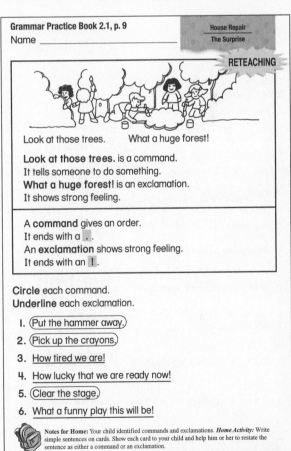

RETEACHING

Look at those trees.   What a huge forest!

Look at those trees. is a command.
It tells someone to do something.
What a huge forest! is an exclamation.
It shows strong feeling.

A **command** gives an order.
It ends with a **.** .
An **exclamation** shows strong feeling.
It ends with an **!** .

Circle each command.
Underline each exclamation.

1. (Put the hammer away.)
2. (Pick up the crayons.)
3. How tired we are!
4. How lucky that we are ready now!
5. (Clear the stage.)
6. What a funny play this will be!

Notes for Home: Your child identified commands and exclamations. **Home Activity:** Write simple sentences on cards. Show each card to your child and help him or her to restate the sentence as either a command or an exclamation.

Use a period after each command.
Use an exclamation mark after each exclamation.

_____ **Possible answers given.** _____

1. Walk to that ride __.__

4. Lock your seat belt __.__

2. What a long line __!__

5. How high up we are __!__

3. Find a seat __.__

6. What a fun ride __!__

Write each command and exclamation.
Use a capital letter and the correct end mark.

7. look for Aunt Meg

Look for Aunt Meg.

8. how far away she seems

How far away she seems!

9. wave to her

Wave to her.

10. i'm so happy to see her

I'm so happy to see her!

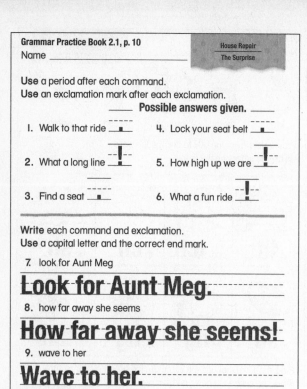

Notes for Home: Your child identified and wrote commands and exclamations. **Home Activity:** Together, look at pictures of friends and family members, or pictures from magazines. Have your child write one command and one exclamation about the pictures.

90 Grammar: Commands and Exclamations

Correct each sentence.
Write it on the line.
Hint: Each sentence should end with a ▪ , a ❓ , or an ❗ .

1. Look at the big dog

Look at the big dog.

2. Is the dog nice

Is the dog nice?

3. The dog barked

The dog barked.

4. Go away, cats

Go away, cats. (or !)

5. We must run fast

We must run fast!

Notes for Home: Your child corrected sentences by adding end marks. **Home Activity:** Write sentences without end marks on slips of paper. Have your child pick a slip of paper and then rewrite the sentence, adding a question mark, a period, or an exclamation mark.

Level 2.1
Writing Process: Edit **91**

Read each sentence.
Circle the word with the **long a** sound.
Write the word on the line.

nail

1. The ducklings (play) in the water.

play

2. Who is that (waiting) in the grass?

waiting

3. Will the cat (stay)?

stay

4. The big ducks are not (afraid) of a cat.

afraid

5. The cat runs (away) as fast as it can.

away

Notes for Home: Your child identified words in which the long a sound is spelled ai or ay (nail, play). **Home Activity:** Have your child read and "collect" sentences with long a words. Together, draw a picture illustrating each sentence.

Level 2.1
Phonics: Long a: ai, ay **95**

Use the word in ( ) to finish each sentence.
Add -s, -es, or -ing to the word.
Write the new word on the line.

Ben shop**s**.   He push**es** a cart.   Ben is walk**ing**.

1. The hen **sits** on her eggs. (sit)

2. She **hears** "chirp, chirp, chirp." (hear)

3. Now one egg **hatches** . (hatch)

4. A chick **pushes** its way out. (push)

5. It is **standing** up. (stand)

Notes for Home: Your child added -s, -es, and -ing to verbs—words that show action (shops, pushes, walking). **Home Activity:** Create sentences for your child like those above. Ask your child whether he or she would add -s, -es, or -ing to the verb to finish each sentence.

96 Phonics: Inflected Endings: -es, -ing, -s
Level 2.1

Pick a word from the box to finish each sentence.
Write the word on the line. Use each word only once.

keep   mother   myself   new   warm

1. That big dog is the pup's **mother**.

2. The dogs stay **warm** in their bed.

3. The pup knows a **new** game.

4. She thinks, "I can carry the stick **myself**."

5. The pup will not get to **keep** the stick.

Notes for Home: This week your child is learning to read the words *keep, mother, myself, new,* and *warm*. Home Activity: Help your child use these words to write about a baby animal that he or she has seen.

Read the words.
Write duck if it tells something about the duck.
Write duckling if it tells something about the duckling.
Write both if it tells something about them both.

duck   duckling

1. beak   **both**

2. big   **duck**

3. little   **duckling**

4. fuzzy down   **duckling**

5. webbed feet   **both**

Notes for Home: Your child identified the ways in which two things are alike and different. Home Activity: Point out two household objects that have something in common, such as a lamp and a flashlight. Ask your child to tell how they are alike and how they are different.

A **noun** is a word that names something.
A noun can name a person, a place, an animal, or a thing.

Duck and lake are nouns.   The <u>duck</u> swims in the <u>lake</u>.

Read each sentence.
Circle all the nouns in each sentence.

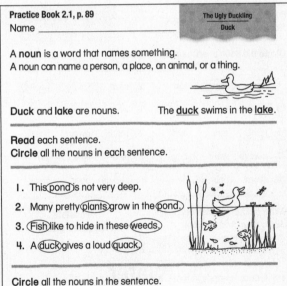

1. This (pond) is not very deep.

2. Many pretty (plants) grow in the (pond.)

3. (Fish) like to hide in these (weeds.)

4. A (duck) gives a loud (quack.)

Circle all the nouns in the sentence.
Draw a picture for the sentence.

5. Big (fish) eat little (bugs.)

**Children should draw more than
one fish eating small bugs.**

Notes for Home: Your child identified nouns—words that name people, places, animals, and things. Home Activity: Help your child find some outdoor pictures in a magazine. Have your child point to the things in the pictures and say the name of each one.

Circle a word to finish each sentence.

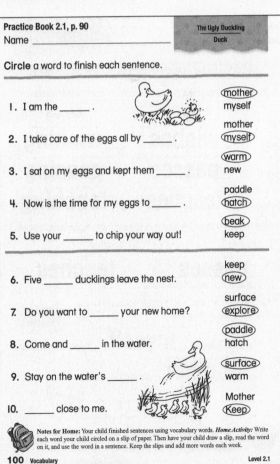

1. I am the _____ .   (mother)
                                 myself

2. I take care of the eggs all by _____ .   mother
                                             (myself)

3. I sat on my eggs and kept them _____ .   (warm)
                                             new

4. Now is the time for my eggs to _____ .   paddle
                                             (hatch)

5. Use your _____ to chip your way out!   (beak)
                                             keep

6. Five _____ ducklings leave the nest.   keep
                                             (new)

7. Do you want to _____ your new home?   surface
                                             (explore)

8. Come and _____ in the water.   (paddle)
                                             hatch

9. Stay on the water's _____ .   (surface)
                                             warm

10. _____ close to me.   Mother
                                             (Keep)

Notes for Home: Your child finished sentences using vocabulary words. Home Activity: Write each word your child circled on a slip of paper. Then have your child draw a slip, read the word on it, and use the word in a sentence. Keep the slips and add more words each week.

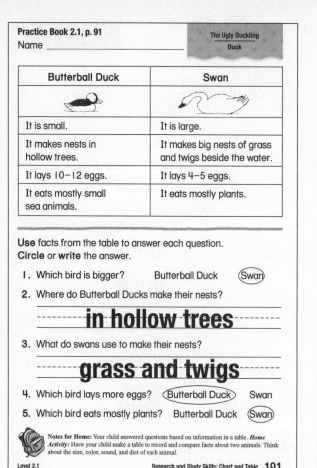

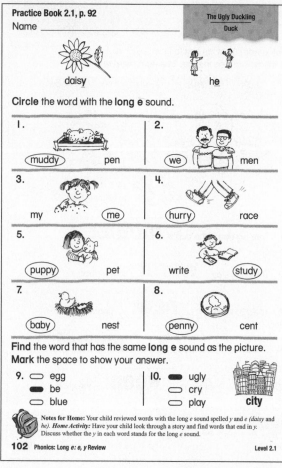

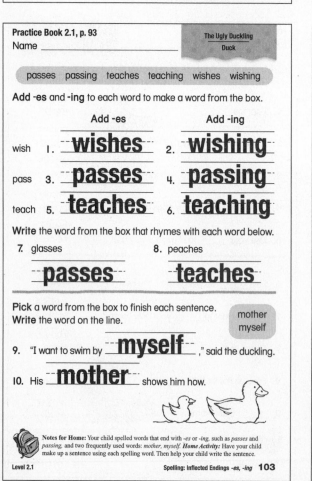

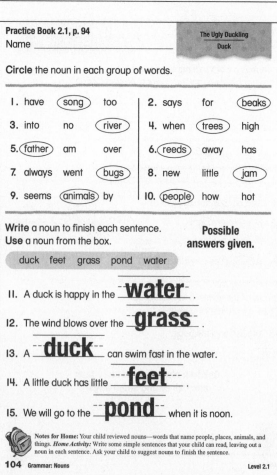

Name _____

The Ugly Duckling
Duck

Part 1: Vocabulary

Find the word that best fits in each sentence.
Mark the space for your answer.

1. The duck eats with its _____ .
   - ● beak   ○ surface   ○ house

2. You can _____ that hat.
   - ○ paddle   ○ explore   ● keep

3. I can read that book _____ .
   - ○ around   ● myself   ○ many

4. The ducks _____ through the water.
   - ● paddle   ○ fix   ○ farm

5. Bugs land on the _____ of the water.
   - ○ warm   ● surface   ○ tool

GO ON ➡

Name _____

Duck

Part 2: Comprehension

Read each question.
Mark the space for your answer.

6. The mother duck sits on her eggs to —
   - ○ hide them.
   - ○ lay them.
   - ● keep them warm.

7. When can the duckling walk?
   - ○ when it is two days old
   - ● as soon as it hatches
   - ○ when it is one week old

8. How is a six-week-old duckling different from a one-week-old duckling?
   - ○ It has webbed feet.
   - ○ It has a beak.
   - ● It has white feathers.

9. Ducklings get food from —
   - ○ the mother duck.
   - ● the water.
   - ○ yellow down.

10. When the ducks grow up, what will they do?
    - ○ talk
    - ○ read
    - ● take care of ducklings

STOP

Name _____

The Ugly Duckling
Duck

Pick the word that rhymes.
Write the word on the line.

hatch**ed**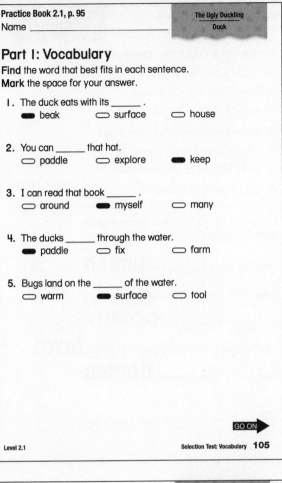

1. pecked

   nest   next   checked

   ## checked

2. rowed

   toad   floated   slow

   ## toad

3. stayed

   play   made   waited

   ## made

4. nested

   west   dressed   rested

   ## rested

5. smelled

   melt   held   helped

   ## held

6. missed

   fizz   list   sled

   ## list

Find the word that has the same ending sound as **lost**.
Mark the space to show your answer.

7. ○ moss
   ● tossed
   ○ posted

8. ● crossed
   ○ tested
   ○ close

Notes for Home: Your child reviewed words that end in -ed. Home Activity: Point out words like these when you read with your child. Help your child say these words aloud. Discuss the different ways that words ending in -ed can sound as in played, rested, or missed.

Name _____

The Ugly Duckling
Duck

passes   passing   teaches   teaching   wishes   wishing

Change one or two letters in each word to make a word from the box.
Write the new word on the line.

1. dishes

   ## wishes

2. beaches

   ## teaches

3. passed

   ## passes

4. fishing

   ## wishing

5. reaching

   ## teaching

6. tossing

   ## passing

Pick a word from the box to finish each sentence.
Write the word on the line.

mother
myself

7. My __ **mother** __ is teaching me to swim.

8. Soon I will swim by __ **myself** __ .

Notes for Home: Your child spelled words ending in -es or -ing, such as passes and passing, and two frequently used words: mother, myself. Home Activity: Help your child think of and spell words that rhyme with some of the spelling words on this page.

Answers **301**

Name _____

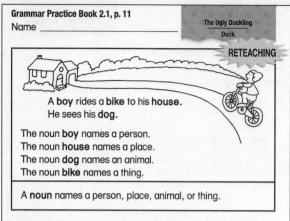

A **boy** rides a **bike** to his **house**.
He sees his **dog**.

The noun **boy** names a person.
The noun **house** names a place.
The noun **dog** names an animal.
The noun **bike** names a thing.

A **noun** names a person, place, animal, or thing.

Circle each noun. There may be more than one in each sentence.

1. My (grandma) is here.
2. (Dad) walks the (dog).
3. My (friend) comes to my (house).
4. My (aunt) calls on the (telephone).
5. (Mr. Jones) cooks in his (kitchen).
6. I play in my (room).
7. (Mom) works in her (office).
8. (Grandpa) works in the (garden).
9. (Dad) shops at the (store).
10. A (bird) sits by my (window).
11. The (cat) licks her (paw).
12. Our (roof) needs to be fixed.

Notes for Home: Your child identified nouns—words for people, places, animals, or things— in sentences. **Home Activity:** Read a story with your child and have him or her point out each noun on one page of the story.

Grammar: Nouns **109**

Name _____

Circle each noun that names a person or an animal.

1. My (uncle) lives by the sea.
2. (Seagulls) like to play in his yard.
3. My (brother) sits on the porch.
4. Sometimes my (dog) hides in the garage.
5. Our (aunt) shows us the flowers.
6. (Neighbors) bring food from the fair.
7. The (family) eats in the kitchen.

Circle each noun. **Possible answers given.**
Write on each line a noun that names a place.

The (father) took the (girl) to the **beach**. Her (friend) came too. There were many (children) swimming. A (man) pointed to a (boat) and a (whale) in the **ocean**. A (woman) watched a (baby). Some (people) walked to the **town homes**. Soon it was (time) to go to their **homes**.

Notes for Home: Your child identified nouns in sentences. **Home Activity:** Have your child write as many nouns as possible on cards. Then he or she can categorize them as people, places, animals, or things.

110 Grammar: Nouns

Name _____

Circle a word to finish each sentence.   sky   night   tie

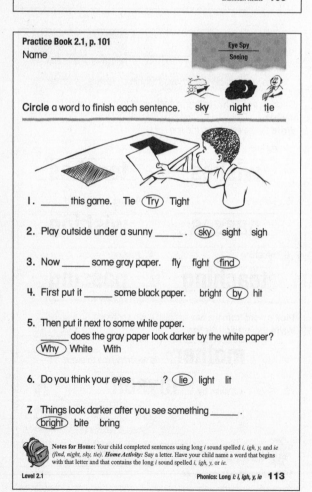

1. _____ this game.   Tie (Try) Tight
2. Play outside under a sunny _____ .   (sky) sight sigh
3. Now _____ some gray paper.   fly fight (find)
4. First put it _____ some black paper.   bright (by) hit
5. Then put it next to some white paper.
   _____ does the gray paper look darker by the white paper?
   (Why) White With
6. Do you think your eyes _____ ?   (lie) light lit
7. Things look darker after you see something _____ .
   (bright) bite bring

Notes for Home: Your child completed sentences using long *i* sound spelled *i, igh, y,* and *ie* (*find, night, sky, tie*). **Home Activity:** Say a letter. Have your child name a word that begins with that letter and that contains the long *i* sound spelled *i, igh, y,* or *ie*.

Level 2.1

Phonics: Long *i*: *i, igh, y, ie* **113**

Name _____

Say the word for each picture.
Write the letter or letters from the box to finish each word.

| g   l   nd   pp   rr | stu**d**ent

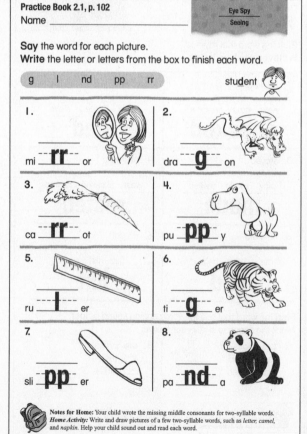

1. mi **rr** or
2. dra **g** on
3. ca **rr** ot
4. pu **pp** y
5. ru **l** er
6. ti **g** er
7. sli **pp** er
8. pa **nd** a

Notes for Home: Your child wrote the missing middle consonants for two-syllable words. **Home Activity:** Write and draw pictures of a few two-syllable words, such as *letter, camel,* and *napkin.* Help your child sound out and read each word.

114 Phonics: Medial Consonants

Level 2.1

---

302 Answers

Pick a word from the box to finish each sentence.
Write the word on the line.

| because | carry | don't | goes | whole |

1. The boy _____**goes**_____ to get the melon.

2. Can he _____**carry**_____ it?

3. I _____**don't**_____ think he can.

4. The _____**whole**_____ melon is too big.

5. He can carry a slice _____**because**_____ it is small.

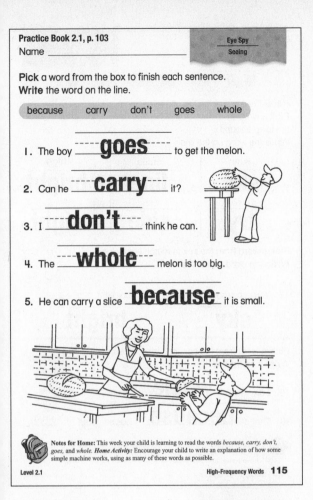

Notes for Home: This week your child is learning to read the words *because, carry, don't, goes,* and *whole.* *Home Activity:* Encourage your child to write an explanation of how some simple machine works, using as many of these words as possible.

Level 2.1   **High-Frequency Words 115**

Look at the pictures. **Read** the steps.
Write a number from **1** to **5** to show the right order.
One is done for you.

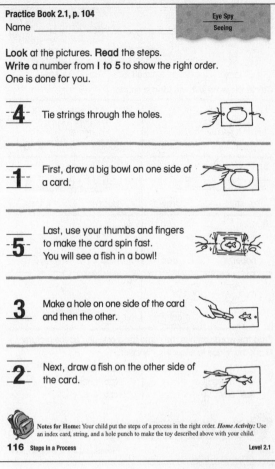

4 Tie strings through the holes.

1 First, draw a big bowl on one side of a card.

5 Last, use your thumbs and fingers to make the card spin fast.
You will see a fish in a bowl!

3 Make a hole on one side of the card and then the other.

2 Next, draw a fish on the other side of the card.

Notes for Home: Your child put the steps of a process in the right order. *Home Activity:* Use an index card, string, and a hole punch to make the toy described above with your child.

116 Steps in a Process   Level 2.1

Proper nouns are special names for people, places, animals, and things.
Proper nouns begin with **capital letters**.
Titles begin with capital letters.
Most titles end with a **·** .

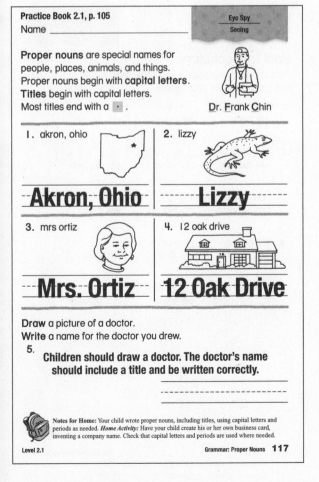

Dr. Frank Chin

1. akron, ohio

Akron, Ohio

2. lizzy

Lizzy

3. mrs ortiz

Mrs. Ortiz

4. 12 oak drive

12 Oak Drive

Draw a picture of a doctor.
Write a name for the doctor you drew.

5. **Children should draw a doctor. The doctor's name should include a title and be written correctly.**

_____

Notes for Home: Your child wrote proper nouns, including titles, using capital letters and periods as needed. *Home Activity:* Have your child create his or her own business card, inventing a company name. Check that capital letters and periods are used where needed.

Level 2.1   **Grammar: Proper Nouns 117**

Pick a word from the box to match each clue.
Write the word on the line.

| brain | hidden | messages | mirror | thumb | whole |

1. _____**thumb**_____

2. _____**mirror**_____

3. what you think with
_____**brain**_____

4. notes you write or tell someone
_____**messages**_____

5. all of something
_____**whole**_____

6. can't be seen
_____**hidden**_____

Notes for Home: Your child used clues to identify vocabulary words learned this week. *Home Activity:* Make a picture dictionary with your child. Draw pictures and write simple definitions for each word in the box.

118 Vocabulary   Level 2.1

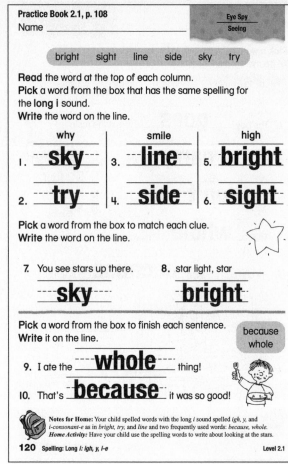

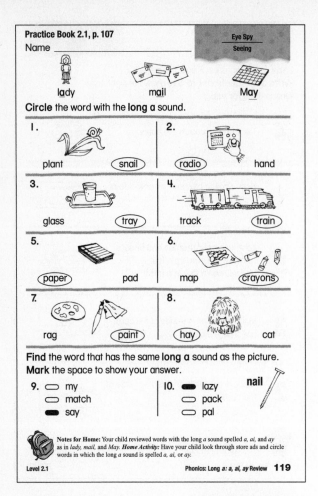 Practice Book 2.1, p. 107
Name _____
Eye Spy / Seeing

lady   mail   May

Circle the word with the long a sound.

1. plant (snail)
2. (radio) hand
3. glass (tray)
4. track (train)
5. (paper) pad
6. map (crayons)
7. rag (paint)
8. (hay) cat

Find the word that has the same long a sound as the picture.
Mark the space to show your answer.

nail

9. ○ my
   ○ match
   ● say

10. ● lazy
    ○ pack
    ○ pal

Notes for Home: Your child reviewed words with the long a sound spelled a, ai, and ay as in lady, mail, and May. Home Activity: Have your child look through store ads and circle words in which the long a sound is spelled a, ai, or ay.

Level 2.1   Phonics: Long a: a, ai, ay Review   119

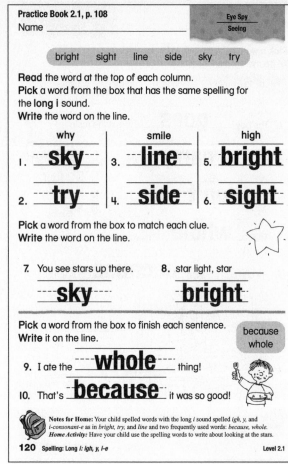 Practice Book 2.1, p. 108
Name _____
Eye Spy / Seeing

bright sight line side sky try

Read the word at the top of each column.
Pick a word from the box that has the same spelling for the long i sound.
Write the word on the line.

why   smile   high
1. sky   3. line   5. bright
2. try   4. side   6. sight

Pick a word from the box to match each clue.
Write the word on the line.

7. You see stars up there.
   sky

8. star light, star _____
   bright

Pick a word from the box to finish each sentence.
Write it on the line.

because whole

9. I ate the whole thing!

10. That's because it was so good!

Notes for Home: Your child spelled words with the long i sound spelled igh, y, and i-consonant-e as in bright, try, and line and two frequently used words: because, whole. Home Activity: Have your child use the spelling words to write about looking at the stars.

120   Spelling: Long i: igh, y, i-e   Level 2.1

Practice Book 2.1, p. 109
Name _____
Eye Spy / Seeing

Write a proper noun that makes sense for each word below.
Use capital letters and periods as needed.
Draw a picture to match your proper noun.

1. doctor
   Dr. Amy

2. Possible answers given. Children's drawings should reflect the proper nouns they wrote.

3. dog
   Max

4.

5. girl
   Kim Lee

6.

7. teacher
   Ms. Brown

8.

9. state
   New York

10.

Notes for Home: Your child wrote and drew pictures of proper nouns—special names for people, animals, places, and things. Home Activity: Help your child make a family tree, listing the family members by their full names.

Level 2.1   Grammar: Proper Nouns   121

Practice Book 2.1, p. 111
Name _____
Eye Spy / Seeing

Part 1: Vocabulary
Find the word that best fits in each sentence.
Mark the space for your answer.

1. You use your _____ to think.
   ○ beak   ● brain   ○ thumb

2. Alex took two _____ for his dad.
   ● messages   ○ world   ○ surface

3. I can see you in the _____ .
   ○ tomorrow   ○ hidden   ● mirror

4. You have one _____ on each hand.
   ● thumb   ○ time   ○ beak

5. My sister ate the _____ cake!
   ○ surprised   ● whole   ○ pleased

GO ON

Level 2.1   Selection Test: Vocabulary   123

Practice Book 2.1, p. 112

Name _____

Seeing

Part 2: Comprehension

Read each question.
Mark the space for your answer.

6. Your pupils let in just the right amount of light by changing —
   - ● size.
   - ○ shape.
   - ○ color.

7. What happens first as the eye sees?
   - ○ Messages go to the brain.
   - ● Light goes into the eye.
   - ○ A picture is made at the back of the eyeball.

8. Which of these did you find out from reading?
   - ○ Your eyeball is not really a ball.
   - ○ People who are far away are smaller.
   - ● Your brain tries to make sense of what you see.

9. Which is a good title for this story?
   - ○ "Two Dogs in a Vase"
   - ● "How Your Eyes Work"
   - ○ "Why Some Eyes Are Blue"

10. Which sentence is true?
    - ● You need your brain and your eyes to see.
    - ○ Light goes into your brain.
    - ○ A friend is smaller than a thumb.

STOP

124 Selection Test: Comprehension

Level 2.1

Practice Book 2.1, p. 113

Name _____

Eye Spy
Seeing

pitch**es**

play**ing**

hits

Read each sentence.
Circle the verb that makes sense in the sentence.

1. Dad _____ the show.   (watches) watching
2. Sam _____ off his hat.   (pulls) pulling
3. Kay _____ a rabbit in the hat.   (puts) putting
4. Sam is _____ the hat with a wand.   taps (tapping)
5. Sam is _____ a skunk out of the hat!   takes (taking)

Find the word that makes sense in the sentences below.
Mark the space to show your answer.

Sam _____ his cape.

6. ● flings
   ○ flinging
   ○ fling

He _____ it over the hat.

7. ○ tossing
   ○ toss
   ● tosses

Notes for Home: Your child reviewed verbs with *-s*, *-es*, and *-ing* endings. **Home Activity:** Read with your child, looking for sentences with verbs ending in *-ing.* (*He is washing the dog.*) Have your child write the sentence using another form of the verb. (*He washes the dog.*)

Level 2.1

Phonics: Inflected Endings *-es, -ing, -s* Review **125**

Practice Book 2.1, p. 114

Name _____

Eye Spy
Seeing

| bright | sight | line | side | sky | try |

Change one letter in each word to make a word from the box.
Write the word on the line.

1. ride   **side**
2. fine   **line**

Write two words that rhyme with knight.

3. **bright**
4. **sight**

Write two words from the box that rhyme with **cry.**

5. **sky**
6. **try**

| because | whole |

Write the word from the box that fits in each puzzle.

7. | b | e | c | a | u | s | e |
8. | w | h | o | l | e |

Notes for Home: Your child spelled words with the long *i* sound spelled *igh, y,* and *i-consonant-e (bright, try,* and *line)* and two frequently used words: *because, whole.* **Home Activity:** Have your child sort the long *i* words according to their long *i* spellings.

126 Spelling: Long *i: igh, y, i-e*

Level 2.1

Grammar Practice Book 2.1, p. 13

Name _____

Eye Spy
Seeing

RETEACHING

Why does Brian go to Littletown?

Pepper gets a checkup from Dr. Williams.

Proper nouns are special names for people, animals, things, and places. They begin with capital letters.
Titles for people begin with capital letters. Most titles end with a period.

Circle each proper noun that should begin with a capital letter.
Circle two proper nouns in each sentence.

1. (wayne crane) lives in the state of (maine).
2. He got his dog, (nick), in the city of (brunswick).
3. His sister (pat) has a cat called (matt).

Write a title or titles from the box in each sentence.

| Ms. | Mr. | Mrs. | Miss | Dr. |

Possible answers given.

4. Today a neighbor, **Miss** Ann Blatt, watches Matt.

5. **Mr.** and **Mrs.** Crane take sick Nick to **Dr.** Moore.

6. **Ms.** Susan Ko works for **Dr.** Moore.

Notes for Home: Your child identified and capitalized proper nouns and titles for people. **Home Activity:** Have your child show you his or her work on this page. Ask your child why each proper noun is capitalized.

Grammar: Proper Nouns **127**

Answers **305**

Circle each title and proper noun that should have a capital letter.

1. My team doctor on our basketball team is (dr. john)
2. My teacher, (mrs. romero), likes him too.
3. My neighbor, (mr. roth), gave our team a pet dog.
4. Its name is (miss sunflower).

Correct each title and proper noun and write it.

5. **Dr. John**
6. **Mrs. Romero**
7. **Mr. Roth**
8. **Miss Sunflower**

Write a proper noun that names someone you know.

Possible answers given.

9. your teacher **Mrs. Long**
10. your friend **Debbie**
11. a pet **Whiskers**

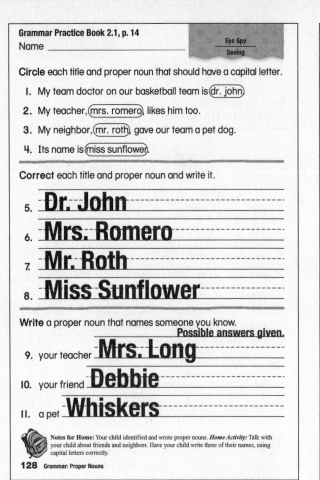

Notes for Home: Your child identified and wrote proper nouns. **Home Activity:** Talk with your child about friends and neighbors. Have your child write three of their names, using capital letters correctly.

Say each word.
Circle 7 words that have the same vowel sound as **shirt**.
Write these words on the lines.

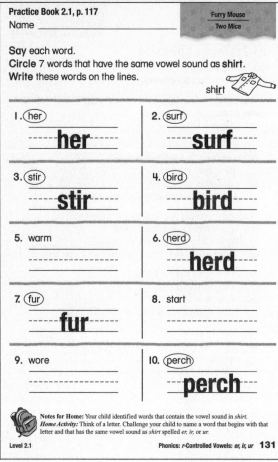

shirt

1. (her)   **her**
2. (surf)   **surf**
3. (stir)   **stir**
4. (bird)   **bird**
5. warm
6. (herd)   **herd**
7. (fur)   **fur**
8. start
9. wore
10. (perch)   **perch**

Notes for Home: Your child identified words that contain the vowel sound in *shirt*. **Home Activity:** Think of a letter. Challenge your child to name a word that begins with that letter and that has the same vowel sound as *shirt* spelled *er, ir,* or *ur.*

---

cats   boxes   babies

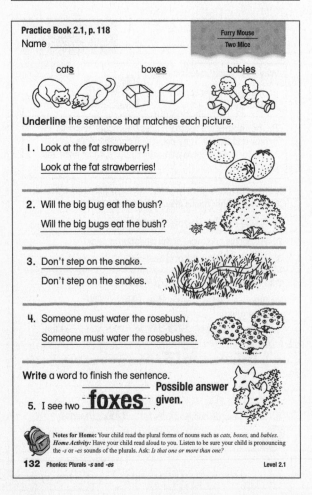

Underline the sentence that matches each picture.

1. Look at the fat strawberry!
   <u>Look at the fat strawberries!</u>

2. <u>Will the big bug eat the bush?</u>
   Will the big bugs eat the bush?

3. <u>Don't step on the snake.</u>
   Don't step on the snakes.

4. Someone must water the rosebush.
   <u>Someone must water the rosebushes.</u>

Write a word to finish the sentence.

Possible answer given.

5. I see two **foxes**

Notes for Home: Your child read the plural forms of nouns such as *cats, boxes,* and *babies.* **Home Activity:** Have your child read aloud to you. Listen to be sure your child is pronouncing the *-s* or *-es* sounds of the plurals. Ask: *Is that one or more than one?*

Pick a word from the box to finish each sentence.
Write the word on the line.

| almost | another | around | food | under |

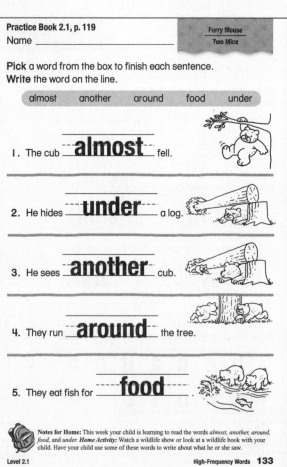

1. The cub **almost** fell.
2. He hides **under** a log.
3. He sees **another** cub.
4. They run **around** the tree.
5. They eat fish for **food**

Notes for Home: This week your child is learning to read the words *almost, another, around, food,* and *under.* **Home Activity:** Watch a wildlife show or look at a wildlife book with your child. Have your child use some of these words to write about what he or she saw.

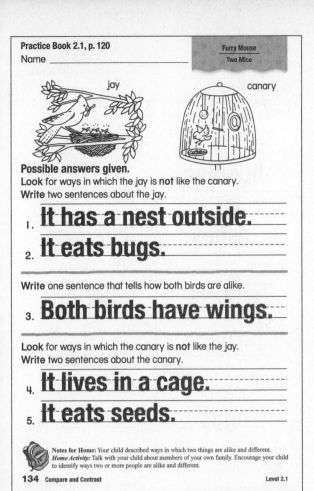

jay

canary

Possible answers given.
Look for ways in which the jay is **not** like the canary.
Write two sentences about the jay.

1. **It has a nest outside.**

2. **It eats bugs.**

Write one sentence that tells how both birds are alike.

3. **Both birds have wings.**

Look for ways in which the canary is **not** like the jay.
Write two sentences about the canary.

4. **It lives in a cage.**

5. **It eats seeds.**

Notes for Home: Your child described ways in which two things are alike and different. *Home Activity:* Talk with your child about members of your own family. Encourage your child to identify ways two or more people are alike and different.

Write the word for each picture.
Add -s or -es if the picture shows more than one.
Use the words in the box to help you.

| ant | cherry | dish | peach | spoon |

1. **spoon**

2. **peaches**

3. **ant**

4. **dishes**

5. **cherries**

Notes for Home: Your child used pictures to write singular and plural nouns. *Home Activity:* Have your child help you write grocery shopping lists. Ask your child to identify which words name one and which name more than one.

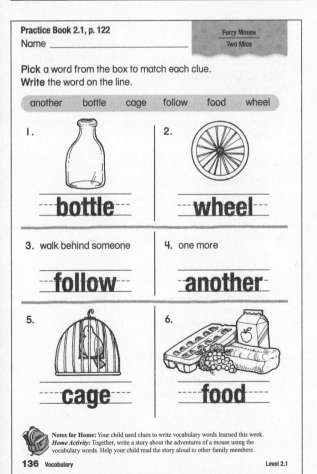

Pick a word from the box to match each clue.
Write the word on the line.

| another | bottle | cage | follow | food | wheel |

1. **bottle**

2. **wheel**

3. walk behind someone

follow

4. one more

another

5. **cage**

6. **food**

Notes for Home: Your child used clues to write vocabulary words learned this week. *Home Activity:* Together, write a story about the adventures of a mouse using the vocabulary words. Help your child read the story aloud to other family members.

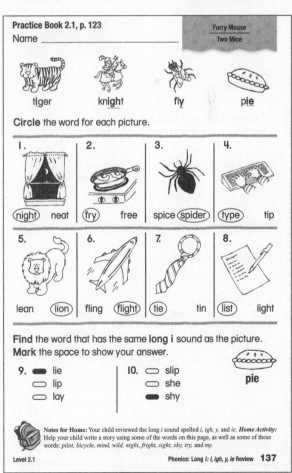

tiger   kn**igh**t   fl**y**   p**ie**

Circle the word for each picture.

1. (night)   neat

2. (fry)   free

3. spice (spider)

4. (type)   tip

5. lean (lion)

6. fling (flight)

7. (tie)   tin

8. (list)   light

Find the word that has the same **long i** sound as the picture.
Mark the space to show your answer.

9. ● lie
   ○ lip
   ○ lay

10. ○ slip
    ○ she
    ● shy

pie

Notes for Home: Your child reviewed the long *i* sound spelled *i, igh, y,* and *ie. Home Activity:* Help your child write a story using some of the words on this page, as well as some of these words: *pilot, bicycle, mind, wild, night, fright, sight, sky, try,* and *my.*

baby babies bunny bunnies friend friends

Read the words above each column.
Write the words from the box in the correct column.

Names One	Names More Than One
1. **baby**	2. **babies**
3. **bunny**	4. **bunnies**
5. **friend**	6. **friends**

Pick a word from the box to match each clue.
Write the word on the line.

7. one pal

friend

8. two rabbits

bunnies

Pick a word from the box to finish each sentence.
Write the word on the line.

another   food

9. Carrots are **food** that bunnies like to eat.

10. They will always eat **another** carrot.

Notes for Home: Your child spelled singular and plural nouns, such as *baby* and *babies,* and two frequently used words: *another, food.* **Home Activity:** Help your child make a list of his or her favorite things. Some of the words on the list should be singular, and others plural.

138 Spelling: Plurals

Level 2.1

Look at the picture.
Circle the word next to the picture if you see just one.
Write a plural word if you see more than one.

1. bunny	2. (bus)
bunnies	
3. dish	4. cherry
dishes	**cherries**
5. wheel	6. light
wheels	**lights**
7. (boy)	8. box
	boxes
9. egg	10. (brush)
eggs	

Notes for Home: Your child identified singular and plural nouns. **Home Activity:** Help your child make a list of the objects in a refrigerator, closet, or drawer. Discuss which plural nouns end in *-s* and which end in *-es.*

Level 2.1

Grammar: Singular and Plural Nouns **139**

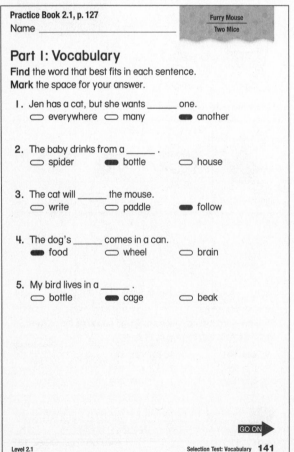

Part 1: Vocabulary

Find the word that best fits in each sentence.
Mark the space for your answer.

1. Jen has a cat, but she wants _____ one.
   ○ everywhere ○ many ● another

2. The baby drinks from a _____ .
   ○ spider ● bottle ○ house

3. The cat will _____ the mouse.
   ○ write ○ paddle ● follow

4. The dog's _____ comes in a can.
   ● food ○ wheel ○ brain

5. My bird lives in a _____ .
   ○ bottle ● cage ○ beak

GO ON

Level 2.1

Selection Test: Vocabulary **141**

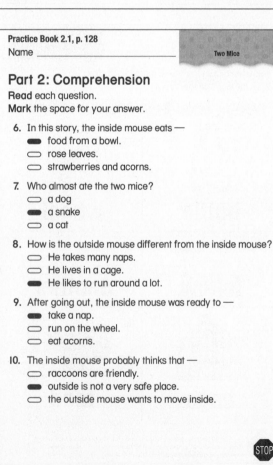

Part 2: Comprehension

Read each question.
Mark the space for your answer.

6. In this story, the inside mouse eats —
   ● food from a bowl.
   ○ rose leaves.
   ○ strawberries and acorns.

7. Who almost ate the two mice?
   ○ a dog
   ● a snake
   ○ a cat

8. How is the outside mouse different from the inside mouse?
   ○ He takes many naps.
   ○ He lives in a cage.
   ● He likes to run around a lot.

9. After going out, the inside mouse was ready to —
   ● take a nap.
   ○ run on the wheel.
   ○ eat acorns.

10. The inside mouse probably thinks that —
    ○ raccoons are friendly.
    ● outside is not a very safe place.
    ○ the outside mouse wants to move inside.

STOP

142 Selection Test: Comprehension

Level 2.1

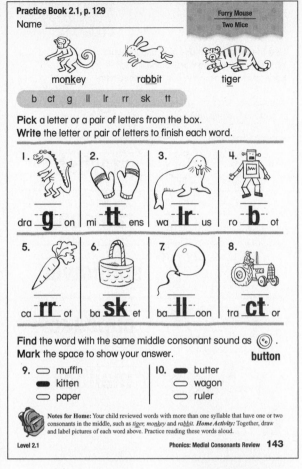

monkey   rabbit   tiger

| b | ct | g | ll | lr | rr | sk | tt |

Pick a letter or a pair of letters from the box.
Write the letter or pair of letters to finish each word.

1. dra **g** on
2. mi **tt** ens
3. wa **lr** us
4. ro **b** ot
5. ca **rr** ot
6. ba **sk** et
7. ba **ll** oon
8. tra **ct** or

Find the word with the same middle consonant sound as ⊙ .
Mark the space to show your answer.

button

9. ○ muffin
   ● kitten
   ○ paper

10. ● butter
    ○ wagon
    ○ ruler

Notes for Home: Your child reviewed words with more than one syllable that have one or two consonants in the middle, such as *tiger*, *monkey* and *rabbit*. **Home Activity:** Together, draw and label pictures of each word above. Practice reading these words aloud.

Level 2.1   Phonics: Medial Consonants Review   **143**

| baby | babies | bunny | bunnies | friend | friends |

Pick a word from the box to finish the math sentence.
Write the word on the line.

1. 👶 + 👶 = 2   **babies**
2. 🧍 + 🧍 = 2   **friends**
3. 🐰 + 🐰 = 3   **bunnies**
4. 🐰🐰🐰 🐰 = 1   **bunny**

Write the word from the box that rhymes with each word below.

5. bend   **friend**
6. maybe   **baby**

Pick a word from the box to match each clue.
Write the word on the line.

| another | food |

7. something to eat   **food**
8. one more   **another**

Notes for Home: Your child spelled singular and plural nouns (*baby* and *babies*) and two frequently used words: *another*, *food*. **Home Activity:** Have your child draw and label pictures of these words: *ponies*, *dog*, *snakes*, and *zebra*.

144   Spelling: Plurals   Level 2.1

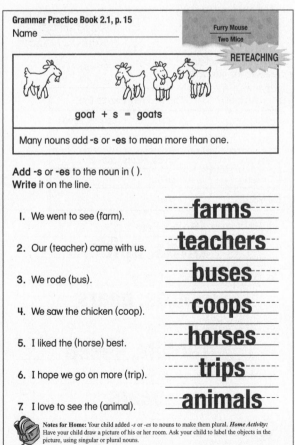

RETEACHING

goat + s = goats

Many nouns add **-s** or **-es** to mean more than one.

Add -s or **-es** to the noun in ( ).
Write it on the line.

1. We went to see (farm).   **farms**
2. Our (teacher) came with us.   **teachers**
3. We rode (bus).   **buses**
4. We saw the chicken (coop).   **coops**
5. I liked the (horse) best.   **horses**
6. I hope we go on more (trip).   **trips**
7. I love to see the (animal).   **animals**

Notes for Home: Your child added *-s* or *-es* to nouns to make them plural. **Home Activity:** Have your child draw a picture of his or her room. Ask your child to label the objects in the picture, using singular or plural nouns.

Grammar: Singular and Plural Nouns   **145**

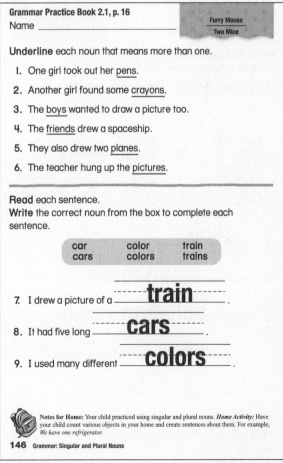

Underline each noun that means more than one.

1. One girl took out her <u>pens</u>.
2. Another girl found some <u>crayons</u>.
3. The <u>boys</u> wanted to draw a picture too.
4. The <u>friends</u> drew a spaceship.
5. They also drew two <u>planes</u>.
6. The teacher hung up the <u>pictures</u>.

Read each sentence.
Write the correct noun from the box to complete each sentence.

| car | color | train |
| cars | colors | trains |

7. I drew a picture of a **train** .
8. It had five long **cars** .
9. I used many different **colors** .

Notes for Home: Your child practiced using singular and plural nouns. **Home Activity:** Have your child count various objects in your home and create sentences about them. For example, *We have one refrigerator.*

146   Grammar: Singular and Plural Nouns

Circle the word in each row with the **long o** sound.
Write the word on the line.

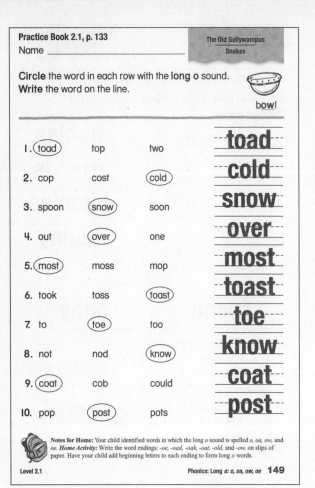
bowl

1. (toad)   top   two
2. cop   cost   (cold)
3. spoon   (snow)   soon
4. out   (over)   one
5. (most)   moss   mop
6. took   toss   (toast)
7. to   (toe)   too
8. not   nod   (know)
9. (coat)   cob   could
10. pop   (post)   pots

toad
cold
snow
over
most
toast
toe
know
coat
post

Notes for Home: Your child identified words in which the long o sound is spelled o, oa, ow, and oe. Home Activity: Write the word endings: -oe, -oad, -oak, -oat, -old, and -ow, on slips of paper. Have your child add beginning letters to each ending to form long o words.

Use the pictures to make a compound word.
Write the compound word on the line.
Look at the words in the box if you need help.

cupcake mailbox raincoat
starfish sunflower

rattlesnake

1. ☆ + 🐟 = **starfish**
2. 🌧 + 🧥 = **raincoat**
3. ☀ + 🌻 = **sunflower**
4. ☕ + 🍰 = **cupcake**
5. ✉ + 📦 = **mailbox**

Notes for Home: Your child formed compound words—words that are made up of two smaller words. Home Activity: Have fun with your child making up picture puzzles for other compound words, such as toothbrush.

Pick a word from the box to finish each sentence.
Write the word on the line.

animals   before   between   knew   Why

1. **Why** did you jump back?
2. I saw some strange **animals**.
3. They were **between** the rock and the dirt.
4. I **knew** snakes lived under rocks.
5. But I've never seen one **before**!

Notes for Home: This week your child is learning to read the words animals, before, between, knew, and why. Home Activity: Read and discuss a book about reptiles with your child. Encourage your child to write a few sentences about the book, using some of these words.

Read the table.
Answer the questions.

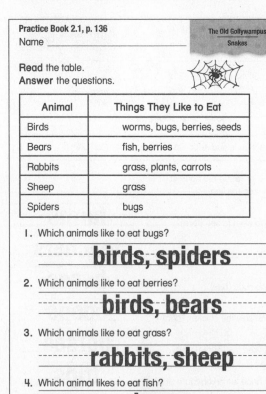

Animal	Things They Like to Eat
Birds	worms, bugs, berries, seeds
Bears	fish, berries
Rabbits	grass, plants, carrots
Sheep	grass
Spiders	bugs

1. Which animals like to eat bugs?
   birds, spiders
2. Which animals like to eat berries?
   birds, bears
3. Which animals like to eat grass?
   rabbits, sheep
4. Which animal likes to eat fish?
   bears

Notes for Home: Your child read a table and used information in it to answer questions. Home Activity: Help your child make a table that tells something about family members, such as favorite foods, songs, or colors.

310   Answers

Name _____

Some **nouns** change to a different word to name more than one.

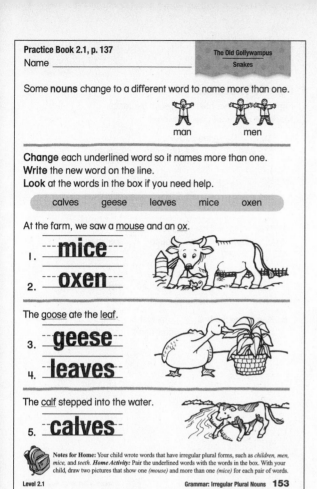

man   men

Change each underlined word so it names more than one.
Write the new word on the line.
Look at the words in the box if you need help.

calves   geese   leaves   mice   oxen

At the farm, we saw a <u>mouse</u> and an <u>ox</u>.

1. **mice**

2. **oxen**

The <u>goose</u> ate the <u>leaf</u>.

3. **geese**

4. **leaves**

The <u>calf</u> stepped into the water.

5. **calves**

Notes for Home: Your child wrote words that have irregular plural forms, such as *children, men, mice,* and *teeth*. Home Activity: Pair the underlined words with the words in the box. With your child, draw two pictures that show one *(mouse)* and more than one *(mice)* for each pair of words.

Level 2.1   Grammar: Irregular Plural Nouns **153**

Name _____

Circle a word to finish each sentence.

between   enemy   medicine
peels   scales   underneath

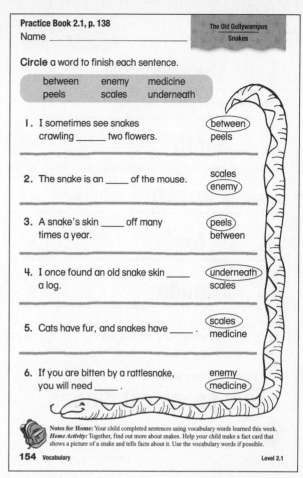

1. I sometimes see snakes crawling _____ two flowers.   (between) / peels

2. The snake is an _____ of the mouse.   scales / (enemy)

3. A snake's skin _____ off many times a year.   (peels) / between

4. I once found an old snake skin _____ a log.   (underneath) / scales

5. Cats have fur, and snakes have _____ .   (scales) / medicine

6. If you are bitten by a rattlesnake, you will need _____ .   enemy / (medicine)

Notes for Home: Your child completed sentences using vocabulary words learned this week. Home Activity: Together, find out more about snakes. Help your child make a fact card that shows a picture of a snake and tells facts about it. Use the vocabulary words if possible.

154 Vocabulary   Level 2.1

Name _____

fern   bird   surf

Circle the word for each picture.

1. (turtle) / towel
2. short / (shirt)
3. (herd) / hard
4. (hurt) / hut

5. (dirt) / drift
6. nose / (nurse)
7. desk / (dessert)
8. (clerk) / clock

Find the word that has the same vowel sound as the picture.
Mark the space to show your answer.

9. ○ trunk   10. ○ here
   ● first   ● her   skirt
   ○ near   ○ horse

Notes for Home: Your child reviewed words with *er, ir,* and *ur* that have the same vowel sound *(fern, bird,* and *surf)*. Home Activity: Use some of the following words to write sentences for your child to read aloud: *germ, herd, her, bird, chirp, dirt, burn, burst, purse.*

Level 2.1   Phonics: r-Controlled Vowels: er, ir, ur Review **155**

Name _____

sold   woke   coat   soap   below   owe

Write the word from the box that rhymes with each word below.

1. toe   2. rope

   owe   **soap**

3. throat   4. cold

   coat   **sold**

Pick a word from the box that is the opposite of each word below.
Write the word on the line.

5. above   6. slept

   below   **woke**

Pick a word from the box to finish each sentence.
Write the word on the line.

animals
between

7. Some **animals** sleep when it is winter.

8. One sleeps **between** two rocks.

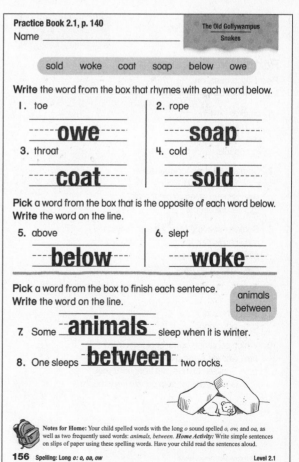

Notes for Home: Your child spelled words with the long *o* sound spelled *o, ow,* and *oa,* as well as two frequently used words: *animals, between.* Home Activity: Write simple sentences on slips of paper using these spelling words. Have your child read the sentences aloud.

156 Spelling: Long *o: o, oa, ow*   Level 2.1

Answers **311**

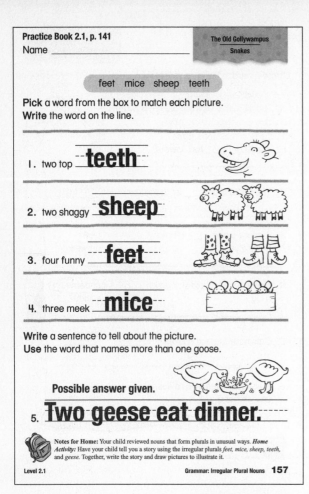

feet   mice   sheep   teeth

Pick a word from the box to match each picture.
Write the word on the line.

1. two top __**teeth**__

2. two shaggy __**sheep**__

3. four funny __**feet**__

4. three meek __**mice**__

Write a sentence to tell about the picture.
Use the word that names more than one goose.

Possible answer given.

5. __Two geese eat dinner.__

Notes for Home: Your child reviewed nouns that form plurals in unusual ways. **Home Activity:** Have your child tell you a story using the irregular plurals *feet, mice, sheep, teeth,* and *geese.* Together, write the story and draw pictures to illustrate it.

Part I: Vocabulary

Find the word that best fits in each sentence.
Mark the space for your answer.

1. We ran _____ the houses.
   ○ with   ● between   ○ so

2. She _____ the banana.
   ● peels   ○ follows   ○ fixes

3. This _____ will help you feel better.
   ○ enemy   ○ ground   ● medicine

4. The snake's _____ are dry.
   ○ beaks   ○ messages   ● scales

5. Ben found the ball _____ his bed.
   ○ there   ● underneath   ○ after

GO ON ▶

Part 2: Comprehension

Read each question.
Mark the space for your answer.

6. Snakes have no —
   ○ eyes.
   ● legs.
   ○ scales.

7. Snakes use their tongues to —
   ○ lick their food.
   ● pick up smells from the air.
   ○ scare people.

8. Snakes "unhook" their jaws so they can —
   ○ chew their food.
   ○ clean their teeth.
   ● open their mouths wide.

9. To tell other animals to stay away, some snakes try to —
   ○ run fast.
   ● look scary.
   ○ sing songs.

10. Which sentence about snakes is true?
    ● Snakes sleep all winter.
    ○ Snakes can see and hear very well.
    ○ Snakes do not help people very much.

STOP

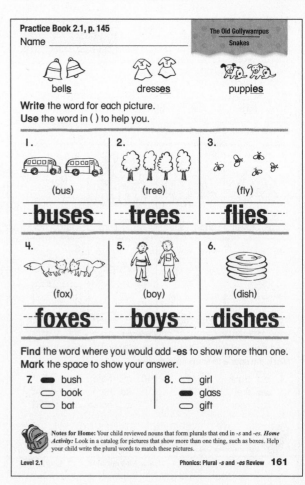

bell**s**   dress**es**   pupp**ies**

Write the word for each picture.
Use the word in ( ) to help you.

1.	2.	3.
(bus)	(tree)	(fly)
__**buses**__	__**trees**__	__**flies**__
4.	5.	6.
(fox)	(boy)	(dish)
__**foxes**__	__**boys**__	__**dishes**__

Find the word where you would add **-es** to show more than one.
Mark the space to show your answer.

7. ● bush   8. ○ girl
   ○ book   ● glass
   ○ bat   ○ gift

Notes for Home: Your child reviewed nouns that form plurals that end in *-s* and *-es.* **Home Activity:** Look in a catalog for pictures that show more than one thing, such as boxes. Help your child write the plural words to match these pictures.

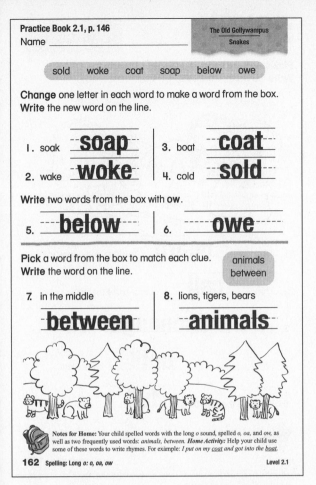

Practice Book 2.1, p. 146

Name _____

The Old Gollywampus
Snakes

sold   woke   coat   soap   below   owe

Change one letter in each word to make a word from the box.
Write the new word on the line.

1. soak **soap**
2. wake **woke**
3. boat **coat**
4. cold **sold**

Write two words from the box with **ow**.

5. **below**
6. **owe**

Pick a word from the box to match each clue.
Write the word on the line.

animals
between

7. in the middle **between**
8. lions, tigers, bears **animals**

Notes for Home: Your child spelled words with the long *o* sound, spelled *o, oa,* and *ow,* as well as two frequently used words: *animals, between.* **Home Activity:** Help your child use some of these words to write rhymes. For example: *I put on my coat and got into the boat.*

162 Spelling: Long *o: o, oa, ow*

Level 2.1

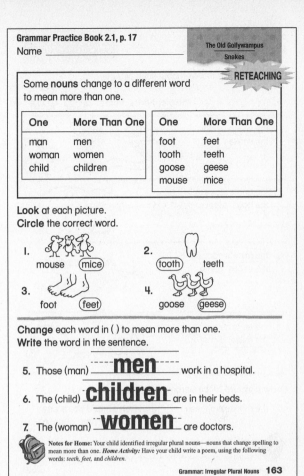

Grammar Practice Book 2.1, p. 17

Name _____

The Old Gollywampus
Snakes

RETEACHING

Some **nouns** change to a different word
to mean more than one.

One	More Than One	One	More Than One
man	men	foot	feet
woman	women	tooth	teeth
child	children	goose	geese
		mouse	mice

Look at each picture.
Circle the correct word.

1. mouse (mice)
2. (tooth) teeth
3. foot (feet)
4. goose (geese)

Change each word in ( ) to mean more than one.
Write the word in the sentence.

5. Those (man) **men** work in a hospital.

6. The (child) **children** are in their beds.

7. The (woman) **women** are doctors.

Notes for Home: Your child identified irregular plural nouns—nouns that change spelling to mean more than one. **Home Activity:** Have your child write a poem, using the following words: *teeth, feet,* and *children.*

Grammar: Irregular Plural Nouns **163**

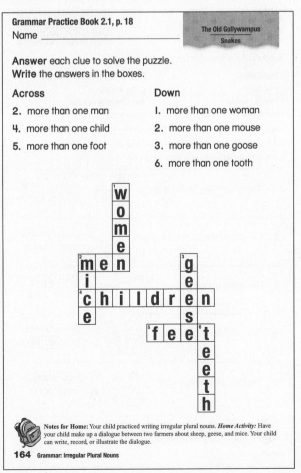

Grammar Practice Book 2.1, p. 18

Name _____

The Old Gollywampus
Snakes

Answer each clue to solve the puzzle.
Write the answers in the boxes.

Across

2. more than one man
4. more than one child
5. more than one foot

Down

1. more than one woman
2. more than one mouse
3. more than one goose
6. more than one tooth

Notes for Home: Your child practiced writing irregular plural nouns. **Home Activity:** Have your child make up a dialogue between two farmers about sheep, geese, and mice. Your child can write, record, or illustrate the dialogue.

164 Grammar: Irregular Plural Nouns

Practice Book 2.1, p. 149

Name _____

Spiders Up Close
Anansi and the Talking Melon

Circle the word for each picture.

mice

1. mouth (mouse)
2. (cheese) cheap
3. (ice) ink
4. (cage) case
5. nice (nose)
6. (page) place

Draw a picture of each word.

7. house

**Children's drawings
should show a house.**

8. face

**Children's drawings
should show a face.**

Notes for Home: Your child practiced using words that end in *ce, ge,* and *se.* **Home Activity:** Give your child practice with words that end in *-ace, -ice, -uce, -aise, -ease, -eese, -ose, -ouse,* and words that end in *-ge,* such as *cage.* Take turns writing and reading rhyming pairs of these words.

Level 2.1

Phonics: Words with *ce, ge, se* **167**

Answers **313**

Circle the words that tell about each picture.

the **elephants'** trunks

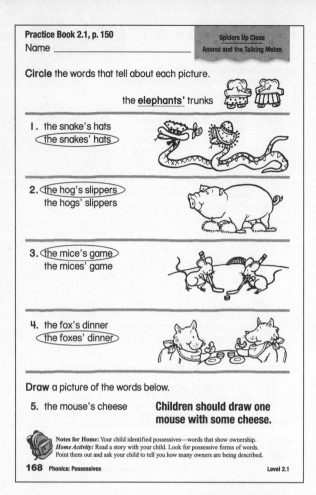

1. the snake's hats
   (The snakes' hats)

2. (The hog's slippers)
   the hogs' slippers

3. (The mice's game)
   the mices' game

4. the fox's dinner
   (The foxes' dinner)

Draw a picture of the words below.

5. the mouse's cheese   **Children should draw one mouse with some cheese.**

Notes for Home: Your child identified possessives—words that show ownership. *Home Activity:* Read a story with your child. Look for possessive forms of words. Point them out and ask your child to tell you how many owners are being described.

Pick a word from the box to finish each sentence.
Write the word on the line.

call   enough   full   heard   until

1. All day we ___**heard**___ the king and queen yell.

2. They ___**call**___ out for more melons.

3. They can never eat **enough** melons.

4. We picked melons ___**until**___ it was dark.

5. We hope they will be ___**full**___ soon.

Notes for Home: This week your child is learning to read the words *call, enough, full, heard,* and *until. Home Activity:* Help your child use these words to write a story about some talking animals. Encourage your child to read the story to others.

Look at the pictures. Read the sentences.
Write 1, 2, 3, 4 to show the right order.

3 a. Then, he picks up the box.

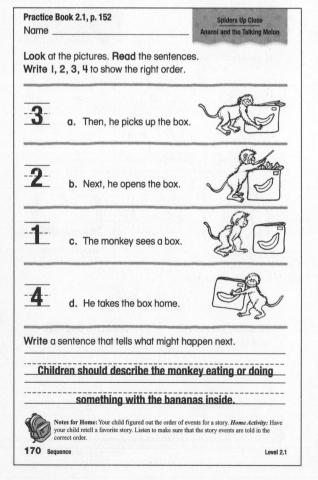

2 b. Next, he opens the box.

1 c. The monkey sees a box.

4 d. He takes the box home.

Write a sentence that tells what might happen next.

**Children should describe the monkey eating or doing**

**something with the bananas inside.**

Notes for Home: Your child figured out the order of events for a story. *Home Activity:* Have your child retell a favorite story. Listen to make sure that the story events are told in the correct order.

A noun can show who owns something.

One Owner
girl**'s** bike
Chris**'s** melon
man**'s** car

More Than One Owner
girls**'** bikes
the Cross**'s** house
men**'s** cars

Circle the words that tell who owns what.
Use the underlined words to help you.

1. The spiders are having a party.   spider's party
   (spiders' party)

2. The geese are carrying a melon.   (geese's melon)
   geese' melon

3. The hippo brings pies.   (hippo's pies)
   hippos' pies

4. The princes wear big hats.   prince's hats
   (princes' hats)

5. The toad sings a silly song.   (toad's song)
   toads' song

Notes for Home: Your child identified singular and plural possessives—words that show who owns something. *Home Activity:* Using possessives (*Bob's bed, dogs' bowls*), take turns with your child making up sentences that tell who owns what in your home.

314 Answers

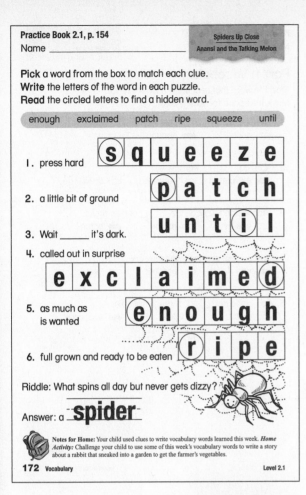

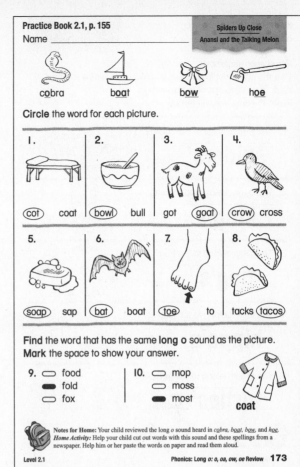

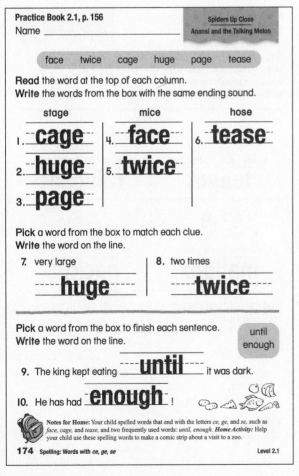

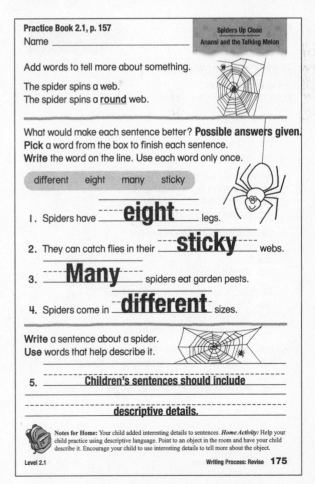

Answers **315**

Spiders Up Close
Anansi and the Talking Melon

Read each sentence.
Use the two underlined words to show who owns each thing.
Add 's or ' to one of the words.
Write the new word on the line.

1. The <u>web</u> belongs to the <u>spiders</u>.

spiders' web

2. The <u>crown</u> belongs to the <u>king</u>.

king's crown

3. The <u>tusks</u> belong to the <u>hog</u>.

hog's tusks

4. The <u>teeth</u> belong to the <u>hippo</u>.

hippo's teeth

5. The <u>shells</u> belong to the <u>turtles</u>.

turtles' shells

Notes for Home: Your child reviewed writing possessive nouns to show who owns something, such as *the elephant's trunk.* **Home Activity:** Look through a book with your child. Ask your child to write descriptive sentences about the pictures (*The cat's fur is black.*).

Spiders Up Close
Anansi and the Talking Melon

Part I: Vocabulary

Find the word that best fits in each sentence.
Mark the space for your answer.

1. Did you have _____ to eat?
   ○ never   ● enough   ○ until

2. "Oh, no!" _____ Pat.
   ● exclaimed   ○ surprised   ○ drew

3. Please don't walk on the _____ of new grass.
   ○ enemy   ○ mirror   ● patch

4. You can eat melons when they are _____ .
   ● ripe   ○ another   ○ later

5. Len could not _____ through the hole.
   ○ clean   ○ peel   ● squeeze

GO ON ▶

Anansi and the Talking Melon

Part 2: Comprehension

Read each question.
Mark the space for your answer.

6. What did Anansi use to make a hole in the melon?
   ○ a rock
   ○ a spoon
   ● a thorn

7. Anansi could not get out of the melon because —
   ● he was too fat from eating.
   ○ the hole had gotten smaller.
   ○ someone had covered the hole.

8. Which animal did Elephant see first?
   ○ Warthog
   ● Hippo
   ○ Ostrich

9. Why did the king get angry at the melon?
   ● The melon insulted him.
   ○ The melon tasted bad.
   ○ The melon would not talk to him.

10. Why will Elephant **not** take talking bananas to the king?
    ○ He will want to keep the bananas for himself.
    ○ He will want to share the bananas with Anansi.
    ● He will be afraid the bananas will get him in trouble.

STOP

Spiders Up Close
Anansi and the Talking Melon

Say the word for each picture.
Use two words to make a compound word that stands for the picture.
Write the compound word on the line.

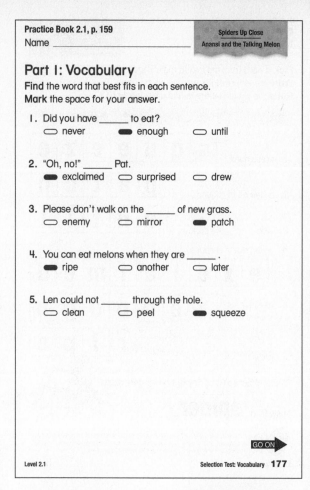 wart + hog = warthog

1. spoon pot table tea

teapot

2. coat shoes rain snow

raincoat

3. air box mail plane

mailbox

4. neck shoe lace tie

necktie

Find the word that you can put together with *meal* to make a compound word.
Mark the space to show your answer.

5. _____ meal
   ○ dinner
   ● oat
   ○ book

6. meal _____
   ● time
   ○ spoon
   ○ napkin

Notes for Home: Your child reviewed compound words—words that are made up of two smaller words, such as *warthog.* **Home Activity:** With your child, use the words listed above to make up other compound words such as *teaspoon* or *snowshoes.*

face   twice   cage   huge   page   tease

Change one or two letters in each word to make a word from the box. **Possible answers given.**
Write the new word on the line.

1. please **tease**   2. hugs **huge**

3. pale **page**   4. slice **twice**

Write the word from the box to match each picture.

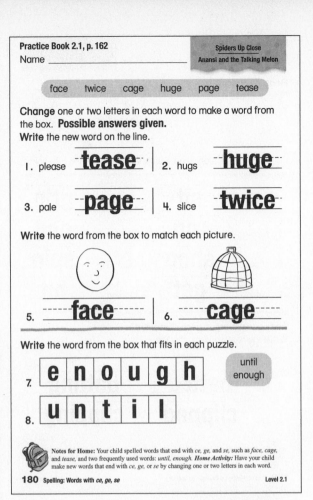

5. **face**   6. **cage**

Write the word from the box that fits in each puzzle.

until
enough

7. | e | n | o | u | g | h |

8. | u | n | t | i | l |

Notes for Home: Your child spelled words that end with *ce*, *ge*, and *se*, such as *face*, *cage*, and *tease*, and two frequently used words: *until*, *enough*. **Home Activity:** Have your child make new words that end with *ce*, *ge*, or *se* by changing one or two letters in each word.

The **flags of the tents** are blowing.
The **tents' flags** are blowing.
Kim holds **the hand of her mother**.
Kim holds **her mother's hand**.
The **'** shows that the flags belong to the tents. The **'s** shows that the hand belongs to the mother.

Many nouns add **'s** or **'** to show ownership.

Match the groups of words that say the same thing in a different way.

1. the face of the clown   a. the elephants' trunks
2. the teeth of the tiger   b. the clown's face
3. the trunks of the elephants   c. the tiger's teeth

Add 's or **'** to each noun in ( ).
Write the noun in the sentence.

4. A (clown) **clown's** nose is red.

5. A (lion) **lion's** roar is loud.

6. The (bears) **bears'** act was fun.

Notes for Home: Your child identified possessive nouns. **Home Activity:** Have your child make two sets of cards, one with people's names and one with names of things. Have him or her pick a card from each pile and write a sentence, using both words. *(This is Jerry's car.)*

Read the story.
Use 's or **'** to write the underlined words in a different way.

The whistle of the train blew. I looked at the watch of my mother. I could not wait to get to the city. The windows of the stores were filled with beautiful things. The eyes of my sister opened wide. We could not see the tops of the buildings. At night we saw the lights of the city. We had a good time!

1. **The train's whistle**

2. **my mother's watch**

3. **The stores' windows**

4. **My sister's eyes**

5. **the buildings' tops**

6. **the city's lights**

Notes for Home: Your child wrote possessive nouns in sentences. **Home Activity:** Ask your child questions about various family members' belongings. For example, *What color is Grandma's car?* Make sure that he or she uses a possessive noun to answer.

One word in each sentence is **not** correct.
Circle the incorrect word.
Write the word correctly on the line.
Hint: Use an **'** to show ownership.

1. Ms. (Goldmans) class is studying insects.

Goldman's

2. An (insects) head is very small.

insect's

3. (Marias) report is about dragonflies.

Maria's

4. (Dragonflies) bodies are long and thin.

Dragonflies'

5. The (class) reports were all interesting.

class's

Notes for Home: Your child used apostrophes to show ownership. **Home Activity:** Make a list of things that belong to members of your family. Help your child use the list to write sentences with possessives to show ownership. (For example: *This is Bill's blue hat.*)

Read each sentence.
Circle the word with the same vowel sound as **cow** or **house**.
Write the word on the line.

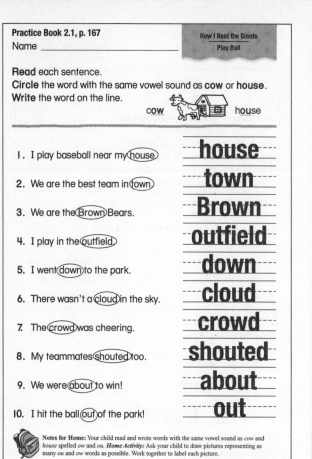

cow   house

1. I play baseball near my (house) **house**

2. We are the best team in (town) **town**

3. We are the (Brown) Bears. **Brown**

4. I play in the (outfield) **outfield**

5. I went (down) to the park. **down**

6. There wasn't a (cloud) in the sky. **cloud**

7. The (crowd) was cheering. **crowd**

8. My teammates (shouted) too. **shouted**

9. We were (about) to win! **about**

10. I hit the ball (out) of the park! **out**

Notes for Home: Your child read and wrote words with the same vowel sound as *cow* and *house* spelled *ow* and *ou*. **Home Activity:** Ask your child to draw pictures representing as many *ou* and *ow* words as possible. Work together to label each picture.

Read each word.
Find the base word.
Write the base word on the line.

stop + -ed = stopp**ed**   hop + -ing = hopp**ing**

1. sitting **sit**   2. gripped **grip**

3. running **run**   4. nodded **nod**

5. shopped **shop**   6. spinning **spin**

7. getting **get**   8. hitting **hit**

Add -ed and **-ing** to each base word.
Write the new words on the line.

     + -ed   + -ing

9. bat **batted** **batting**

10. clip **clipped** **clipping**

Notes for Home: Your child read and wrote words whose final consonants are doubled before adding the endings *-ed* and *-ing*. **Home Activity:** Read a story together. Ask your child to point out words with *-ed* and *-ing* that have had their final consonants doubled.

Pick a word from the box to finish each sentence.
Write the word on the line.

| been | friends | show | since | those |

1. Tom and I are best **friends**

2. We have **been** pals for a long time.

3. We don't know **those** new boys.

4. They have only lived here **since** last night.

5. We will **show** them how to play!

Notes for Home: This week your child is learning to read the words *been, friends, show, since,* and *those.* **Home Activity:** Encourage your child to write sentences about his or her best friend using these words.

Read the story.
Answer the questions.

A New Bike for Matt

Matt had a bike. He rode his bike all over.

One day, Matt left his bike out. The next day, the bike was gone!

Matt wanted a new bike.

He did extra chores around the house. He cut the grass. Soon Matt had enough money.

Matt's dad was proud. Matt got his new bike. Now Matt always puts it in a safe place!

1. What did Matt want? **Possible answers given.**

He wanted a new bike.

2. Why did he want it?

His bike was taken.

3. What did he do to get it?

He did extra chores to make money.

Notes for Home: Your child summarized what happened in a story. **Home Activity:** Watch a video or TV show with your child. Encourage your child to summarize what happened in the story in a few sentences.

A **verb** is a word that can show action.
Sandy <u>kicks</u> the ball.
Kicks is a verb.

Circle the verb in each sentence.

1. Ann (hits) the ball.

2. She (runs) to first base.

3. Deb (throws) the ball to Ken.

4. He (catches) the ball.

5. Ann (gets) there just in time.

Notes for Home: Your child identified verbs that are action words. *Home Activity:* Read a story with your child. Encourage your child to point out the action words. Make a list of these words and continue adding to it as you and your child read other stories.

Level 2.1

Grammar: Verbs **191**

Pick a word from the box to match each clue.
Write the word on the line.

baseball	friend	pitching	returned
since	terrible	those	

1. pal

friend

2. the ones over there

those

3. throwing a ball to a batter

pitching

4. gave back

returned

5. awful

terrible

6. game played with a bat and ball

baseball

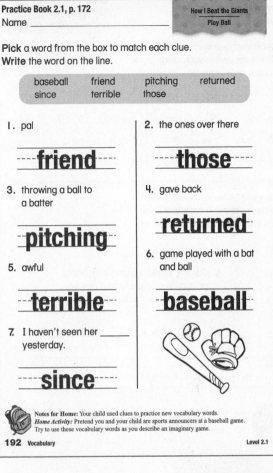

7. I haven't seen her _____ yesterday.

since

Notes for Home: Your child used clues to practice new vocabulary words. *Home Activity:* Pretend you and your child are sports announcers at a baseball game. Try to use these vocabulary words as you describe an imaginary game.

192 Vocabulary

Level 2.1

---

fence   stage   house   nose

Circle the word for each picture.

1. (mouse) moth

2. (face) fact

3. (rose) rope

4. cake (cage)

5. eyes (ice)

6. (rack) race

7. (orange) order

8. (blouse) blue

Find the word that has the same ending sound as the picture.
Mark the space to show your answer.

9. ○ host
   ● hose
   ○ hotel

10. ○ test
    ○ taste
    ● tease

nose

Notes for Home: Your child reviewed words that end in *ce, ge,* and *se. Home Activity:* Write *fence, stage, house,* and *nose* in a row across the top of a sheet of paper. Encourage your child to think of at least two more words that have the same ending sound as each word.

Level 2.1

Phonics: Words with *ce, ge, se* Review **193**

---

hugged hugging nodded nodding skipped skipping

Add -ed or **-ing** to each word below to make a word from the box.
Write the new word on the line.

	Add -ed		Add -ing
hug	1. **hugged**	2.	**hugging**
nod	3. **nodded**	4.	**nodding**
skip	5. **skipped**	6.	**skipping**

Pick a word from the box to finish each sentence.
Write the word on the line.

7. We are **skipping** rope.

8. Before I left, I **hugged** my friends.

Pick a word from the box to match each clue.
Write the word on the line.

since those

9. not these

those

10. from then until now

since

Notes for Home: Your child practiced spelling words that end with *-ed* and *-ing* and two frequently used words: *since, those. Home Activity:* Have your child use each spelling word in a sentence. Work together to write each sentence.

194 Spelling: Inflected Endings *-ed* and *-ing*

Level 2.1

Read each group of words.
Circle the verb in each group.

1. (sing)   song   son | 2. white   with   (writes)
3. plaid   pail   (played) | 4. (rang)   wrong   runny
5. Chris   (cries)   crust | 6. (cut)   cot   cold
7. buns   (runs)   tons | 8. (read)   real   red

Pick one of the verbs you circled.
Draw a picture to show that verb.
Write a sentence about the picture.

9.

**Children's drawings and sentences
should correctly show and use one
of the verbs circled above.**

10. _____

Notes for Home: Your child practiced identifying verbs that show action. *Home Activity:* Take a walk with your child. Point out people and objects that are doing things. Ask your child to tell you, in a complete sentence, what action they are performing.

Part I: Vocabulary

Find the word that best fits in each sentence.
Mark the space for your answer.

1. Scott hit the _____ hard.
   ⬭ hundred   ⬤ baseball   ⬭ terrible

2. Ken was _____ the ball fast.
   ⬭ going   ⬤ pitching   ⬭ peeling

3. Lina _____ from her trip yesterday.
   ⬤ returned   ⬭ exclaimed   ⬭ followed

4. I will make a cake for you _____ it is your birthday.
   ⬭ after   ⬭ until   ⬤ since

5. I like _____ apples better than these red ones.
   ⬭ terrible   ⬤ those   ⬭ enough

GO ON ➤

Part 2: Comprehension

Read each question.
Mark the space for your answer.

6. When it was Lionel's turn at bat, he —
   ⬭ swung and missed.
   ⬭ threw the ball to Ellen.
   ⬤ hit the ball over the fence.

7. When he heard the crash, Lionel felt —
   ⬤ terrible.
   ⬭ glad.
   ⬭ surprised.

8. Lionel and his friends will —
   ⬭ pay for the broken window.
   ⬤ help Mr. Barrie fix the window.
   ⬭ never play baseball again.

9. Which sentence best tells what happens in this story?
   ⬤ When Lionel breaks a window, all his friends help him.
   ⬭ Max said that he hit the ball over the fence.
   ⬭ Lionel tries to play baseball, but his friends know he is not very good.

10. If Lionel lost his coat, his friends probably would —
    ⬭ tell his parents.
    ⬭ laugh at him.
    ⬤ help him find it.

STOP

Add 's or ' to the word in ( ) to show
who owns something.
Write the new words on the lines below.

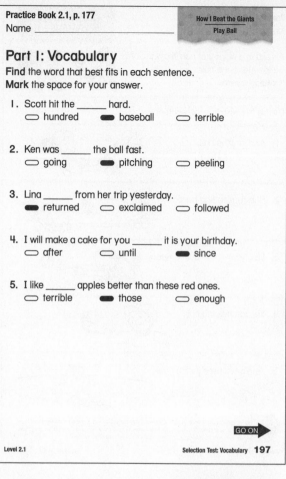
Joe's bat

1. This is my **sister's** cap. (sister)
2. Here are the **girls'** bats. (girls)
3. Here are the **teams'** coaches. (teams)
4. Where is **Jan's** mitt? (Jan)
5. I found the **boys'** missing ball. (boys)
6. How was **Kim's** game? (Kim)

Find the word that shows who owns something.
Mark the space to show your answer.

7.	8.	9.	10.
⬭ crowds	⬭ fan	⬭ girls	⬤ kitten's
⬭ crowd	⬤ fans'	⬭ girl	⬭ kittens
⬤ crowd's	⬭ fans	⬤ girls'	⬭ kitten

Notes for Home: Your child reviewed possessives—words that show ownership or belonging. *Home Activity:* Read a story together. Ask your child to point out any possessive words. Make sure your child can tell the difference between possessive words and contractions.

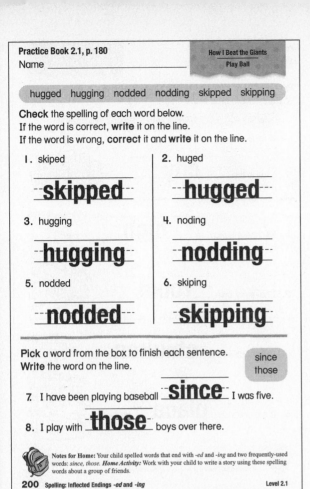

hugged   hugging   nodded   nodding   skipped   skipping

Check the spelling of each word below.
If the word is correct, **write** it on the line.
If the word is wrong, **correct** it and **write** it on the line.

1. skiped

skipped

2. huged

hugged

3. hugging

hugging

4. noding

nodding

5. nodded

nodded

6. skiping

skipping

Pick a word from the box to finish each sentence.
Write the word on the line.

since
those

7. I have been playing baseball **since** I was five.

8. I play with **those** boys over there.

Notes for Home: Your child spelled words that end with -ed and -ing and two frequently-used words: *since, those.* **Home Activity:** Work with your child to write a story using these spelling words about a group of friends.

200 Spelling: Inflected Endings -ed and -ing   Level 2.1

RETEACHING

The children **skip** to the music.

The word **skip** is a verb.
It tells what the children do.

A word that can show action is a **verb**.

Find the verb in each sentence.
Then **write** the verb.

1. The girls dance well.   **dance**

2. They spin around the room.   **spin**

3. All the children look.   **look**

4. Now some boys sing.   **sing**

5. Friends listen to the song.   **listen**

6. They clap loudly.   **clap**

Notes for Home: Your child identified verbs in sentences. **Home Activity:** Watch a television show with your child. Ask him or her to tell you sentences about what people are doing. Write the sentences. Have your child circle the verbs in the sentences.

Grammar: Verbs **201**

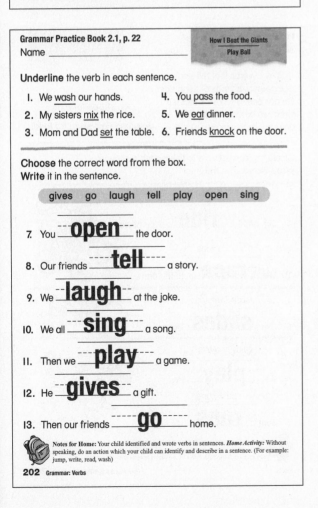

Underline the verb in each sentence.

1. We <u>wash</u> our hands.
2. My sisters <u>mix</u> the rice.
3. Mom and Dad <u>set</u> the table.
4. You <u>pass</u> the food.
5. We <u>eat</u> dinner.
6. Friends <u>knock</u> on the door.

Choose the correct word from the box.
Write it in the sentence.

gives   go   laugh   tell   play   open   sing

7. You **open** the door.
8. Our friends **tell** a story.
9. We **laugh** at the joke.
10. We all **sing** a song.
11. Then we **play** a game.
12. He **gives** a gift.
13. Then our friends **go** home.

Notes for Home: Your child identified and wrote verbs in sentences. **Home Activity:** Without speaking, do an action which your child can identify and describe in a sentence. (For example: jump, write, read, wash)

202 Grammar: Verbs

Circle the word for each picture.

bark

1. pair / **park**
2. **barn** / band
3. **arm** / hair
4. **yarn** / yam
5. hard / **herd**
6. cold / **card**
7. stare / **star**
8. cat / **cart**
9. **car** / care
10. **jar** / jam

Notes for Home: Your child read words that contain the letters *ar* that represent the vowel sound in *car.* **Home Activity:** Name several words that contain *ar.* Challenge your child to think of a word that rhymes with each one.

Level 2.1   Phonics: r-Controlled Vowels: ar **205**

Name _____

Add the ending to each word.
Write the new word on the line.

bake   bak**ed**   bak**ing**

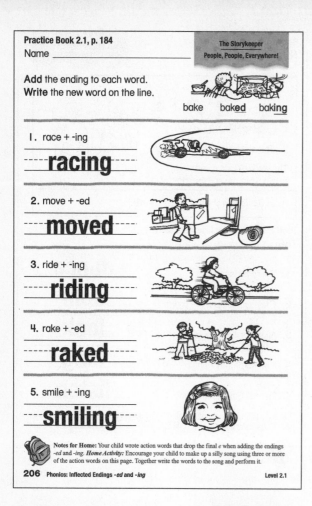

1. race + -ing

racing

2. move + -ed

moved

3. ride + -ing

riding

4. rake + -ed

raked

5. smile + -ing

smiling

Notes for Home: Your child wrote action words that drop the final *e* when adding the endings *-ed* and *-ing*. *Home Activity:* Encourage your child to make up a silly song using three or more of the action words on this page. Together write the words to the song and perform it.

Name _____

Pick a word from the box to finish each sentence.
Write the word on the line.

children   city   high   place   room

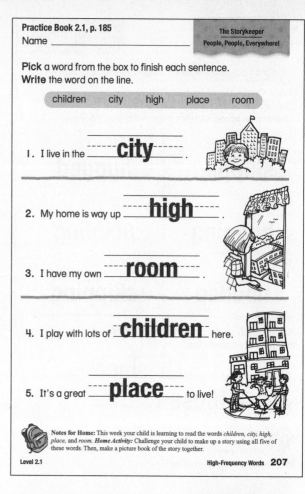

1. I live in the **city** .

2. My home is way up **high** .

3. I have my own **room**

4. I play with lots of **children** here.

5. It's a great **place** to live!

Notes for Home: This week your child is learning to read the words *children, city, high, place,* and *room*. *Home Activity:* Challenge your child to make up a story using all five of these words. Then, make a picture book of the story together.

Name _____

Look at the picture.
Read the sentence with the underlined word.
Pick the word from the box to finish the second sentence.
Write the word on the line.

boat   car   cried   run   sells

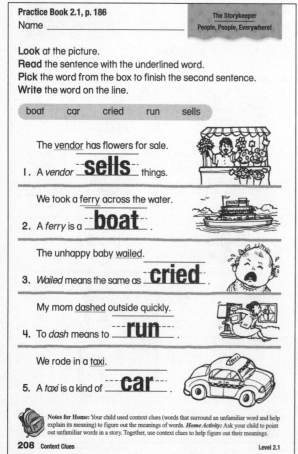

The <u>vendor</u> has flowers for sale.

1. A *vendor* **sells** things.

We took a <u>ferry</u> across the water.

2. A *ferry* is a **boat** .

The unhappy baby <u>wailed</u>.

3. *Wailed* means the same as **cried** .

My mom <u>dashed</u> outside quickly.

4. To *dash* means to **run** .

We rode in a <u>taxi</u>.

5. A *taxi* is a kind of **car** .

Notes for Home: Your child used context clues (words that surround an unfamiliar word and help explain its meaning) to figure out the meanings of words. *Home Activity:* Ask your child to point out unfamiliar words in a story. Together, use context clues to help figure out their meanings.

Name _____

Add **-s** to verbs that tell what one person, animal, or thing does.
Do **not** add **-s** to verbs that tell what two or more people, animals, or things do.

Dad **shops** for food.

Sally and Pam **shop** for food.

Circle the correct verb to finish each sentence.
Write the verb on the line.

1. Jim and I (ride) rides **ride** our bikes.

2. We (race) races **race** to the park.

3. Jim slide (slides) **slides** down.

4. We (play) plays **play** tag.

5. Tom run (runs) **runs** to tag me.

Notes for Home: Your child chose verbs that agree with a singular or plural subject. *Home Activity:* Say a verb aloud to your child. Help him or her use the verb correctly in a sentence to tell about the action of one person or more than one person.

Pick a word from the box to match each clue.
Write the word on the line.

| children | city | country | dashing |
| high | place | room | sealing |

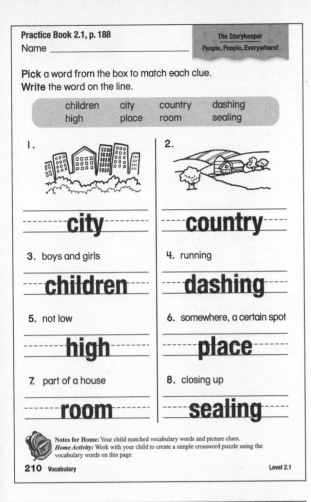

1. **city**

2. **country**

3. boys and girls
children

4. running
dashing

5. not low
high

6. somewhere, a certain spot
place

7. part of a house
room

8. closing up
sealing

Notes for Home: Your child matched vocabulary words and picture clues.
Home Activity: Work with your child to create a simple crossword puzzle using the vocabulary words on this page.

flowers   house

Circle the word for each picture.

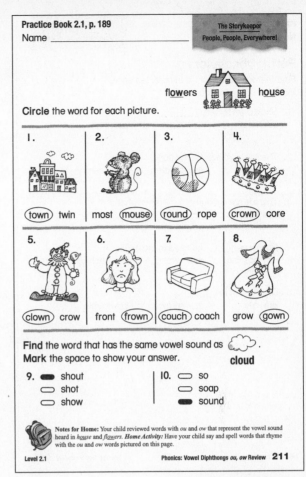

1. (town) twin
2. most (mouse)
3. (round) rope
4. (crown) core

5. (clown) crow
6. front (frown)
7. (couch) coach
8. grow (gown)

Find the word that has the same vowel sound as ☁.
Mark the space to show your answer.

cloud

9. ● shout
   ○ shot
   ○ show

10. ○ so
    ○ soap
    ● sound

Notes for Home: Your child reviewed words with *ou* and *ow* that represent the vowel sound heard in *house* and *flowers*. **Home Activity:** Have your child say and spell words that rhyme with the *ou* and *ow* words pictured on this page.

| arm barn farm hard park start |

Write two words from the box that rhyme with **harm**.

1. **arm**   2. **farm**

Pick a word from the box that rhymes with each word below.
Write the word on the line.

3. yarn **barn**   4. part **start**

5. card **hard**   6. dark **park**

Pick a word that is the opposite of each word below.
Write the word on the line.

7. soft **hard**   8. stop **start**

Pick a word from the box to match each clue.   city   place
Write the word on the line.

9. It rhymes with *face*. **place**

10. It is a very large town. **city**

Notes for Home: Your child spelled words with the *r*-controlled vowel *ar* where the letter *r* changes the vowel sound, as well as two frequently used words: *city*, *place*. **Home Activity:** Work with your child to write simple rhymes using these spelling words.

Pick a verb from the box to finish each sentence.
Write the verb on the line.

| jump reads rings walk works |

1. The girls **jump** rope.

2. Mom **works** at home.

3. Tom **reads** a book.

4. The phone **rings** .

5. They **walk** to school.

Notes for Home: Your child practiced using verbs in sentences. **Home Activity:** Read a magazine or newspaper with your child. Ask him or her to identify the verb in each sentence.

Part 1: Vocabulary

Find the word that best fits in each sentence.
Mark the space for your answer.

1. My kite will fly very _____ .
   ○ ripe   ○ place   ● high

2. The _____ played in the park.
   ○ wheel   ● children   ○ country

3. There is not enough _____ for all of us.
   ● room   ○ bottle   ○ patch

4. Rose was _____ the leaks in the house.
   ○ dashing   ● sealing   ○ pitching

5. Dick lives in the _____ .
   ● city   ○ surface   ○ thumb

GO ON

Part 2: Comprehension

Read each question.
Mark the space for your answer.

6. In this story, people wait in line to —
   ● get on the bus.
   ○ buy tickets.
   ○ eat food.

7. You can tell from the clues in the story that vendors —
   ● sell things.
   ○ clean the streets.
   ○ ride in cars.

8. You can tell that the people in this story are very —
   ● busy.
   ○ tired.
   ○ happy.

9. How is the country different from the city?
   ○ There are more cars and noise.
   ○ There are more people.
   ● There is more room, and it is quiet.

10. What happens when many people move to the country?
    ○ They do not work.
    ○ They ride in taxis.
    ● The country starts to look like a city.

STOP

Add -ed and **-ing** to each word below.
Write the new words on the lines.

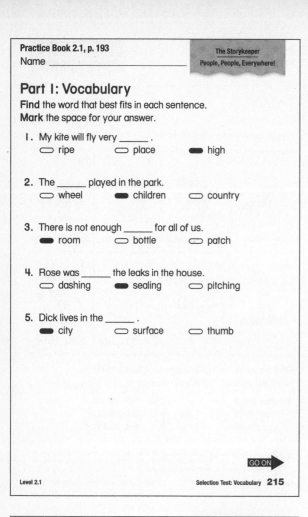

drop dropp**ing** dropp**ed**

	Add -ed		Add -ing
rub	1. **rubbed**	2.	**rubbing**
fix	3. **fixed**	4.	**fixing**
jog	5. **jogged**	6.	**jogging**
hop	7. **hopped**	8.	**hopping**

Find the word where you would double the last consonant before adding **-ed** or **-ing**.
Mark the space to show your answer.

9. ○ help   ● drum   ○ ask
10. ● stop   ○ work   ○ mix

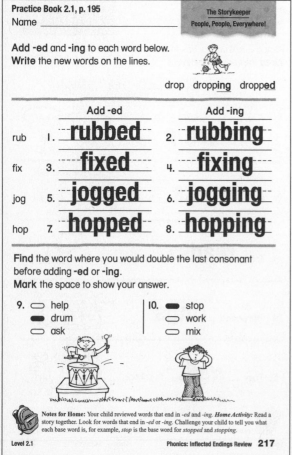

Notes for Home: Your child reviewed words that end in *-ed* and *-ing*. **Home Activity:** Read a story together. Look for words that end in *-ed* or *-ing*. Challenge your child to tell you what each base word is, for example, *stop* is the base word for *stopped* and *stopping*.

---

arm barn farm hard park start

Pick a word from the box to match each picture.
Write the word on the line.

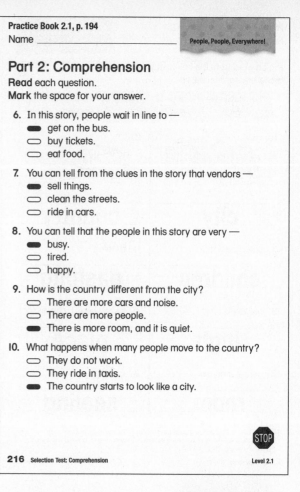

1. **farm**   2. **park**   3. **arm**

Change one letter in each word to make a word from the box.
Write the new word on the line.

4. stars   5. card   6. yarn

start   **hard**   **barn**

Pick a word from the box to finish each tongue twister.
Write the word on the line.

city   place

7. Polly picked a pretty **place** to play.

8. Six seals sit sipping tea in the **city** .

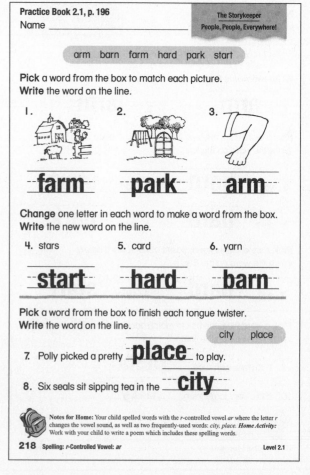

Notes for Home: Your child spelled words with the *r*-controlled vowel *ar* where the letter *r* changes the vowel sound, as well as two frequently-used words: *city, place.* **Home Activity:** Work with your child to write a poem which includes these spelling words.

---

324 Answers

Grammar Practice Book 2.1, p. 23

Name _____

RETEACHING

One dog **barks**.   Two dogs **bark**.

Add **-s** to a verb to tell what one person, animal, or thing does. Do **not** add **-s** to a verb that tells what two or more people, animals, or things do.

Choose a verb in ( ).
Write the verb on the line.

1. Two cats (meow/meows). **meow**

2. One mouse (climb/climbs). **climbs**

3. Three dogs (run/runs). **run**

Choose the correct verb.
Write it in the sentence.

4. Three fish (swim/swims) **swim** .

5. A turtle (swim/swims) **swims** fast.

Notes for Home: Your child wrote verbs which agree with the subjects of sentences. **Home Activity:** Read a story with your child and have him or her identify all the singular subjects and verbs on one page. Do the same with plural subjects and verbs.

Grammar: Subject/Verb Agreement **219**

Grammar Practice Book 2.1, p. 24

Name _____

Match each subject to the correct predicate.
Draw a line.

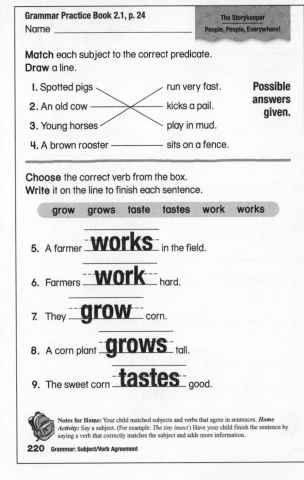

1. Spotted pigs — run very fast.
2. An old cow — kicks a pail.
3. Young horses — play in mud.
4. A brown rooster — sits on a fence.

Possible answers given.

Choose the correct verb from the box.
Write it on the line to finish each sentence.

grow   grows   taste   tastes   work   works

5. A farmer **works** in the field.

6. Farmers **work** hard.

7. They **grow** corn.

8. A corn plant **grows** tall.

9. The sweet corn **tastes** good.

Notes for Home: Your child matched subjects and verbs that agree in sentences. **Home Activity:** Say a subject. (For example: *The tiny insect*.) Have your child finish the sentence by saying a verb that correctly matches the subject and adds more information.

220 Grammar: Subject/Verb Agreement

Practice Book 2.1, p. 199

Name _____

Circle all the words that have the same vowel sound as **new**.

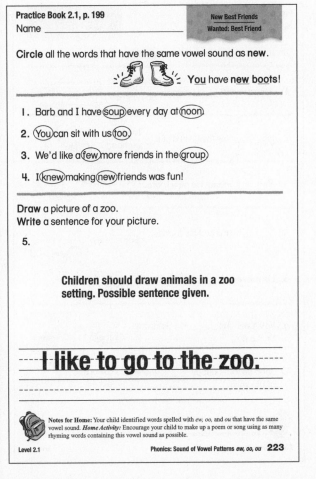 **Y**ou have **new** **boots**!

1. Barb and I have (soup) every day at (noon).

2. (You) can sit with us (too).

3. We'd like a (few) more friends in the (group).

4. I (knew) making (new) friends was fun!

Draw a picture of a zoo.
Write a sentence for your picture.

5.

Children should draw animals in a zoo setting. Possible sentence given.

I like to go to the zoo.

Notes for Home: Your child identified words spelled with *ew*, *oo*, and *ou* that have the same vowel sound. **Home Activity:** Encourage your child to make up a poem or song using as many rhyming words containing this vowel sound as possible.

Level 2.1   Phonics: Sound of Vowel Patterns *ew, oo, ou* **223**

Practice Book 2.1, p. 200

Name _____

Pick the contraction that is formed from each pair of words.
Write the contraction on the line.

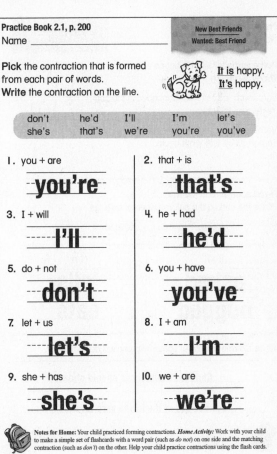 **It is** happy.
It's happy.

don't   he'd   I'll   I'm   let's
she's   that's   we're   you're   you've

1. you + are **you're**

2. that + is **that's**

3. I + will **I'll**

4. he + had **he'd**

5. do + not **don't**

6. you + have **you've**

7. let + us **let's**

8. I + am **I'm**

9. she + has **she's**

10. we + are **we're**

Notes for Home: Your child practiced forming contractions. **Home Activity:** Work with your child to make a simple set of flashcards with a word pair (such as *do not*) on one side and the matching contraction (such as *don't*) on the other. Help your child practice contractions using the flash cards.

224 Phonics: Contractions   Level 2.1

Answers **325**

Circle a word to finish each sentence.

across   best   either   sometimes   toward

1. We are _____ friends.
   across
   (best)

2. Kim lives _____ the street.
   either
   (across)

3. I play at her house _____ .
   (sometimes)
   toward

4. I'm careful when I walk _____ her house.
   (toward)
   best

5. _____ my sister or my mom helps me.
   Across
   (Either)

Look at each picture.
Answer the questions.

Possible answers given.   I hurt myself **because** I fell down.

1. Why does Pat go to the doctor?

Pat feels sick.

2. Why does the baby smile?

Mom hugs the baby.

3. Why can't Pete play ball?

It is raining.

Some verbs tell what is happening **now**.
Today Jill **walks**.

Verbs with **-ed** tell what happened in the past.
Yesterday Jill **walked**.

Verbs with **will** tell about the future.
Tomorrow Jill **will walk** again.

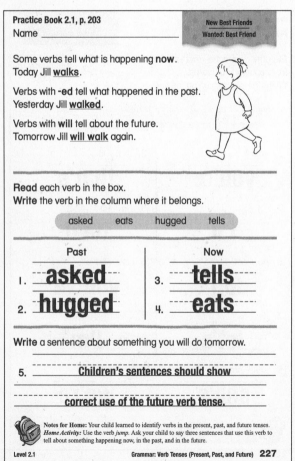

Read each verb in the box.
Write the verb in the column where it belongs.

asked   eats   hugged   tells

Past	Now
1. **asked**	3. **tells**
2. **hugged**	4. **eats**

Write a sentence about something you will do tomorrow.

5. _____ Children's sentences should show
   _____ correct use of the future verb tense.

Circle a word to finish each sentence.

1. John moved _____ town.
   (across)
   sometimes

2. He _____ his things in a pile.
   toward
   (dumped)

3. He _____ about his new room.
   (complained)
   best

4. _____ he missed his friends.
   Across
   (Sometimes)

5. He missed his _____ friend most.
   toward
   (best)

6. Kevin will visit _____ on Saturday or Sunday.
   across
   (either)

7. John became happy _____ the end of the week.
   (toward)
   either

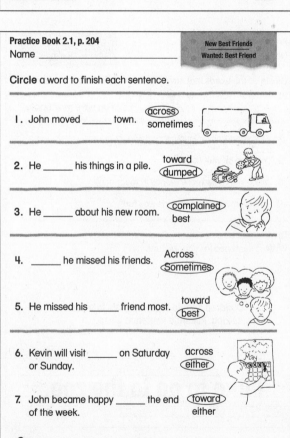

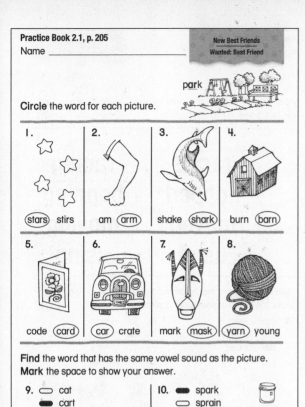

p**ark**

Circle the word for each picture.

1. (stars) stirs	2. am (arm)	3. shake (shark)	4. burn (barn)
5. code (card)	6. (car) crate	7. mark (mask)	8. (yarn) young

Find the word that has the same vowel sound as the picture.
Mark the space to show your answer.

9. ◯ cat
   ⬤ cart
   ◯ act

10. ⬤ spark
    ◯ sprain
    ◯ speak

jar

Notes for Home: Your child reviewed words with the *r*-controlled vowel *ar* where the letter *r* changes the vowel sound. *Home Activity:* Ask your child to think of a word that rhymes with one of the words with *ar* pictured above. Have your child spell both words.

Level 2.1   Phonics: *r*-Controlled Vowels: *ar* Review   **229**

I'll	I'm	can't	didn't	he's	she's

Put each pair of words together to make a word from the box.
Write the word on the line.

1. I will **I'll**
3. I am **I'm**
5. can not **can't**

2. did not **didn't**
4. he is **he's**
6. she is **she's**

Pick a word from the box to finish each sentence. Write the word on the line. Begin with a capital letter.

7. **He's** my brother.
8. **She's** my sister.

Pick a word from the box to match each clue.
Write the word on the line.

best
sometimes

9. very good **best**
10. once in a while **sometimes**

Notes for Home: Your child practiced spelling contractions such as *I'll* and *can't* and two frequently used words: *best, sometimes.* *Home Activity:* Have your child use each of these spelling words in a sentence. Work together to write each sentence.

230   Spelling: Contractions   Level 2.1

Underline the verb or verbs in each sentence.
Circle now, past, or future to tell when the action happens.

1. Amy <u>likes</u> her best friend Barb. (now) past future
2. Yesterday, they <u>played</u> at Barb's house. now (past) future
3. They <u>baked</u> cookies with Barb's mom. now (past) future
4. Tomorrow, they <u>will swim</u> at the pond. now past (future)
5. Today, they <u>kick</u> a ball. (now) past future

Use the verb *play.*
Write three sentences to tell about something now, in the past, and in the future.

6. (now)   **Possible answers given.**

We play games.

7. (past)

We played tag yesterday.

8. (future)

We will play soccer Friday.

Notes for Home: Your child used verbs in the present, past, and future tenses. *Home Activity:* Name a simple verb that your child might know, such as *jump, walk,* or *hop.* Encourage your child to use that verb to describe actions now, in the past, and in the future.

Level 2.1   Grammar: Verb Tenses (Present, Past, and Future)   **231**

Part 1: Vocabulary

Find the word that best fits in each sentence.
Mark the space for your answer.

1. I get to stay up late _____ .
   ⬤ sometimes ◯ around ◯ either

2. Josie _____ that she felt sick.
   ◯ dumped ⬤ complained ◯ returned

3. Mel rode her bike _____ me.
   ◯ through ◯ across ⬤ toward

4. Dad walked _____ the street.
   ◯ since ⬤ across ◯ sometimes

5. You can _____ come with us or stay home.
   ◯ best ◯ once ⬤ either

GO ON ➡

Level 2.1   Selection Test: Vocabulary   **233**

Answers **327**

Part 2: Comprehension

Read each question.
Mark the space for your answer.

6. Why did Mouse go home?
   - ● Cat did not want to play crazy eights.
   - ○ Cat had a new friend.
   - ○ Mouse was tired of games.

7. Cat called *The Hollow Log Gazette* because he wanted to —
   - ○ buy a newspaper.
   - ● try to find a friend.
   - ○ buy a new game.

8. Who made the biggest mess in Cat's house?
   - ○ Raccoon
   - ○ Mouse
   - ● Mole

9. When Cat and Mouse play crazy eights, Cat will —
   - ○ try to find a new friend.
   - ○ ask Otter to come and watch.
   - ● be nicer to Mouse.

10. What did Cat learn in this story?
    - ○ Mouse would never come back again.
    - ● Mouse was his best friend after all.
    - ○ He could not beat Mouse at checkers.

STOP

Add -ed and **-ing** to each word below.   smil∅ + -ed = smil**ed**
Write the new words on the lines.   smil∅ + -ing = smil**ing**

	Add -ed		Add -ing
race	1. **raced**	2.	**racing**
hop	3. **hopped**	4.	**hopping**
move	5. **moved**	6.	**moving**
use	7. **used**	8.	**using**

Find the new word that is formed by adding **-ed** or **-ing**.
Mark the space to show your answer.

9. dance + -ed =
   - ○ danceed
   - ● danced
   - ○ dancced

10. give + -ing =
    - ● giving
    - ○ givving
    - ○ giveing

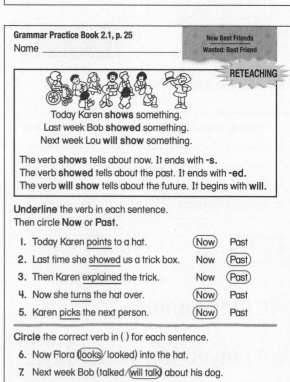

Notes for Home: Your child reviewed words that end with *-ed* and *-ing*. **Home Activity:** Ask your child to draw pictures showing the actions named by two or more of the words above. Help your child write a sentence to go with each picture.

> I'll   I'm   can't   didn't   he's   she's

Pick a word from the box to replace the underlined words.
Write the word on the line.

1. <u>I am</u> glad I met Gina and Tony.   **I'm**

2. I <u>did not</u> know them last year.   **didn't**

3. <u>He is</u> so funny.   **He's**

4. <u>She is</u> funny too.   **She's**

5. We <u>cannot</u> stop laughing sometimes.   **can't**

6. <u>I will</u> see them both tomorrow.   **I'll**

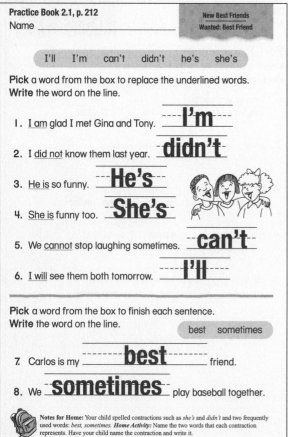

Pick a word from the box to finish each sentence.
Write the word on the line.

> best   sometimes

7. Carlos is my **best** friend.

8. We **sometimes** play baseball together.

Notes for Home: Your child spelled contractions such as *she's* and *didn't* and two frequently used words: *best, sometimes*. **Home Activity:** Name the two words that each contraction represents. Have your child name the contraction and write it.

Today Karen **shows** something.
Last week Bob **showed** something.
Next week Lou **will show** something.

The verb **shows** tells about now. It ends with **-s**.
The verb **showed** tells about the past. It ends with **-ed**.
The verb **will show** tells about the future. It begins with **will**.

Underline the verb in each sentence.
Then circle **Now** or **Past**.

1. Today Karen <u>points</u> to a hat.   (Now)   Past
2. Last time she <u>showed</u> us a trick box.   Now   (Past)
3. Then Karen <u>explained</u> the trick.   Now   (Past)
4. Now she <u>turns</u> the hat over.   (Now)   Past
5. Karen <u>picks</u> the next person.   (Now)   Past

Circle the correct verb in ( ) for each sentence.

6. Now Flora ((looks)/ looked) into the hat.
7. Next week Bob (talked /(will talk)) about his dog.
8. Now Karen ((pulls)/ pulled) out a picture.
9. She (shows /(will show)) the picture tomorrow too.
10. Last Monday Greg (learns /(learned)) a new game.

Notes for Home: Your child identified verbs in the present, past, and future tenses. **Home Activity:** Take a walk with your child and talk about what you see and hear. Help your child use verbs in the correct tenses.

Name _____

Underline the correct verb in ( ) for each sentence.

1. Jessie says she (<u>wants</u>/wanted) to see a movie.

2. A few hours ago she (picks/<u>picked</u>) a show.

3. After that she (walks/<u>walked</u>) to town.

4. Now the movie (<u>ends</u>/ended).

5. Jessie (laughs/<u>laughed</u>) when the movie was over.

6. The same movie (<u>will play</u>/played) next week.

Add -s, -ed, or **will** to each word in the box.
Write the correct verb in each sentence.

Answers may vary.

| talk | ask | learn | explain |

7. Last night Jessie ___**talked**___ about the movie.

8. Today Dad ___**asks**___ questions.

9. Later Jessie ___**will explain**___ the story.

10. Jessie ___**learned**___ the story well.

Notes for Home: Your child identified and wrote verbs in the present, past, and future tenses. **Home Activity:** Talk with your child about a family event. Help him or her use the present, past, and future tenses correctly.

Name _____

Pick a word from the box to match each clue.
Write the word on the line.

| tore | store | horn | door |
| pour | fork | corn | sport |

Order in the court!

1. something you knock on ___**door**___

2. something on a bull ___**horn**___

3. ripped ___**tore**___

4. a place where you buy things ___**store**___

5. something to eat with ___**fork**___

6. you can play or watch this ___**sport**___

7. something you do with a pitcher ___**pour**___

8. something you can pop and eat ___**corn**___

Notes for Home: Your child read and wrote words with *or, ore, oor,* where the letter *r* changes the vowel sound. **Home Activity:** Ask your child to think of other words that rhyme with each of the words in the box.

Name _____

Add -ed and **-es** to each word below.
Write the new words on the lines.

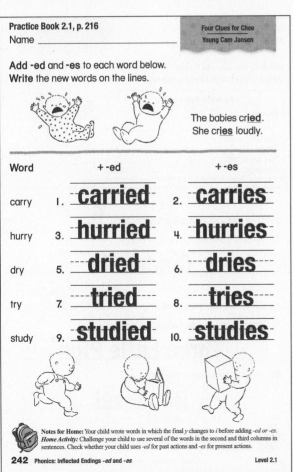

The babies cr**ied**.
She cr**ies** loudly.

Word	+ -ed	+ -es
carry	1. **carried**	2. **carries**
hurry	3. **hurried**	4. **hurries**
dry	5. **dried**	6. **dries**
try	7. **tried**	8. **tries**
study	9. **studied**	10. **studies**

Notes for Home: Your child wrote words in which the final *y* changes to *i* before adding *-ed or -es.* **Home Activity:** Challenge your child to use several of the words in the second and third columns in sentences. Check whether your child uses *-ed* for past actions and *-es* for present actions.

Name _____

Pick a word from the box to finish each sentence.
Write the word on the line.

| bring | brought | next | picture | read |

1. What kind of present did you ___**bring**___ Lil?

2. I ___**brought**___ a book.

3. I hope she hasn't ___**read**___ it yet.

4. It has a nice ___**picture**___ of a cat on the cover.

5. Lil will open my present ___**next**___!

Notes for Home: This week your child is learning to read the words *bring, brought, next, picture,* and *read.* **Home Activity:** Challenge your child to make up a story about a party using these words.

Answers **329**

Write a word from the box to name each person.

| doctor | painter | teacher | vet |

1. I help sick people. I take care of them. I help them feel well.

I am a **doctor** .

2. I help you learn. I read lots of books. I work in a school.

I am a **teacher** .

3. I take care of cats and dogs. I help them feel well.

I am a **vet** .

4. I draw and paint. I use lots of pretty colors.

I am a **painter** .

Draw a picture of one of the people described.
Show something this person does.

5. **Children should draw a doctor, painter, teacher, or vet doing a typical work activity.**

Notes for Home: Your child identified characters based on things they say and do.
Home Activity: Read a story with your child. Name characters from the story. Have your child describe each character and tell how he or she knows what the character is like.

244 Character

Level 2.1

Be sure to use the correct verb to show something happening in the past, now, or in the future.

Today we **study**.
Yesterday she **studied**.
Tomorrow we **will study**.

Circle the correct verb to finish each sentence.
Write the verb on the line.

1. Yesterday it   rains   (rained)   **rained**

2. We ran and   hurry   (hurried)   **hurried** inside.

3. Tomorrow it   rained   (will rain)   **will rain** again.

4. Now the sun   (shines)   will shine   **shines**

5. Now we   (play)   played   **play** outside!

Notes for Home: Your child chose the correct verb to show actions in the past, present, and future. **Home Activity:** Have your child tell you what he or she did yesterday, what he or she is doing now, and what he or she will do tomorrow. Listen for the correct verb tenses.

Level 2.1

Grammar: Correct Verb Tenses **245**

Pick a word from the box to finish each sentence.
Write the word on the line.

| brought | camera | dinosaurs |
| exact | next | order |

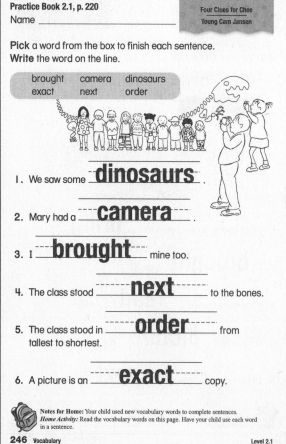

1. We saw some **dinosaurs**

2. Mary had a **camera** .

3. I **brought** mine too.

4. The class stood **next** to the bones.

5. The class stood in **order** from tallest to shortest.

6. A picture is an **exact** copy.

Notes for Home: Your child used new vocabulary words to complete sentences.
Home Activity: Read the vocabulary words on this page. Have your child use each word in a sentence.

246 Vocabulary

Level 2.1

Look at the table of contents from a book of fairy tales.
Write the answer to each question.

Favorite Fairy Tales	
Contents	
Cinderella	3
Sleeping Beauty	10
Three Little Pigs	15
Rumpelstiltskin	21
Rapunzel	26

1. How many stories are in this book? **5**

2. What is the name of the first story?

Cinderella

3. On what page does "Sleeping Beauty" start? **10**

4. Which story comes before "Rumpelstiltskin"?

Three Little Pigs

5. What is the name of the last story?

Rapunzel

Notes for Home: Your child read a table of contents and answered questions about it. **Home Activity:** Look through books in your home or at the library. Compare different tables of contents and talk about the information each one shows.

Level 2.1

Research and Study Skills: Parts of a Book: Table of Contents **247**

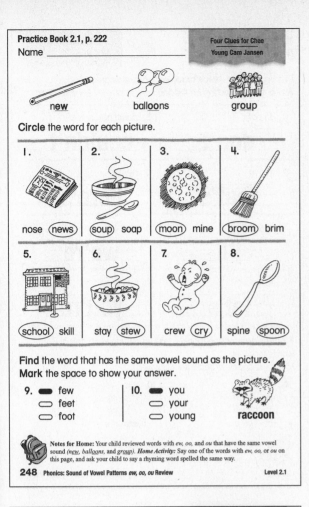

new   balloons   group

Circle the word for each picture.

1.	2.	3.	4.
nose (news)	(soup) soap	(moon) mine	(broom) brim

5.	6.	7.	8.
(school) skill	stay (stew)	crew (cry)	spine (spoon)

Find the word that has the same vowel sound as the picture.
Mark the space to show your answer.

9. ▬ few
   ▭ feet
   ▭ foot

10. ▬ you
    ▭ your
    ▭ young

raccoon

Notes for Home: Your child reviewed words with *ew, oo,* and *ou* that have the same vowel sound (*new, balloons,* and *group*). Home Activity: Say one of the words with *ew, oo,* or *ou* on this page, and ask your child to say a rhyming word spelled the same way.

---

door	corn	horse	more	pour	store

Write four words from the box that rhyme with **snore**.

1. **door**   2. **more**

3. **pour**   4. **store**

Pick a word from the box to match each picture.
Write the word on the line.

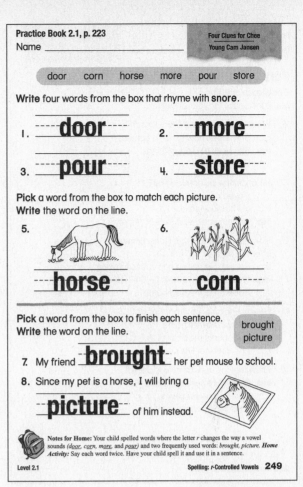

5. **horse**   6. **corn**

Pick a word from the box to finish each sentence.
Write the word on the line.

brought
picture

7. My friend **brought** her pet mouse to school.

8. Since my pet is a horse, I will bring a

picture of him instead.

Notes for Home: Your child spelled words where the letter *r* changes the way a vowel sounds (*door, corn, more,* and *pour*) and two frequently used words: *brought, picture.* Home Activity: Say each word twice. Have your child spell it and use it in a sentence.

Circle the correct verb to finish each sentence.

1. Last week, we (plays (played)) a guessing game in school.

2. We (will guess (guessed)) how many pencils were in a jar.

3. My friend Bill and I (studied) study) the jar all week long.

4. Today, we (talks (talk)) about who will win.

5. Tomorrow, the teacher (counted (will count)) the pencils.

6. The winner (walked (will walk)) first in line all next week.

7. Yesterday, Bill (will change (changed)) his guess.

8. Today, I (hope) hoped) that I win.

9. I (finds (will find)) out tomorrow.

10. We (played (will play)) another game next week!

Notes for Home: Your child chose verbs in the present, past, and future tenses. Home Activity: Write *today, yesterday,* and *tomorrow* on three sheets of paper. Work with your child to write sentences using present, past, and future tenses to describe different actions.

Part 1: Vocabulary

Find the word that best fits in each sentence.
Mark the space for your answer.

1. Lee _____ a dog to school.
   ▭ drew   ▭ giggled   ▬ brought

2. Will you take a picture with my _____?
   ▭ order   ▬ camera   ▭ mirror

3. _____ were very big animals.
   ▬ Dinosaurs   ▭ Scales   ▭ Friends

4. Who is _____ in line?
   ▭ toward   ▭ clean   ▬ next

5. Les knew the _____ number.
   ▭ either   ▬ exact   ▭ between

GO ON ▶

Answers **331**

Part 2: Comprehension

Read each question.
Mark the space for your answer.

6. What is special about Cam Jansen?
   - ○ She knows how to use a camera.
   - ● She does not forget things.
   - ○ She gets lost.

7. What did the children do first?
   - ○ played musical chairs
   - ○ ate birthday cake
   - ● wrote numbers on slips of paper

8. How did Cam know that Robert made his guess after the others?
   - ○ Robert told her he had guessed twice.
   - ● There was some cake on the paper.
   - ○ Robert had the best guess.

9. How is Eric different from Robert?
   - ○ Eric wins every game.
   - ● Eric shares the dinosaurs.
   - ○ Eric does not like cake.

10. Of all the children, Cam was best at —
    - ● finding answers to questions.
    - ○ playing musical chairs.
    - ○ guessing the right numbers.

STOP

Put each pair of words together to make a contraction.
Write the contraction on the line.   I + am = **I'm**

1. do not	2. could not
don't	**couldn't**
3. that is	4. here is
that's	**here's**
5. I will	6. we are
I'll	**we're**
7. let us	8. you are
let's	**you're**

Find the contraction that is made by putting each pair of words together.
Mark the space to show your answer.

9. we have
   - ● we've
   - ○ wave
   - ○ we'd

10. it is
    - ○ its
    - ○ its'
    - ● it's

 **Notes for Home:** Your child reviewed contractions such as *don't, I'll,* and *couldn't.* **Home Activity:** With your child, make a list of other contractions you know. For each contraction you list, write the two words it represents.

| door | corn | horse | more | pour | store |

Pick a word from the box to match each clue.
Write the word on the line.

1. an animal you can ride	2. a greater amount
horse	**more**
3. a place to shop	4. something you eat or pop
store	**corn**
5. something you knock on	6. something you do to milk
door	**pour**

Pick a word from the box to finish each sentence.
Write the word on the line.

brought
picture

7. I **brought** this drawing to show you.

8. That's a great **picture** of a dinosaur!

 Notes for Home: Your child spelled words where the letter *r* changes the way a vowel sounds (*door, corn, more,* and *pour*) and two frequently used words: *brought, picture.* **Home Activity:** Scramble the letters of each spelling word and have your child unscramble each word.

RETEACHING

Today it **rains**.
Yesterday it **rained**.
Tomorrow it **will rain**.

Be sure to use the correct verb to show something happening now, in the past, or in the future.

Circle the verb in each sentence.
Then **write** the verb.

1. They (stayed) inside.   **stayed**

2. Jason (plays) a game.   **plays**

3. Kim (will watch) TV.   **will watch**

4. Ann (cleaned) her room.   **cleaned**

Underline the correct verb in ( ) for each sentence.

5. Yesterday Jason (paint / **painted**) a picture.

6. Tomorrow Kim (color / **will color**) with crayons.

7. Now the dog (**jumps** / jumped) on them.

 **Notes for Home:** Your child identified and wrote verbs in the correct tenses in sentences. **Home Activity:** Write a sentence on a piece of paper, leaving out the verb. (*Yesterday we _____ a movie.*) Have your child write a verb in the correct tense.

Four Clues for Chee
Young Cam Jansen

Add -ed, -s, or **will** to the words in ( ).

1. An hour ago we (turn) **turned** the lights off.

2. Soon Mike (walk) **will walk** into the room.

3. Then Barbara (yell) **will yell**, "Surprise!"

4. Now she (hide) **hides**.

Complete each sentence with a verb from the box.

| will open   play   thanked   laughed |

5. Mike **laughed** at our trick.

6. Soon Mike **will open** his presents.

7. He **thanked** everyone for the surprise.

8. Now we **play** the new games.

 **Notes for Home:** Your child completed sentences by adding verbs in the correct tenses. **Home Activity:** Choose a verb and have your child write sentences, using that verb in the present, past, and future tenses.

256 Grammar: Correct Verb Tenses

A Good Laugh for Cookie
Moonbear's Pet

Write the letters **oo** or **ou** on the lines to make a word.
Look at the words in the box if you need help.

| cook   could   foot   look |
| should   took   would   wood |

b<u>oo</u>k

1. sh **ou** ld

2. l **oo** k

3. w **oo** d

4. t **oo** k

5. c **oo** k

6. c **ou** ld

7. w **ou** ld

8. f **oo** t

Write two sentences.
Use a word from the box in each sentence.

9. _____ **Each sentence should contain at least** _____

10. _____ **one word from the box.** _____

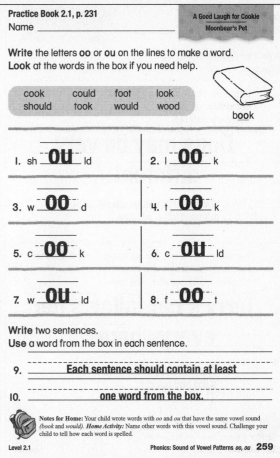 **Notes for Home:** Your child wrote words with *oo* and *ou* that have the same vowel sound (*book* and *would*). **Home Activity:** Name other words with this vowel sound. Challenge your child to tell how each word is spelled.

Level 2.1   Phonics: Sound of Vowel Patterns *oo, ou* **259**

A Good Laugh for Cookie
Moonbear's Pet

Circle a word to finish each sentence.

Spot is **big**.
Rover is **bigger**.
Spike is **biggest**!

1. Bobby is _____ than Jimmy.
   sadder / saddest

2. The spotted one is the _____ .
   smaller / **smallest**

3. Jack is _____ than Ned.
   taller / tallest

4. Jill is the _____ of all.
   wetter / **wettest**

5. This clown is _____ than that one.
   fatter / fattest

 **Notes for Home:** Your child used adjectives that end in *-er* and *-est* to complete sentences. **Home Activity:** Look for objects or people in your neighborhood. Ask your child to compare them, using adjectives such as *bigger*, *smallest*, *tallest*, and *younger*.

260 Phonics: Comparative Endings *-er, -est*   Level 2.1

A Good Laugh for Cookie
Moonbear's Pet

Pick a word from the box to finish each sentence.
Write the word on the line.

| beautiful   become   even   great   together |

1. They keep their pets **together** .

2. They have a **great** time with them.

3. They **even** feed them at the same time.

4. One day their pets will **become** frogs.

5. Frogs are not ugly. They're **beautiful** .

Notes for Home: This week your child is learning to read the words *beautiful, become, even, great,* and *together.* **Home Activity:** Have your child use these sentences as models for writing his or her own sentences about a pet he or she has or would like to have.

Level 2.1   High-Frequency Words **261**

Answers **333**

Write a sentence that tells what each passage is mostly about.
Draw a picture that shows what each passage is mostly about.

> Dogs may be different in many ways.
> Some dogs are long and thin. Some are small.
> Some are very big.

1. **Dogs may be very different.**

2. Children's drawings should show
different kinds of dogs.

> Barney is Terry's cat. Barney follows Terry everywhere.
> He sleeps on her bed every night.
> He even sits by her when she eats.

3. **Terry's cat follows her everywhere.**

4. Children's drawings should show
a girl and her cat.

Notes for Home: Your child read a passage and wrote a sentence to tell what it was mostly about.
Home Activity: Talk about a story your child is familiar with. Ask him or her to tell what the
story is mostly about in just a few sentences.

The verbs **is**, **are**, **was**, **were**, and **will be** do not show action.
The verbs **is** and **are** tell about now.
The verbs **was** and **were** tell about the past.
The verb **will be** tells about the future.

Circle the correct verb to finish each sentence.
Write the verb on the line.

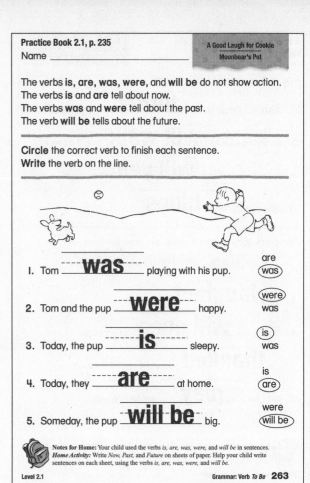

1. Tom ___**was**___ playing with his pup.
   are (was)

2. Tom and the pup ___**were**___ happy.
   (were) was

3. Today, the pup ___**is**___ sleepy.
   (is) was

4. Today, they ___**are**___ at home.
   is (are)

5. Someday, the pup ___**will be**___ big.
   were (will be)

Notes for Home: Your child used the verbs *is, are, was, were,* and *will be* in sentences.
Home Activity: Write *Now, Past,* and *Future* on sheets of paper. Help your child write
sentences on each sheet, using the verbs *is, are, was, were,* and *will be.*

Pick a word from the box to match each clue.
Write the word on the line.

beautiful	become	bubbles
decide	paws	quite

1.

bubbles

2. very pretty

beautiful

3. to make up your mind

decide

4. That dog made _____
a mess!

quite

5. another name for a
dog's feet

paws

6. turn into

become

Notes for Home: Your child matched vocabulary words with word and picture clues.
Home Activity: Make a list of four or five words that your child thinks are challenging.
Work together to write a clue like those above for each word.

---

thorn   core   door   four

Circle the word for each picture.

1.	2.	3.	4.
(acorn) actor	(corn) coin	(snore) snare	floor (flower)

5.	6.	7.	8.
stare (store)	turn (torn)	hers (horse)	peer (pour)

Find the word that has the same vowel sound as the picture.
Mark the space to show your answer.

horn

9. ● stork
   ○ stock
   ○ stir

10. ○ firm
    ● four
    ○ few

Notes for Home: Your child reviewed words that contain the *r*-controlled vowels *or, ore, oor,*
and *our,* found in *thorn, core, door,* and *four.* **Home Activity:** Ask your child to draw pictures
illustrating some of the words on this page. Help your child label each picture.

book   hood   shook   stood   took   wood

Write three words from the box that rhyme with **good**.

1. **hood**   2. **stood**   3. **wood**

Write three words from the box that rhyme with **look**.

4. **book**   5. **shook**   6. **took**

Pick a word from the box to match each picture.
Write the word on the line.

7.
book

8.
wood

Pick a word from the box to finish each sentence.
Write the word on the line.

become
even

9. When I read, I **become** part of the story.

10. I **even** pretend I am the hero!

Notes for Home: Your child spelled words with *oo* that have the same vowel sound heard in *book* and two frequently used words: *become, even*. Home Activity: Have your child use each spelling word in a sentence. Together, write each sentence.

Use words that help show how two things are alike or different.

Cats need water.
Dogs **also** need water.

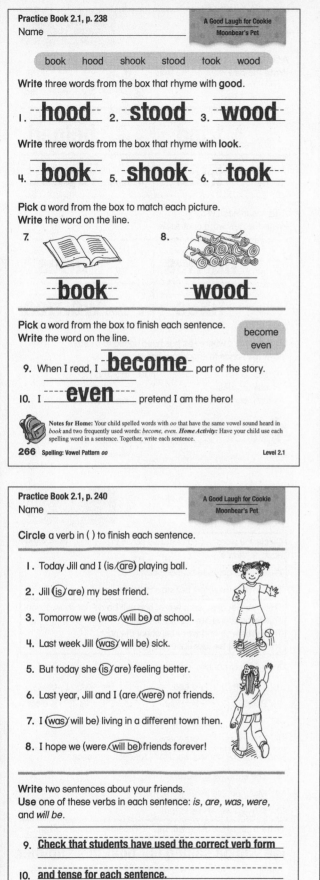

Circle a word in ( ) to finish each sentence.

1. (Both/Two) cats and dogs like living with people.

2. Cats make good pets. But lions do (know/not).

3. Pets need love just (like/same) people do.

4. A dog's needs are (same/different) from a bird's needs.

Write a sentence that compares two animals.
Use the word **both** in your sentence.   **Possible answer given.**

5. **Both cats and dogs like to play.**

Notes for Home: Your child identified words that show comparisons and contrasts. Home Activity: Ask your child to compare and contrast two different animals. Have him or her tell how they are alike and how they are different.

Circle a verb in ( ) to finish each sentence.

1. Today Jill and I (is/are) playing ball.

2. Jill (is/are) my best friend.

3. Tomorrow we (was/will be) at school.

4. Last week Jill (was/will be) sick.

5. But today she (is/are) feeling better.

6. Last year, Jill and I (are/were) not friends.

7. I (was/will be) living in a different town then.

8. I hope we (were/will be) friends forever!

Write two sentences about your friends.
Use one of these verbs in each sentence: *is, are, was, were,*
and *will be.*

9. **Check that students have used the correct verb form**

10. **and tense for each sentence.**

Notes for Home: Your child practiced using the verbs *is, are, was, were,* and *will be.* Home Activity: Write these verbs on slips of paper. Take turns picking a verb and using it in a sentence.

Part 1: Vocabulary

Find the word that best fits in each sentence.
Mark the space for your answer.

1. Sue saw a _____ red bird.
   ○ mirror   ● beautiful   ○ ripe

2. Ted will _____ a fireman when he grows up.
   ● become   ○ decide   ○ keep

3. A dog has four _____ .
   ○ brains   ○ tools   ● paws

4. Kat blew big _____ .
   ○ messages   ● bubbles   ○ wheels

5. Ben is _____ tall for his age.
   ● quite   ○ around   ○ between

GO ON →

Answers **335**

Part 2: Comprehension

Read each question.
Mark the space for your answer.

6. What happens first in this story?
   - ◯ Moonbear goes shopping.
   - ◯ Splash grows four legs.
   - ● Moonbear finds a pet.

7. You can tell that Bear —
   - ● likes his new pet a lot.
   - ◯ does not take good care of his pet.
   - ◯ is mean to his new pet.

8. Little Bird thought that Splash —
   - ◯ should be in a pool.
   - ● wanted to be a bird.
   - ◯ was growing paws.

9. How did Splash get out of the pool?
   - ● She hopped out.
   - ◯ Someone took her out.
   - ◯ She flew out.

10. This story is about two friends who learn that —
    - ● they should not fight about silly things.
    - ◯ everyone should be a bird.
    - ◯ fish grow up to be frogs.

STOP

Add -ed to each verb.
Write the new word on the line.

crỵ + -es = cr**ies**

crỵ + -ed = cr**ied**

1. fry	**fried**	2. help	**helped**
3. try	**tried**	4. reply	**replied**

Add -es to each verb.
Write the new word on the line.

5. hurry	**hurries**	6. dry	**dries**
7. fix	**fixes**	8. worry	**worries**

Find the word where **-es** has been added to a verb.
Mark the space to show your answer.

9.
- ◯ cars
- ● carries
- ◯ canes

10.
- ◯ mares
- ◯ marry
- ● marries

Notes for Home: Your child reviewed words that end with *-ed* and *-es*, including words where the final *y* is changed to an *i* before *-ed* or *-es* is added. **Home Activity:** Ask your child to spell other words in which *y* changes to *i* before *-ed* or *-es* is added, such as *bury*, *study*, and *carry*.

Find the words from the box in the puzzle.
They may go across or down.
Circle each word in the puzzle.
Write the words on the lines.

book	hood	shook
stood	took	wood

```
s  t  o  o  d  x  g  l  b  w
b  v  y  b  o  o  k  o  p  o
t  a  c  y  u  w  e  u  i  o
o  h  o  o  d  h  q  w  y  d
o  h  j  g  o  s  y  k  e  c
k  s  s  h  o  o  k  n  y  v
```

Order may vary.

1. **book**   2. **hood**
3. **shook**   4. **stood**
5. **took**   6. **wood**

Pick a word from the box to finish each sentence.
Write the word on the line.

become
even

7. A tadpole will **become** a frog.

8. It will **even** grow legs!

Notes for Home: Your child spelled words with the letters *oo* that have the same vowel sound heard in *book* and two frequently used words: *become*, *even*. **Home Activity:** Work with your child to write and illustrate a story using these spelling words.

RETEACHING

Circle the word in ( ) that makes sense in each sentence.

We (**are**/ is) going to school today.

Tomorrow I (was /**will be**) staying home.

The verbs **is, are, was, were,** and **will be** do not show action.
The verbs **is** and **are** tell about now.
The verbs **was** and **were** tell about the past.
The verb **will be** tells about the future.

Draw lines to connect sentence parts and make sentences.

1. The sun — is cool.
2. Boats — is bright.
3. The lake — are ready.
4. The races —— are today.
5. The sky — are up.
6. The sails — is clear.
7. Dina —— is busy.

Underline the correct word in ( ) for each sentence.

8. The show (**was**/ were) exciting.

9. Many people (was /**were**) there.

10. It (**was**/ were) lots of fun.

Write a sentence using **will be**.   **Possible answers given.**

We will be sailing our boat this summer.

They will be here tomorrow.

Notes for Home: Your child wrote forms of the verb *to be*, such as *is, was, are, were,* and *will be*, in sentences. **Home Activity:** Talk with your child about what he or she did last year that is different from this year. Remind your child to use the correct forms of the verb *to be*.

A Good Laugh for Cookie
Moonbear's Pet

Write **is, are, was, were,** or **will be** to complete each sentence correctly. **Possible answers given.**

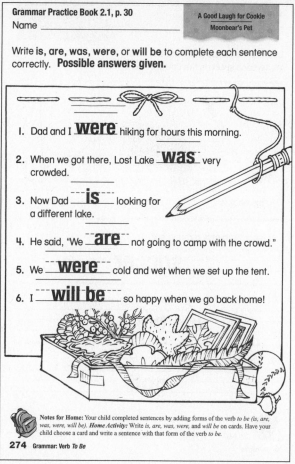

1. Dad and I **were** hiking for hours this morning.

2. When we got there, Lost Lake **was** very crowded.

3. Now Dad **is** looking for a different lake.

4. He said, "We **are** not going to camp with the crowd."

5. We **were** cold and wet when we set up the tent.

6. I **will be** so happy when we go back home!

Notes for Home: Your child completed sentences by adding forms of the verb *to be (is, are, was, were, will be)*. **Home Activity:** Write *is, are, was, were,* and *will be* on cards. Have your child choose a card and write a sentence with that form of the verb *to be*.

274 Grammar: Verb *To Be*

A Good Laugh for Cookie
Moonbear's Pet

Correct each sentence.
Write it on the line.
Hint: Make sure that verbs are used correctly.

1. They plays together.

They play together.

2. Now the big cat roll over.

Now the big cat rolls over.

3. Now the kitten are jumping up.

Now the kitten is jumping up.

4. It is born last month.

It was born last month.

5. It is big someday.

It will be big someday.

Notes for Home: Your child corrected verbs in sentences. **Home Activity:** Read a sentence from a story aloud to your child, leaving out the verb. Have your child give a verb that makes sense in the sentence.

Level 2.1

Writing Process: Edit **275**

Hear the Cheers
The Great Ball Game

Circle a word to finish each sentence.
Write the word on the line.

year   steer

1. Did you **hear** ?
   - hear
   - heart

2. It was a singing **deer** !
   - dare
   - deer

3. He sat very **near** to us.
   - near
   - next

4. I had no **fear** .
   - fair
   - fear

5. It was **clear** that he was friendly.
   - clear
   - close

Notes for Home: Your child read and wrote words with *ear* and *eer*, such as *year* and *steer*. **Home Activity:** Ask your child to write a silly poem with words that rhyme with *year* and *steer*. Challenge your child to use as many *ear* and *eer* words as possible.

Level 2.2

Phonics: *r*-Controlled Vowels: *ear, eer*   **3**

Hear the Cheers
The Great Ball Game

Add -ly to each word.
Write the new word on the line.

happily

1. lucky **luckily**   2. quick **quickly**

3. loud **loudly**   4. near **nearly**

5. slow **slowly**   6. final **finally**

7. sure **surely**   8. soft **softly**

Draw a picture of an animal that moves slowly and one that moves quickly.

9. slowly   10. quickly

Children should draw a slow animal such as a turtle. | Children should draw a fast animal such as a rabbit.

Notes for Home: Your child has learned to form words with the suffix *-ly*. **Home Activity:** Help your child make a list of words with the suffix *-ly*. Work together to use these words in sentences.

4 Phonics: Suffix *-ly*   Level 2.2

Answers **337**

Pick a word from the box to finish each sentence.
Write the word on the line.

| ago | better | head | idea | still |

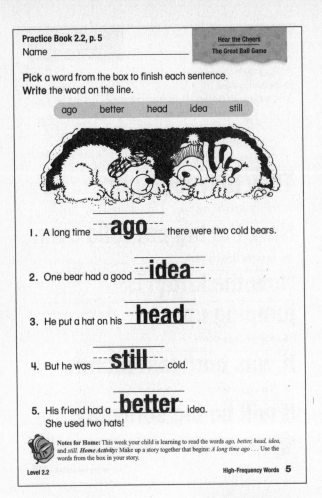

1. A long time __**ago**__ there were two cold bears.

2. One bear had a good __**idea**__.

3. He put a hat on his __**head**__.

4. But he was __**still**__ cold.

5. His friend had a __**better**__ idea.
She used two hats!

Notes for Home: This week your child is learning to read the words *ago, better, head, idea,* and *still*. **Home Activity:** Make up a story together that begins: *A long time ago . . .* Use the words from the box in your story.

Level 2.2

High-Frequency Words **5**

Look at the words and pictures.
Write each sport on the correct line.

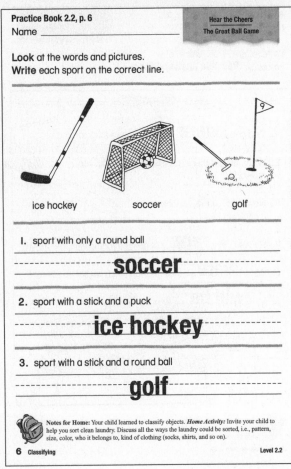

ice hockey   soccer   golf

1. sport with only a round ball

__**soccer**__

2. sport with a stick and a puck

__**ice hockey**__

3. sport with a stick and a round ball

__**golf**__

Notes for Home: Your child learned to classify objects. **Home Activity:** Invite your child to help you sort clean laundry. Discuss all the ways the laundry could be sorted, i.e., pattern, size, color, who it belongs to, kind of clothing (socks, shirts, and so on).

6 Classifying

Level 2.2

An **adjective** describes a noun.
An adjective may tell how many, what size, or what shape.

Two bears play ball.
A **small** bat flies by.
The ball is **round**.

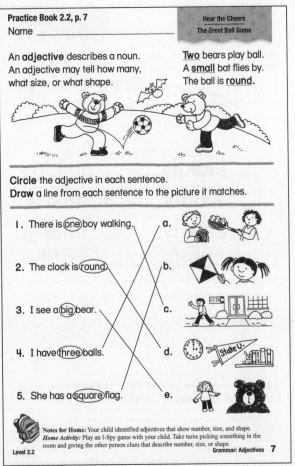

Circle the adjective in each sentence.
Draw a line from each sentence to the picture it matches.

1. There is (one) boy walking.   a.

2. The clock is (round).   b.

3. I see a (big) bear.   c.

4. I have (three) balls.   d.

5. She has a (square) flag.   e.

Notes for Home: Your child identified adjectives that show number, size, and shape. **Home Activity:** Play an I-Spy game with your child. Take turns picking something in the room and giving the other person clues that describe number, size, or shape.

Level 2.2

Grammar: Adjectives **7**

Pick a word from the box to match each clue.
Write the word in the puzzles. The circled letters spell two words.

| ago | better | creature | head | lose | still | team |

1. sounds like *hill*

2. where your eyes and ears are

3. not worse

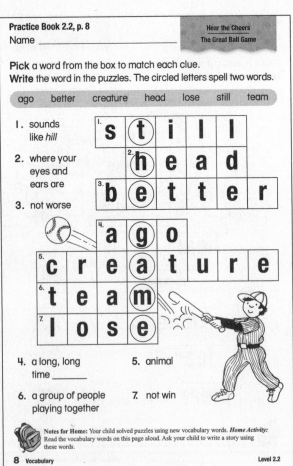

1. s (t) i l l
2. (h) e a d
3. b (e) t t e r
4. (a) g o
5. c r (e) a t u r e
6. t e a (m)
7. l o s (e)

4. a long, long time _____

5. animal

6. a group of people playing together

7. not win

Notes for Home: Your child solved puzzles using new vocabulary words. **Home Activity:** Read the vocabulary words on this page aloud. Ask your child to write a story using these words.

8 Vocabulary

Level 2.2

---

338 Answers

He c**ou**ldn't reach the b**oo**ks.

Circle the word for each picture.

1. (hood) hide
2. (hook) hike
3. (shore) should
4. (shook) sock
5. (crook) creak
6. cork (cook)
7. could (cold)
8. fold (foot)

Find the word that has the same vowel sound as the picture.
Mark the space to show your answer.

9. ○ won
   ● would
   ○ world

10. ● took
    ○ top
    ○ too

cookie

Notes for Home: Your child reviewed words with *oo* and *ou* that have the same vowel sound heard in *couldn't* and *books*. Home Activity: Ask your child to tell you about things he or she could do, using words with this vowel sound. *(I could look at a book.)*

---

bravely   friendly   lightly   slowly   softly   weekly

Add -ly to each word below to make a word from the box.
Write the new word on the line.

1. light
   lightly

2. week
   weekly

3. soft
   softly

4. brave
   bravely

5. slow
   slowly

6. friend
   friendly

Pick a word from the box to finish each sentence.
Write the word on the line.

ago   head

7. We had a contest two days **ago** .

8. I raced with a book on my **head** .

Notes for Home: Your child spelled words that end with *-ly* and two frequently used words: *ago, head*. Home Activity: Say each spelling word, then use it in a sentence. Invite your child to act out the sentence.

Pick an adjective from the box to finish each sentence.
Write the adjective on the line. Use each word only once.

best   great   many   round   tall

1. We are playing a **great** game.

2. We try to kick a **round** ball into the net.

3. Our team has two **tall** players.

4. We score **many** goals.

5. Soccer is the **best** sport.

Some answers may vary. Check that children give reasonable answers.

Notes for Home: Your child completed sentences using adjectives for number, size, and shape. Home Activity: Take turns describing an object in a room using adjectives. The other player tries to guess the object being described.

Part I: Vocabulary

Find the word that best fits in each sentence.
Mark the space for your answer.

1. It is time for lunch, but Meg is _____ sleeping.
   ● still   ○ between   ○ across

2. The dinosaurs lived a long time _____ .
   ○ tomorrow   ○ quite   ● ago

3. Jed will _____ the game.
   ○ climb   ● lose   ○ peel

4. The ant is a tiny _____ .
   ○ surface   ● creature   ○ picture

5. Put a hat on your _____ !
   ○ city   ○ team   ● head

GO ON →

Answers **339**

Part 2: Comprehension

Read each question.
Mark the space for your answer.

6. The Birds and Animals have a —
   - ● ball game.
   - ○ card game.
   - ○ jumping game.

7. Which one belongs on the same team as a dog?
   - ● Fox
   - ○ Crane
   - ○ Hawk

8. How is Bat **not** like all the others?
   - ● He has wings and teeth.
   - ○ He plays in the game.
   - ○ He can fly.

9. Who takes the ball from Crane at the end of the game?
   - ○ Bear
   - ○ Hawk
   - ● Bat

10. You can tell from this story that bats do not —
    - ○ come out at night.
    - ● fly south for the winter.
    - ○ use their wings much.

STOP

---

big   bigg**er**   bigg**est**

Circle a word in ( ) to finish each sentence.

1. The football is (**bigger**/ biggest) than the baseball.

2. The basketball is the (larger /**largest**) ball.

3. The baseball is the (smaller /**smallest**).

4. The (heavier /**heaviest**) ball is the bowling ball.

5. Jan is (**taller**/ tallest) than Bill.

6. Jill is the (faster /**fastest**) runner of all.

7. Bill is (**slower**/ slowest) than Jill.

8. Is Bill (**quicker**/ quickest) than Jan?

Find the word that you could use to compare three things.
Mark the space to show your answer.

9. ○ wet
   ○ wetter
   ● wettest

10. ○ loud
    ○ louder
    ● loudest

Notes for Home: Your child reviewed words with the comparative endings *-er* and *-est*, such as *bigger* and *biggest*. **Home Activity:** Help your child write a story about bigger animals helping smaller animals play a game, using comparative *-er* and *-est* words.

---

bravely   friendly   lightly   slowly   softly   weekly

Pick a word from the box to match each clue.
Write the word on the line.

1. every seven days

   weekly

2. without fear

   bravely

3. not loudly

   softly

4. not fast

   slowly

5. nice

   friendly

6. with a light touch

   lightly

Pick a word from the box to match each clue.
Write the word in the puzzle.

ago   head

7. It is on top of your body.
8. It means "in the past."

⁷h	e	a	⁸d
			g
			o

Notes for Home: Your child spelled words ending with *-ly* and two frequently used words: *ago, head.* **Home Activity:** Have your child look through a newspaper and list words with *-ly* endings. Help your child figure out what each word means.

RETEACHING

Words for number, size, and shape are **adjectives**.

Ten leaves fall. The tree has **large** leaves.
The leaves have **pointed** edges.

Underline the adjective for number, size, or shape in each sentence.

1. The <u>round</u> leaves are gone.

2. The boy puts leaves in <u>two</u> piles.

3. The children collect <u>big</u> leaves.

4. A <u>small</u> squirrel climbs on the tree.

Circle the adjective for number, size, or shape in each sentence.
Write the adjective on the line.

5. The squirrel looks for (large) nuts.

   large

6. Its (round) ears hear the children.

   round

7. (Two) girls smile at the squirrel.

   Two

Notes for Home: Your child identified and wrote adjectives that tell more about number, size, and shape in sentences. **Home Activity:** Have your child draw a picture of a familiar place. Then have him or her label the picture with at least three adjectives.

Write the adjective in ( ) on the line.

1. Chris wears a __**big**__ hat in the school play.
(shoe/big)

2. Kara is the girl in the __**small**__ coat.
(small/slowly)

3. They have __**three**__ parrots.
(three/fly)

Complete each sentence with an adjective from the box.

| tall | little | two | square |

Possible answers given.

4. Kara looks at the __**little**__ parrots.

5. The parrots hide in a __**tall**__ tree.

6. Kara puts the parrots in __**two**__ cages.

7. The cages have __**square**__ doors.

Notes for Home: Your child identified and wrote adjectives that tell more about size, shape, and number in sentences. *Home Activity:* Have your child write sentences about family members. Challenge him or her to use at least one adjective in each sentence.

Circle a word to finish each sentence.
Write the word on the line.

b**oi**l

1. I have three ~~cans~~ (coins) __**coins**__

2. I wanted a new (toy) tab __**toy**__

3. I ~~planted~~ (pointed) __**pointed**__ at it.

4. It makes lots of (noise) nuts __**noise**__ .

5. It brings lots of job (joy) __**joy**__

Notes for Home: Your child practiced using words with *oi* and *oy*, such as *coin* and *joy*. **Home Activity:** Work with your child to list other words with *oi* and *oy* that have the same vowel sound as *coin* and *joy*.

Add -ful to each word in ( ).
Write the word on the line to finish each sentence.

help + -ful = help**ful**

1. It was a __**wonderful**__ party. (wonder)

2. The room looked __**joyful**__ . (joy)

3. The children were __**playful**__ . (play)

4. The music was __**cheerful**__ . (cheer)

5. It was __**peaceful**__ after the party. (peace)

Notes for Home: Your child wrote words with the suffix *-ful*, such as *helpful*. **Home Activity:** Read a story with your child. Challenge your child to find words in the story that can have the suffix *-ful* added to them, such as *care, help,* and *play (careful, helpful, playful)*.

Pick a word from the box to finish each sentence.
Write the word on the line.

| about | different | father | important | told |

1. My __**father**__ was born in Korea.

2. He has __**told**__ me stories about Korea.

3. One is __**about**__ a Korean boy like me.

4. Life there is a bit __**different**__ from life here.

5. These stories are __**important**__ to me.

Notes for Home: This week your child is learning to read the words *about, different, father, important,* and *told*. **Home Activity:** Encourage your child to write a story with a character who is a father, using as many of these words as possible.

Read each story. **Follow** the directions.

I have a birthday party every year. My family is all there.
My friends come too. There are games and cake.
It is a lot of fun.

1. Circle the sentence that tells the big idea of this story.

   (My birthday party is always fun)

   I am growing up.

2. Underline the parts of the story that helped you tell
   the big idea.

I was going out to play, but my mom got sick. I had
to take care of my little brother. He can be a pest.
I know it is important to help out, so I didn't mind.

3. Circle the sentence that is the
   big idea of this story.

   (Helping your family is important.)

   A little brother can be a pest.

4. Underline the parts of the story that
   helped you tell the big idea.

Notes for Home: Your child practiced finding the big idea in a story. **Home Activity:** Work with
your child to come up with an idea you both think is important, such as: *Always plan ahead.*
Help your child write about something that has happened in his or her life that conveys that idea.

24 Theme

Level 2.2

An **adjective** describes a noun.
An adjective can tell how something
looks, sounds, tastes, feels, or smells.

Apples taste **sweet.**

Circle the adjective in each sentence.
Draw a line from each adjective to the sense it goes with.

1. The ball looks (red.)   a.

2. The soap smells (fruity.)   b.

3. The tree bark feels (rough.)   c.

4. The music sounds (loud.)   d.

5. The stew tastes (salty.)   e.

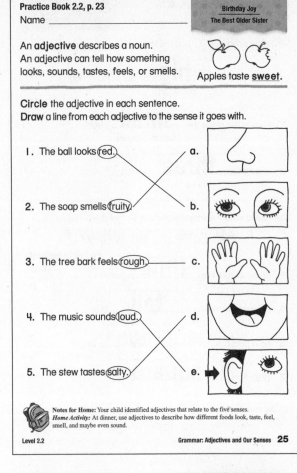

Notes for Home: Your child identified adjectives that relate to the five senses.
Home Activity: At dinner, use adjectives to describe how different foods look, taste, feel,
smell, and maybe even sound.

Level 2.2

Grammar: Adjectives and Our Senses **25**

Pick a word from the box to match each clue.
Write the word on the line.

attention   different   important
interesting   secretly   special   told

1. I found a _____ map.   **special**

2. not boring   **interesting**

3. not the same   **different**

4. done in secret   **secretly**

5. I _____ him a story.   **told**

6. It's _____ to be on time.   **important**

7. When you listen carefully,   **attention**
   you are paying _____ .

Notes for Home: Your child used word clues to practice new vocabulary words.
Home Activity: Read the vocabulary words on this page aloud. Work with your child to
use each word in a sentence.

26 Vocabulary

Level 2.2

---

ear   p**ee**ring

Circle the word for each picture.

1.	2.	3.	4.
(spear) share	door (deer)	(rear) read	clear (corn)

5.	6.	7.	8.
tires (tears)	(hear) hire	store (steer)	(fear) four

Find the word that has the same vowel sound as the picture.
Mark the space to show your answer.

9. ● near   10. ○ yarn
   ○ nail   ○ yard
   ○ snare   ● year   ear

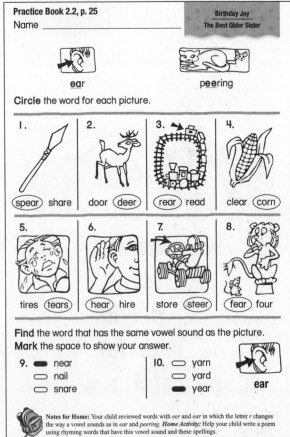

Notes for Home: Your child reviewed words with *eer* and *ear* in which the letter *r* changes
the way a vowel sounds as in *ear* and *peering*. **Home Activity:** Help your child write a poem
using rhyming words that have this vowel sound and these spellings.

Level 2.2

Phonics: *r*-Controlled Vowels: *ear, eer* Review **27**

boil   coin   point   spoil   voice   enjoy

Write the word from the box that rhymes with each word below.

1. choice

voice

2. toy

enjoy

Write two words that rhyme with **foil**.

3. **boil**

4. **spoil**

Pick a word from the box to match each clue.
Write the word on the line.

5. a penny

coin

6. the end of a sharp pencil

point

Pick a word from the box to finish each sentence.
Write the word on the line.

father
told

7. My **father** was born in China.

8. He **told** me stories about it.

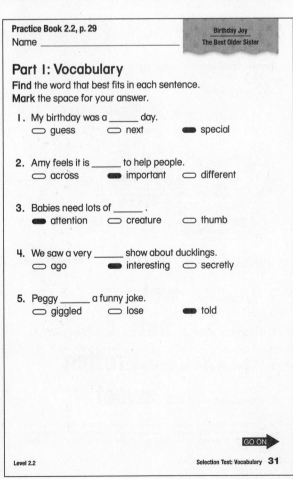

Notes for Home: Your child spelled words with *oy* and *oi*, such as *enjoy* and *coin*, and two frequently used words: *father, told*. **Home Activity:** Say each spelling word, and use it in a sentence. Repeat the word, and have your child write it.

28 Spelling: Vowel /oi/: *oy, oi*   Level 2.2

Draw a line from each adjective to the sense it matches.

1. stinky
2. pretty
3. loud
4. warm
5. salty

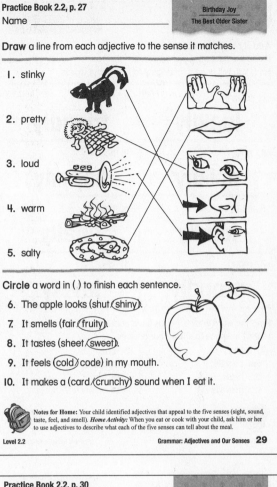

Circle a word in ( ) to finish each sentence.

6. The apple looks (shut (shiny)).

7. It smells (fair (fruity)).

8. It tastes (sheet (sweet)).

9. It feels ((cold) code) in my mouth.

10. It makes a (card (crunchy)) sound when I eat it.

Notes for Home: Your child identified adjectives that appeal to the five senses (sight, sound, taste, feel, and smell). **Home Activity:** When you eat or cook with your child, ask him or her to use adjectives to describe what each of the five senses can tell about the meal.

Level 2.2   Grammar: Adjectives and Our Senses 29

Part 1: Vocabulary

Find the word that best fits in each sentence.
Mark the space for your answer.

1. My birthday was a _____ day.
   - guess
   - next
   - ● special

2. Amy feels it is _____ to help people.
   - across
   - ● important
   - different

3. Babies need lots of _____ .
   - ● attention
   - creature
   - thumb

4. We saw a very _____ show about ducklings.
   - ago
   - ● interesting
   - secretly

5. Peggy _____ a funny joke.
   - giggled
   - lose
   - ● told

GO ON

Level 2.2   Selection Test: Vocabulary 31

Part 2: Comprehension

Read each question.
Mark the space for your answer.

6. After Kiju was born, Sunhi missed her time with —
   - Robin.
   - ● Halmoni.
   - Jenny.

7. At first, Sunhi thinks that —
   - ● everyone likes Kiju better than her.
   - she is the best older sister.
   - it would be great to have more babies.

8. Which sentence tells what this story is about?
   - Sunhi told Halmoni about her day at school.
   - Kiju always made such a mess.
   - ● Everything changed for Sunhi when Kiju was born.

9. Why did Halmoni give Sunhi her surprise early?
   - She could not keep it a secret.
   - ● She wanted Sunhi to know that she loved her.
   - She was afraid that Sunhi would find it.

10. In this story, Sunhi learned that —
   - Halmoni is not her friend.
   - it is better to be an only child.
   - ● everyone is special.

STOP

32 Selection Test: Comprehension   Level 2.2

Answers **343**

Add -ly to each word below.
Write the new word on the line.
Hint: You will need to change **y** to **i** for some words.

1. lucky

   luckily

2. friend

   friendly

3. noisy

   noisily

4. happy

   happily

5. loud

   loudly

6. final

   finally

7. proud

   proudly

8. love

   lovely

Find the word where **-ly** has been added correctly.
Mark the space to show your answer.

9. brave
   - ● bravely
   - ○ bravly
   - ○ bravelly

10. busy
   - ○ busyly
   - ● busily
   - ○ busilly

Notes for Home: Your child reviewed words that have the suffix *-ly*. **Home Activity:** Words with *-ly* tell how an action is done. Name some action verbs *(run, sing)* and have your child use words with the suffix *-ly* to describe how each action could be done *(swiftly, sweetly)*.

Level 2.2

Phonics: Suffix *-ly* Review **33**

---

boil   coin   point   spoil   voice   enjoy

Pick a word from the box to match each clue.
Write the word on the line.

1. You'll find it at the end of a needle.   **point**

2. You use it to speak.   **voice**

3. You do this to water to make tea.   **boil**

4. You can use it to buy something.   **coin**

5. It means "to be happy" with something.   **enjoy**

6. It means "to become bad or rotten."   **spoil**

Change one letter in each word to make a word from the box.
Write the new word on the line.

father   told

7. gold   **told**

8. father   **father**

Notes for Home: Your child spelled words with *oi* and *oy*, such as *coin* and *enjoy*, and two frequently used words: *father, told.* **Home Activity:** Write each spelling word on a slip of paper. Take turns picking words and giving clues about each word for the other player to spell.

34 Spelling: Vowel /oi/: *oy, oi*

Level 2.2

RETEACHING

An **adjective** describes a person, place, animal, or thing.

An adjective can tell how something looks, sounds, tastes, feels, or smells.

The cake tastes **sweet**.

Circle the adjective in each sentence.
Draw a line from each adjective to the sense it matches.

1. Our kittens feel (soft)   a.

2. My soup tastes (spicy)   b.

3. The trees look (green)   c.

4. The air smells (fresh)   d.

5. The drum sounds (loud)   e.

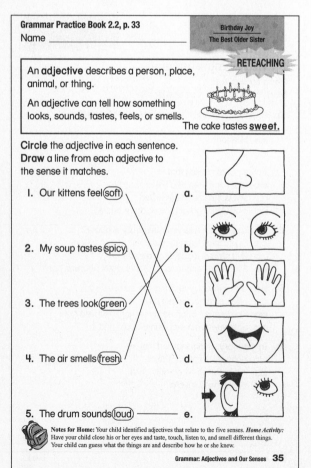

Notes for Home: Your child identified adjectives that relate to the five senses. **Home Activity:** Have your child close his or her eyes and taste, touch, listen to, and smell different things. Your child can guess what the things are and describe how he or she knew.

Grammar: Adjectives and Our Senses **35**

Choose an adjective from the box that makes sense in each sentence.
Write it on the line.

hot   sweet   wet   rotten   loud

Possible answers given.

1. My sister's voice is   **loud**

2. The apples feel   **wet**   in the water.

3. Be careful of the   **hot**   tea on the stove!

4. There is a bad apple that smells   **rotten**

5. Our apple pies will taste   **sweet**

Notes for Home: Your child identified adjectives that describe sight, sound, taste, feel, and smell. **Home Activity:** Have your child choose things that he or she sees, hears, tastes, feels, and smells. Your child can write each thing on one side of a card and list adjectives on the other side.

36 Grammar: Adjectives and Our Senses

Circle a word to finish each sentence.
Write the word on the line.

h**ea**d

(read) rode

1. I **read** a good book.

(bread) braid

2. It was about **bread** .

(healthful) helping

3. Bread is **healthful** .

(ready) reedy

4. I'm **ready** to eat!

(spread) spare

5. I **spread** the jam.

Notes for Home: Your child read and wrote words in which the short *e* sound is spelled *ea* as in *head*. Home Activity: Ask your child to write short rhyming sentences using words that rhyme with *head*.

Add -er to each word in ( ).
Write the word on the line to finish each sentence.

run + -er = runn**er**

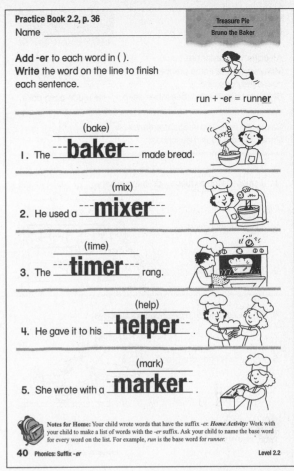

(bake)

1. The **baker** made bread.

(mix)

2. He used a **mixer** .

(time)

3. The **timer** rang.

(help)

4. He gave it to his **helper** .

(mark)

5. She wrote with a **marker** .

Notes for Home: Your child wrote words that have the suffix *-er*. Home Activity: Work with your child to make a list of words with the *-er* suffix. Ask your child to name the base word for every word on the list. For example, *run* is the base word for *runner*.

Pick a word from the box to finish each sentence.
Write the word on the line.

large   ready   says   today   wash

1. We will bake a pie **today** .

2. We **wash** the apples.

3. We'll make a **large** pie.

4. Dad **says** it will take about an hour.

5. Now we are **ready** to eat!

Notes for Home: This week your child is learning to read the words *large, ready, says, today,* and *wash*. Home Activity: Work with your child to write a story about some food you like to make together. Use the words in the box in your story.

Read each sentence.
Write Y if it tells something that could really happen.
Write N if it tells something that could not really happen.

Y   1. Jake has a dog.

N   2. The dog says words to Jake.

Y   3. The dog plays with Jake.

Y   4. Jake walks to school with the dog.

N   5. The dog reads stories to Jake.

Notes for Home: Your child identified whether a story event could really happen. Home Activity: Ask your child to make up two stories, one realistic (can really happen) and one a fantasy (includes events that can't really happen).

Answers **345**

Treasure Pie
Bruno the Baker

An **adjective** describes a noun.
Many adjectives come before the
nouns they describe.
Big is an adjective that describes **cake**.   He made a **big** cake.

Circle the adjective in each sentence.
Underline the noun it describes.

1. I smelled (wonderful) breads in the bakery.

2. I like the (round) loaves.

3. My mom bought (long) rolls.

4. She uses them to make (huge) sandwiches.

5. Her sandwiches are (great)!

🎒 **Notes for Home:** Your child has identified adjectives in sentences and the nouns they describe. **Home Activity:** Name an object in your home. Ask your child to think of adjectives to describe that object and use them in a sentence.

Level 2.2   **Grammar: Writing with Adjectives   43**

Treasure Pie
Bruno the Baker

Pick a word from the box to match each clue.
Write the word on the line.

| kitchen   large   oven   present   ready   says   today   wash |

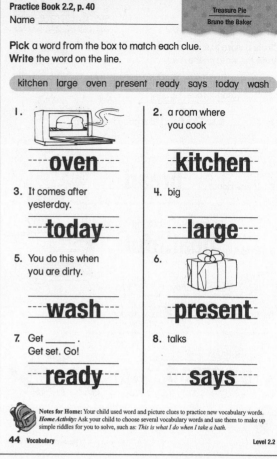

1. **oven**

2. a room where you cook
   kitchen

3. It comes after yesterday.
   today

4. big
   large

5. You do this when you are dirty.
   wash

6. **present**

7. Get _____ .
   Get set. Go!
   ready

8. talks
   says

🎒 **Notes for Home:** Your child used word and picture clues to practice new vocabulary words. **Home Activity:** Ask your child to choose several vocabulary words and use them to make up simple riddles for you to solve, such as: This is what I do when I take a bath.

44   Vocabulary   Level 2.2

Treasure Pie
Bruno the Baker

co**i**ns   to**y**s

Circle the word for each picture.

| 1. bay (boy) | 2. sail (soil) | 3. (point) paint | 4. (boil) bull |
| 5. outer (oyster) | 6. nurse (noise) | 7. roll (royal) | 8. (jet) joint |

Find the word that has the same vowel sound as the picture.
Mark the space to show your answer.

9. ● spoil   10. ○ most
   ○ spoon   ● moist   co**i**ns
   ○ snail   ○ moose

🎒 **Notes for Home:** Your child reviewed words spelled with *oi* and *oy* such as *coins* and *toys*. **Home Activity:** Have your child use the words with *oi* and *oy* in sentences. Together, draw pictures to go with the sentences.

Level 2.2   **Phonics: Vowel Diphthongs oi, oy Review   45**

Treasure Pie
Bruno the Baker

| bread   breath   spread   sweat   thread   weather |

Pick a word from the box to match each picture.
Write the word on the line.

1. **sweat**   2. **bread**   3. **thread**

Pick a word from the box to match each clue.
Write the word on the line.

4. You hold this if you're under water. **breath**

5. You can do this with jam or butter. **spread**

6. You check this before going outside. **weather**

Pick a word from the box to finish each sentence.
Write the word on the line.

ready   today

7. **Today** is Monday.

8. I'm getting **ready** for school.

🎒 **Notes for Home:** Your child spelled words in which the short *e* sound is spelled *ea* (bread) and two frequently used words: *ready, today*. **Home Activity:** Help your child write new short *e* words by changing some letters in each spelling word, for example, *bread* becomes *break*.

46   Spelling: Short e: ea   Level 2.2

Circle the adjective or adjectives in each sentence.

1. Dad makes (wonderful) desserts.

2. He bakes (many, tasty) pies.

3. He only uses (fresh, ripe) fruit.

4. The pies taste (sweet).

5. I like to eat pies when they are (warm).

6. I once helped Dad make (ten) pies.

7. They were for a (big) party at my school.

Write a sentence on each line about something you eat.
Use at least one adjective from the box in each sentence.

| four | good | hot | red | round | small | sweet |

Possible answers given.

8. I like red apples.

9. They taste sweet.

10. Apples are a good snack.

Notes for Home: Your child identified adjectives in sentences and wrote sentences with adjectives. **Home Activity:** Have your child write a sentence using one adjective. Then, you repeat the sentence, adding a second adjective. Switch roles and repeat.

Part I: Vocabulary

Find the word that best fits in each sentence.
Mark the space for your answer.

1. Please _____ the dishes.
   ○ follow   ○ peel   ● wash

2. Are you _____ to go?
   ○ high   ● ready   ○ enough

3. That hat is too _____ for you.
   ○ whole   ● large   ○ still

4. Grandma is in the _____ baking a cake.
   ○ oven   ● kitchen   ○ present

5. We will go to school _____ .
   ● today   ○ important   ○ until

GO ON

Part 2: Comprehension

Read each question.
Mark the space for your answer.

6. Why do Bruno and Felix make a cake?
   ○ Grandma tells them to make one.
   ● It is Bruno's birthday.
   ○ Felix likes to mix the batter.

7. What does Bruno do first?
   ○ He mixes the eggs.
   ○ He turns on the oven.
   ● He puts some butter in a pan.

8. You can tell that Bruno and Felix —
   ● work well together.
   ○ eat too much cake.
   ○ don't like to read directions.

9. Why do Bruno's friends give him a new mixing bowl?
   ○ His other bowl broke.
   ● They know he likes to bake.
   ○ He needs a bowl to put flowers in.

10. Which part of the story could **not** really happen?
    ○ A kitchen gets a little messy.
    ○ Butter melts in a pan.
    ● Animals bake a cake.

STOP

Add -ful to each word below.
Write the new word on the line.

a beauti**ful** cake

1. use	2. plenty
useful	**plentiful**

3. hope	4. color
hopeful	**colorful**

5. help	6. peace
helpful	**peaceful**

Find the base word for each word below.
Mark the space to show your answer.

7. careful
   ○ car
   ● care
   ○ caring

8. wonderful
   ● wonder
   ○ won
   ○ wand

Notes for Home: Your child reviewed words with the suffix -ful. **Home Activity:** Give your child some base words, such as *truth, pain, harm, fear, rest, cheer,* or *wonder.* Ask her or him to add -ful to each word and then use the new word in a sentence.

Answers **347**

bread   breath   spread   sweat   thread   weather

Pick words from the box to finish each sentence.
Write the words on the lines.

1.–2. I like to **spread**

jam on **bread** .

3.–4. If the **weather** is hot,

I **sweat** a lot.

5.–6. Hold your **breath** Ned.

It will help you **thread** .

Write the word from the box that rhymes with each word below.

ready   today

7. play

today

8. steady

ready

Notes for Home: Your child spelled words in which the short *e* sound is spelled *ea* and two frequently used words: *ready, today.* Home Activity: Ask your child to write a letter to a friend or relative using as many of these spelling words as possible.

52 Spelling Short *e: ea*   Level 2.2

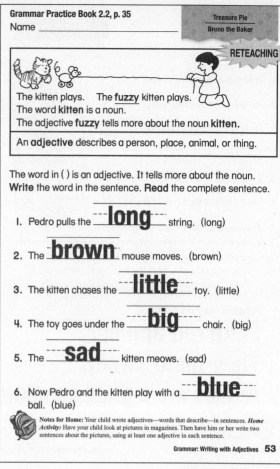

RETEACHING

The kitten plays.   The **fuzzy** kitten plays.
The word **kitten** is a noun.
The adjective **fuzzy** tells more about the noun **kitten**.

An **adjective** describes a person, place, animal, or thing.

The word in ( ) is an adjective. It tells more about the noun.
Write the word in the sentence. **Read** the complete sentence.

1. Pedro pulls the **long** string. (long)

2. The **brown** mouse moves. (brown)

3. The kitten chases the **little** toy. (little)

4. The toy goes under the **big** chair. (big)

5. The **sad** kitten meows. (sad)

6. Now Pedro and the kitten play with a **blue** ball. (blue)

Notes for Home: Your child wrote adjectives—words that describe—in sentences. Home Activity: Have your child look at pictures in magazines. Then have him or her write two sentences about the pictures, using at least one adjective in each sentence.

Grammar: Writing with Adjectives **53**

Draw one line under the adjective in each sentence.
Draw two lines under the noun it tells more about.

1. The silly movie starts.
2. The happy children sit.
3. Then fast music begins.
4. A gray donkey runs.
5. A tiny donkey trots.
6. They step on a large hat.
7. A tall cowboy comes.
8. Is he a brave man?

Choose the better adjective in ( ) to tell more about the noun.
Write the adjective in the sentence.

9. The **loud** thunder crashes. (loud/quiet)

10. The **scared** cattle run away. (safe/scared)

11. The cowboy calls the **gray** donkey. (pink/gray)

12. The donkey chases the **wild** cattle. (wild/dry)

13. The cattle sleep in the **big** barn. (tiny/big)

14. The **tired** cowboy goes home. (tired/new)

Notes for Home: Your child identified and wrote adjectives—words that tell more about nouns—in sentences. Home Activity: Have your child draw an imaginary creature. Then help him or her write a short story about the creature, using at least four adjectives.

54 Grammar: Writing with Adjectives

Circle the word for each picture.   ch**al**k

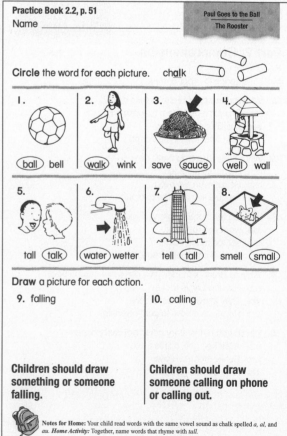

1. **ball** bell
2. **walk** wink
3. save **sauce**
4. **well** wall

5. tall **talk**
6. **water** wetter
7. tell **tall**
8. smell **small**

Draw a picture for each action.

9. falling

Children should draw something or someone falling.

10. calling

Children should draw someone calling on phone or calling out.

Notes for Home: Your child read words with the same vowel sound as *chalk* spelled *a, al,* and *au.* Home Activity: Together, name words that rhyme with *tall.*

Level 2.2   Phonics: /ô/Vowel Patterns *a, al, au* **57**

---

348 Answers

Write **k** or **b** to finish each word.

knee   lamb

1.
k nock

2.
com **b**

3.
k nob

4.
k nit

5.
thum **b**

6.
k not

7.
crum **b** s

8.
plum **b** er

Notes for Home: Your child read and completed words with *kn* and *mb* that have silent consonants. **Home Activity:** Work with your child to write sentences using the *kn* and *mb* words on this page.

58 Phonics: Silent Consonants *kn, mb*   Level 2.2

Pick a word from the box to finish each sentence.
Write the word on the line.

able   early   own   story   thought

1. Grandma told me a funny **story** .

2. She got ready for a party a day **early** .

3. She **thought** it was on Saturday.

4. Luckily, she was **able** to go the next day.

5. It was easy because it was at her **own** house!

Notes for Home: This week your child is learning to read the words *able, early, own, story,* and *thought.* **Home Activity:** Write these words on slips of paper. Ask your child to choose slips at random, read each word aloud, and use it in a sentence.

Level 2.2   High-Frequency Words **59**

Write a number next to each sentence to show the right order.

1. On July 4, everybody came with food. **2**

2. For weeks, our family planned a big picnic. **1**

3. We ate the food and had a lot of fun. **3**

4. He played a lot and got better and better. **2**

5. John started to learn to play the piano. **1**

6. John won the piano contest. **3**

Notes for Home: Your child identified the order of story events. **Home Activity:** Ask your child to tell you the beginning, middle, and end of a story you have read together. Listen for your child to focus on important story events.

60 Plot   Level 2.2

Add -er to an adjective when you compare two nouns.
The striped balloon is **bigger** than the dotted balloon.

Add -est when you compare more than two nouns.
The plain balloon is the **biggest** balloon he has.

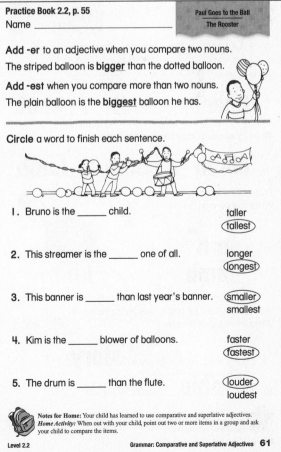

Circle a word to finish each sentence.

1. Bruno is the _____ child.
   taller
   (tallest)

2. This streamer is the _____ one of all.
   longer
   (longest)

3. This banner is _____ than last year's banner.
   (smaller)
   smallest

4. Kim is the _____ blower of balloons.
   faster
   (fastest)

5. The drum is _____ than the flute.
   (louder)
   loudest

Notes for Home: Your child has learned to use comparative and superlative adjectives. **Home Activity:** When out with your child, point out two or more items in a group and ask your child to compare the items.

Level 2.2   Grammar: Comparative and Superlative Adjectives **61**

Pick a word from the box to match each clue.
Write the word on the line.

able	brook	early	feathers
	growl	own	story

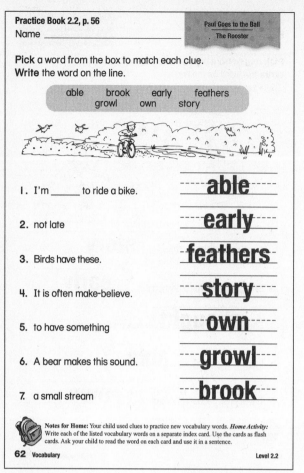

1. I'm _____ to ride a bike. **able**

2. not late **early**

3. Birds have these. **feathers**

4. It is often make-believe. **story**

5. to have something **own**

6. A bear makes this sound. **growl**

7. a small stream **brook**

Notes for Home: Your child used clues to practice new vocabulary words. *Home Activity:* Write each of the listed vocabulary words on a separate index card. Use the cards as flash cards. Ask your child to read the word on each card and use it in a sentence.

62 Vocabulary

Level 2.2

Circle the word for each picture. br**ea**kfast

1.	2.	3.	4.
(head) heard	(heavy) have	(thread) three	leather (letter)

5.	6.	7.	8.
father (feather)	swap (sweat)	(bread) braid	speed (spread)

Find the word that has the same **short e** sound as the picture.
Mark the space to show your answer.

9. ○ peach
   ● weather
   ○ bean

10. ○ meeting
    ○ meaning
    ● meadow

sweater

Notes for Home: Your child reviewed words in which the short *e* sound is spelled *ea*, as in *breakfast*. **Home Activity:** Ask your child to write a poem using words in which the short *e* sound is spelled *ea*.

Level 2.2

Phonics: Short *e: ea* Review **63**

---

climb	comb	lamb	kneel	knit	knot

Write three words from the box that begin with **kn**.

1. **kneel** 2. **knit** 3. **knot**

Write three words from the box that end in **mb**.

4. **climb** 5. **comb** 6. **lamb**

Pick a word from the box to match each picture.
Write the word on the line.

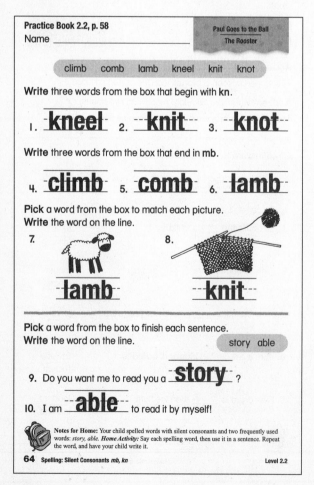

7. **lamb**

8. **knit**

Pick a word from the box to finish each sentence.
Write the word on the line.

story able

9. Do you want me to read you a **story** ?

10. I am **able** to read it by myself!

Notes for Home: Your child spelled words with silent consonants and two frequently used words: *story, able.* **Home Activity:** Say each spelling word, then use it in a sentence. Repeat the word, and have your child write it.

64 Spelling: Silent Consonants *mb, kn*

Level 2.2

Circle an adjective to finish each sentence.

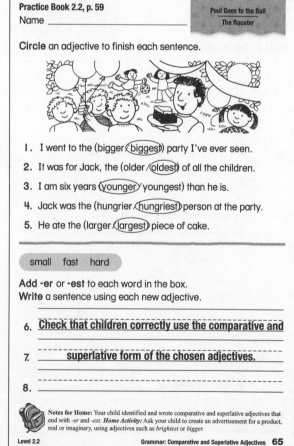

1. I went to the (bigger (biggest)) party I've ever seen.

2. It was for Jack, the (older (oldest)) of all the children.

3. I am six years (younger) youngest) than he is.

4. Jack was the (hungrier (hungriest)) person at the party.

5. He ate the (larger (largest)) piece of cake.

small fast hard

Add -er or **-est** to each word in the box.
Write a sentence using each new adjective.

6. **Check that children correctly use the comparative and**

7. **superlative form of the chosen adjectives.**

8. _____

Notes for Home: Your child identified and wrote comparative and superlative adjectives that end with *-er* and *-est*. **Home Activity:** Ask your child to create an advertisement for a product, real or imaginary, using adjectives such as *brightest* or *bigger*.

Level 2.2

Grammar: Comparative and Superlative Adjectives **65**

Part 1: Vocabulary

Find the word that best fits in each sentence.
Mark the space for your answer.

1. He swims in the _____ .
   ○ field   ● brook   ○ feathers

2. Pat told us a long _____ .
   ● story   ○ able   ○ picture

3. The dog began to _____ .
   ○ decide   ○ peel   ● growl

4. Carlos got up _____ today.
   ● early   ○ between   ○ able

5. Liz has her _____ room.
   ○ ripe   ● own   ○ early

GO ON ➤

Part 2: Comprehension

Read each question.
Mark the space for your answer.

6. What did the rooster do first?
   ○ He crowed at the sun.
   ● He got ready for the wedding.
   ○ He asked the grass for help.

7. The rooster got his beak dirty when he —
   ● ate some corn.
   ○ walked into the brook.
   ○ ate the grass.

8. The rooster talked to the grass, the lamb, and the others because he —
   ○ was a friendly bird.
   ○ wanted them to go to the wedding.
   ● needed some help.

9. Which of these could really happen?
   ○ A dog talks.
   ● A stick burns.
   ○ The grass cries.

10. Why did everyone but the sun say no to the rooster?
    ● The rooster had not done anything for them.
    ○ Everyone was too busy helping someone else.
    ○ They did not want to be late for the wedding.

STOP

Add -er to each word below to make a word that matches the picture.
Write the new word on the line.

bak**er**

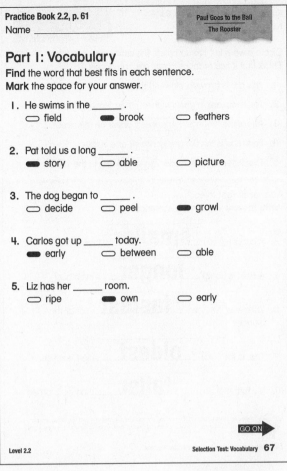

1. time — **timer**
2. sing — **singer**
3. bat — **batter**
4. farm — **farmer**
5. help — **helper**
6. run — **runner**

Find the word where the final **e** was dropped before **-er** was added.
Mark the space to show your answer.

7. ● diner
   ○ worker
   ○ drummer

8. ● skater
   ○ cleaner
   ○ jogger

Notes for Home: Your child wrote words that end with *-er*. **Home Activity:** Ask your child to make a list of different occupations that end with *-er*. Discuss what each person does and how it relates to the base word, such as *baker* and *bake*.

climb   comb   lamb   kneel   knit   knot

Pick a word from the box to match each clue.
Write the word on the line.

1. You do this to a hill. **climb**

2. It rhymes with *heel*. **kneel**

Change one letter in each word to make a word from the box.
Write the new word on the line.

3. come — **comb**
4. lame — **lamb**
5. know — **knot**
6. knot — **knit**

Pick a word from the box to finish each sentence.
Write the word on the line.

story   able

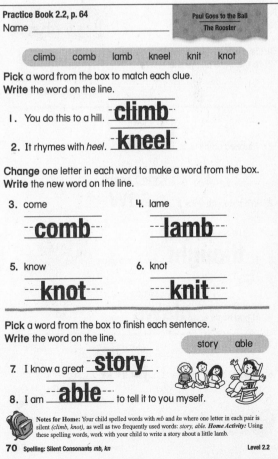

7. I know a great **story** .

8. I am **able** to tell it to you myself.

Notes for Home: Your child spelled words with *mb* and *kn* where one letter in each pair is silent (*climb, knot*), as well as two frequently used words: *story, able*. **Home Activity:** Using these spelling words, work with your child to write a story about a little lamb.

Answers **351**

Paul Goes to the Ball
The Rooster

RETEACHING

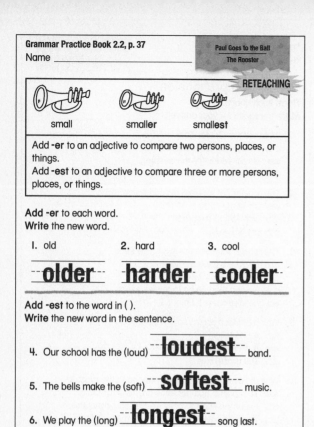

small   smaller   smallest

Add **-er** to an adjective to compare two persons, places, or things.
Add **-est** to an adjective to compare three or more persons, places, or things.

Add -er to each word.
Write the new word.

1. old   2. hard   3. cool

older   **harder**   **cooler**

Add -est to the word in ( ).
Write the new word in the sentence.

4. Our school has the (loud) **loudest** band.

5. The bells make the (soft) **softest** music.

6. We play the (long) **longest** song last.

Notes for Home: Your child wrote comparative and superlative adjectives in sentences. **Home Activity:** Have your child choose three objects in your home (shoes, glasses, pictures) and use comparative and superlative adjectives to compare the objects.

Grammar: Comparative and Superlative Adjectives   **71**

Paul Goes to the Ball
The Rooster

Circle a word in ( ) to complete the sentence.
Think first if two or more things are compared.

1. This car is (slower / slowest) than that car.
2. The seats are (higher / highest) than those in Jo's car.
3. Abe is the (younger / youngest) driver on the street.
4. This road is the (longer / longest) one in town.
5. That kitten is the (smaller / smallest) one in the litter.

Add -er or **-est** to each word in ( ).
Write the new word in the sentence.

6. A car is (small) **smaller** than a bus.

7. A train is (long) **longer** than a bus.

8. This jet is the (fast) **fastest** of all the planes.

9. That is the (old) **oldest** ship I have seen.

10. My father is (tall) **taller** than his brother.

Notes for Home: Your child wrote comparative and superlative adjectives. **Home Activity:** Have your child compare family members. Remind them to use comparative and superlative adjectives.

72   Grammar: Comparative and Superlative Adjectives

Yawning Dawn
Missing: One Stuffed Rabbit

Circle a word to finish each sentence.
Write the word on the line.

He **bought** a dr**aw**ing.

1. I looked at the _loan (lawn)_ **lawn** .

2. What do you think I _(saw) swamp_ **saw** ?

3. I _toad (thought)_ **thought** it was a dragon.

4. It had nasty _(claws) climbs_ **claws**

5. It was Tom inside the _jays (jaws)_ **jaws** !

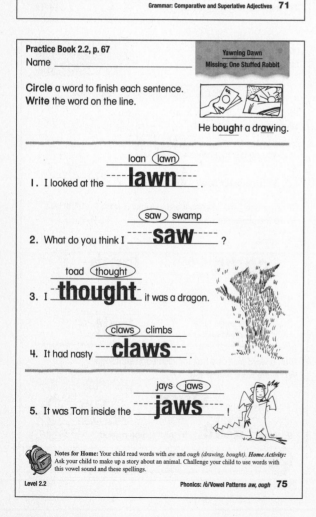

Notes for Home: Your child read words with aw and ough (drawing, bought). **Home Activity:** Ask your child to make up a story about an animal. Challenge your child to use words with this vowel sound and these spellings.

Level 2.2   Phonics: /ô/Vowel Patterns aw, ough   **75**

Yawning Dawn
Missing: One Stuffed Rabbit

Circle a word to finish each sentence.
Write the word on the line.

wrench

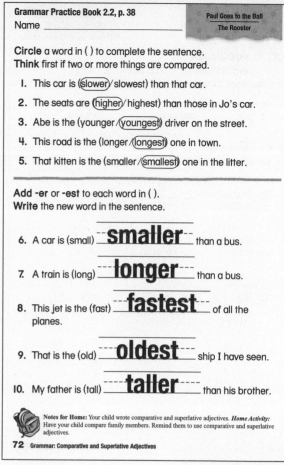

1. The teacher _right (wrote)_ **wrote** the problem.

2. The _hill (whole)_ **whole** class watched her.

3. She drew a plus _(sign) swan_ **sign** .

4. She asked _how (who)_ **who** knew the answer.

5. I was happy my answer wasn't _(wrong) rode_ **wrong** .

Notes for Home: Your child read words with the letters pairs gn, wh, and wr in which one consonant is silent, as in sign, whole, and write. **Home Activity:** Ask your child to make a sign for a new household product using words with these letter pairs.

76   Phonics: Silent Consonants gn, wh, wr   Level 2.2

Pick a word from the box to finish each sentence.
Write the word on the line.

| family | finally | morning | paper | really |

1. I get up early every **morning** .

2. First I get the **paper** .

3. Next, my **family** cooks.

4. **Finally** , we eat.

5. I **really** like mornings!

Notes for Home: This week your child is learning to read the words *family, finally, morning, paper,* and *really.* **Home Activity:** Ask your child to make the front page of a newspaper and write a story about a family activity. Encourage your child to use the listed words.

Level 2.2   **High-Frequency Words** 77

Read the story.
Answer the questions.

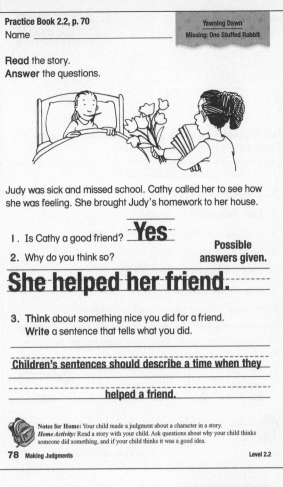

Judy was sick and missed school. Cathy called her to see how she was feeling. She brought Judy's homework to her house.

1. Is Cathy a good friend? **Yes**

2. Why do you think so?

Possible answers given.

She helped her friend.

3. **Think** about something nice you did for a friend.
Write a sentence that tells what you did.

Children's sentences should describe a time when they

helped a friend.

Notes for Home: Your child made a judgment about a character in a story. **Home Activity:** Read a story with your child. Ask questions about why your child thinks someone did something, and if your child thinks it was a good idea.

78   **Making Judgments**   Level 2.2

Adverbs can tell how, when, or where something happens.
Quickly is an **adverb**.

Jane runs **quickly**.

Circle the adverb in each sentence.
Write the adverb on the line.

1. Our Thanksgiving play is (today.)   **today**

2. We came to school (early.)   **early**

3. We practice (inside.)   **inside**

4. We sing (loudly.)   **loudly**

5. We walk (softly.)   **softly**

Notes for Home: Your child identified adverbs—words that tell how, when, or where something happens. **Home Activity:** Give your child simple commands that use adverbs to tell how to do the action. *(Clap your hands softly.)*

Level 2.2   **Grammar: Adverbs** 79

Pick a word from the box to match each clue.
Write the word on the line.

| calm | family | finally | gathered |
| hospital | morning | paper | really |

1. a place where sick or hurt people go   **hospital**

2. something to write on   **paper**

3. mother, father, brothers, and sisters   **family**

4. came together   **gathered**

5. quiet   **calm**

6. at last   **finally**

7. beginning of the day   **morning**

8. very much, truly   **really**

Notes for Home: Your child used word clues to practice new vocabulary words. **Home Activity:** Make a simple crossword puzzle with your child using some of these vocabulary words. Use the clues above or write your own clues.

80   **Vocabulary**   Level 2.2

Answers   **353**

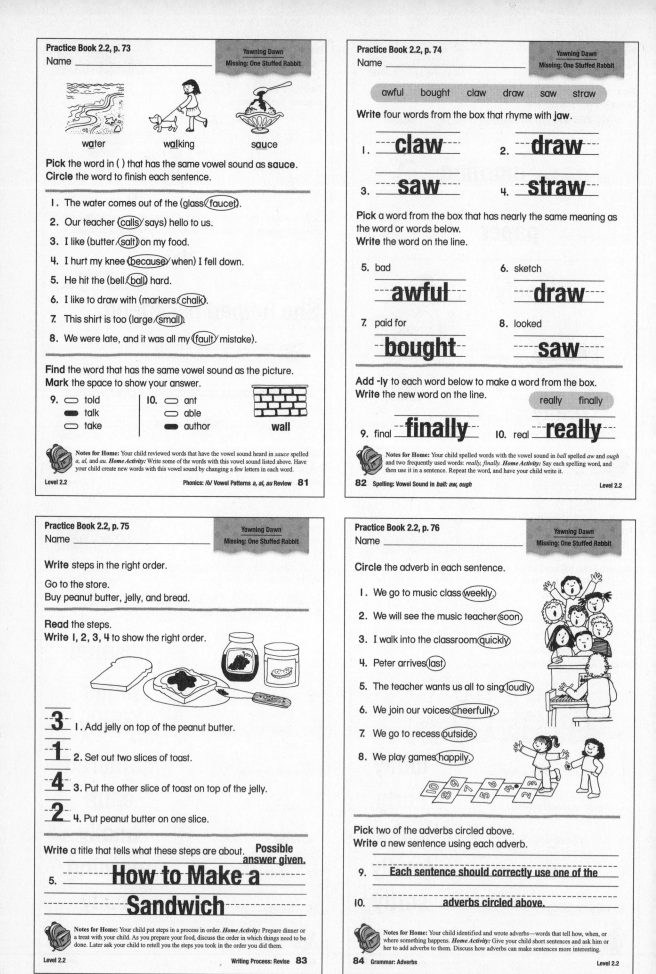

Practice Book 2.2, p. 73

Name _____

Yawning Dawn
Missing: One Stuffed Rabbit

water   walking   sauce

Pick the word in ( ) that has the same vowel sound as **sauce**.
Circle the word to finish each sentence.

1. The water comes out of the (glass/(faucet)).
2. Our teacher ((calls)/says) hello to us.
3. I like (butter/(salt)) on my food.
4. I hurt my knee ((because)/when) I fell down.
5. He hit the (bell/(ball)) hard.
6. I like to draw with (markers/(chalk)).
7. This shirt is too (large/(small)).
8. We were late, and it was all my ((fault)/mistake).

Find the word that has the same vowel sound as the picture.
Mark the space to show your answer.

9. ⬡ told
   ⬤ talk
   ⬡ take

10. ⬡ ant
    ⬡ able
    ⬤ author

wall

Notes for Home: Your child reviewed words that have the vowel sound heard in *sauce* spelled *a, al,* and *au.* *Home Activity:* Write some of the words with this vowel sound listed above. Have your child create new words with this vowel sound by changing a few letters in each word.

Level 2.2

Phonics: /ȯ/ Vowel Patterns *a, al, au* Review **81**

Practice Book 2.2, p. 74

Name _____

Yawning Dawn
Missing: One Stuffed Rabbit

awful   bought   claw   draw   saw   straw

Write four words from the box that rhyme with **jaw**.

1. **claw**   2. **draw**

3. **saw**   4. **straw**

Pick a word from the box that has nearly the same meaning as the word or words below.
Write the word on the line.

5. bad   6. sketch
   awful   **draw**

7. paid for   8. looked
   bought   **saw**

Add -ly to each word below to make a word from the box.
Write the new word on the line.

really   finally

9. final **finally**   10. real **really**

Notes for Home: Your child spelled words with the vowel sound in *ball* spelled *aw* and *ough* and two frequently used words: *really, finally.* *Home Activity:* Say each spelling word, and then use it in a sentence. Repeat the word, and have your child write it.

82 Spelling: Vowel Sound in *ball: aw, ough*

Level 2.2

Practice Book 2.2, p. 75

Name _____

Yawning Dawn
Missing: One Stuffed Rabbit

Write steps in the right order.

Go to the store.
Buy peanut butter, jelly, and bread.

Read the steps.
Write 1, 2, 3, 4 to show the right order.

3 1. Add jelly on top of the peanut butter.

1 2. Set out two slices of toast.

4 3. Put the other slice of toast on top of the jelly.

2 4. Put peanut butter on one slice.

Write a title that tells what these steps are about. **Possible answer given.**

5. **How to Make a Sandwich**

Notes for Home: Your child put steps in a process in order. *Home Activity:* Prepare dinner or a treat with your child. As you prepare your food, discuss the order in which things need to be done. Later ask your child to retell you the steps you took in the order you did them.

Level 2.2

Writing Process: Revise **83**

Practice Book 2.2, p. 76

Name _____

Yawning Dawn
Missing: One Stuffed Rabbit

Circle the adverb in each sentence.

1. We go to music class (weekly).
2. We will see the music teacher (soon).
3. I walk into the classroom (quickly).
4. Peter arrives (last).
5. The teacher wants us all to sing (loudly).
6. We join our voices (cheerfully).
7. We go to recess (outside).
8. We play games (happily).

Pick two of the adverbs circled above.
Write a new sentence using each adverb.

9. **Each sentence should correctly use one of the**

10. **adverbs circled above.**

Notes for Home: Your child identified and wrote adverbs—words that tell how, when, or where something happens. *Home Activity:* Give your child short sentences and ask him or her to add adverbs to them. Discuss how adverbs can make sentences more interesting.

84 Grammar: Adverbs

Level 2.2

Part 1: Vocabulary

Find the word that best fits in each sentence.
Mark the space for your answer.

1. We went to see Grandpa in the _____ .
   ⬡ team ⬤ hospital ⬡ family

2. The sun comes up in the _____ .
   ⬡ paper ⬡ head ⬤ morning

3. Mom told me to _____ down.
   ⬡ clean ⬤ calm ⬡ fix

4. Sam _____ all his toys together.
   ⬡ giggled ⬤ gathered ⬡ exclaimed

5. His shirt is _____ yellow.
   ⬡ another ⬡ finally ⬤ really

GO ON ➡

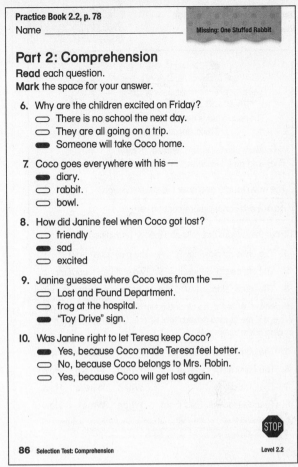

Part 2: Comprehension

Read each question.
Mark the space for your answer.

6. Why are the children excited on Friday?
   ⬡ There is no school the next day.
   ⬡ They are all going on a trip.
   ⬤ Someone will take Coco home.

7. Coco goes everywhere with his —
   ⬤ diary.
   ⬡ rabbit.
   ⬡ bowl.

8. How did Janine feel when Coco got lost?
   ⬡ friendly
   ⬤ sad
   ⬡ excited

9. Janine guessed where Coco was from the —
   ⬡ Lost and Found Department.
   ⬡ frog at the hospital.
   ⬤ "Toy Drive" sign.

10. Was Janine right to let Teresa keep Coco?
    ⬤ Yes, because Coco made Teresa feel better.
    ⬡ No, because Coco belongs to Mrs. Robin.
    ⬡ Yes, because Coco will get lost again.

STOP

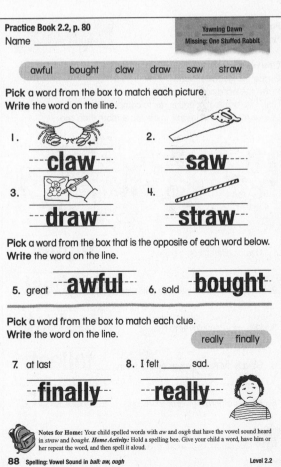

Circle the word for each picture.   k̲nee   lim̲b

1. (comb) cub
2. nice (knife)
3. (lamb) lab
4. nut (knot)
5. club (climb)
6. kite (knight)
7. (thumb) thumb
8. (kitten) knit

Find the word that has a silent consonant.
Mark the space to show your answer.

9. ⬤ know
   ⬡ kind
   ⬡ kiss

10. ⬡ plums
    ⬤ plumber
    ⬡ plank

Notes for Home: Your child reviewed words with *kn* and *mb* where one letter in each pair is silent as in *knee* and *limb*. **Home Activity:** Make picture cards of words with *kn* and *mb* with your child. Take turns picking cards and writing a sentence about each word pictured.

awful   bought   claw   draw   saw   straw

Pick a word from the box to match each picture.
Write the word on the line.

1. claw
2. saw
3. draw
4. straw

Pick a word from the box that is the opposite of each word below.
Write the word on the line.

5. great   awful   6. sold   bought

Pick a word from the box to match each clue.
Write the word on the line.

really   finally

7. at last   8. I felt _____ sad.

   finally   really

Notes for Home: Your child spelled words with *aw* and *ough* that have the vowel sound heard in *straw* and *bought*. **Home Activity:** Hold a spelling bee. Give your child a word, have him or her repeat the word, and then spell it aloud.

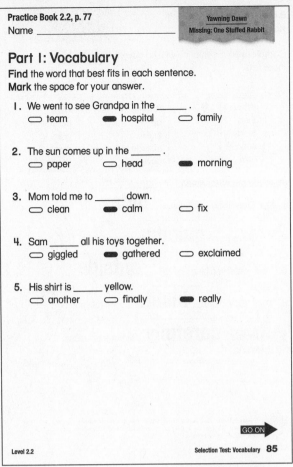

Answers **355**

Name _____

RETEACHING

The music plays **now.**   The children walk **around.**
The children laughed **loudly.**

An adverb can tell **when, where,** or **how.**
The word **now** tells **when** the music plays.
The word **around** tells **where** the children walk.
The word **loudly** tells **how** the children laugh.

An **adverb** can tell more about a verb.

Circle the adverb that tells about each underlined verb.

1. The children <u>play</u> (inside)
4. The players <u>sit</u> (now)

2. The chairs <u>stand</u> (there)
5. Two children <u>stand</u> (up)

3. The music <u>stops</u> (quickly)
6. A boy <u>takes</u> a chair (carefully)

Underline When if the circled adverb tells when. **Underline Where** if the circled adverb tells where. **Underline How** if the circled adverb tells how.

7. The game ends (soon) — When Where How

8. The children go (outside) — When <u>Where</u> How

9. They walk (slowly) — When Where <u>How</u>

10. (Then) the teacher calls them. — <u>When</u> Where How

 Notes for Home: Your child identified and wrote adverbs in sentences. *Home Activity:* Have your child draw a picture of himself or herself doing something at school. Then have your child write sentences about the drawing, using at least one adverb.

Grammar: Adverbs **89**

Name _____

Complete each sentence with an adverb from one of these lists.

When	Where	How
then	up	carefully
today	inside	quickly
soon	outside	quietly
now	down	loudly

Possible answers given.

1. Our class visited a museum **today**

2. We drove there **quietly** in a school bus.

3. First, we saw a plant exhibit **outside**

4. Then, we walked **inside** the museum.

5. We looked **carefully** at huge dinosaur skeletons.

Notes for Home: Your child wrote adverbs in sentences. *Home Activity:* Read a favorite story with your child. Have him or her point out three adverbs. Then have him or her write new sentences, using the adverbs.

90 Grammar: Adverbs

Name _____

One word in each sentence is **not** correct.
Circle the incorrect word.
Write the word correctly on the line.
Hint: Use words that end in **-er** to compare two things.
Use words that end in **-est** to compare more than two.

1. Use a ball (big) than a softball. — **bigger**

2. The (higher) score you can get is ten. — **highest**

3. Use your (fast) player to run. — **fastest**

4. Sara is the (taller) player on our team. — **tallest**

5. Mike is a (hardest) kicker than Tom. — **harder**

Notes for Home: Your child corrected comparative adjectives that end in *-er* and superlative adjectives that end in *-est*. *Home Activity:* Look through a picture book with your child. Have him or her make comparisons about the characters using adjectives that end in *-er* or *-est*.

Level 2.2

Writing Process: Edit **91**

Name _____

Pick the word with the **short u** sound you hear in **double.**
Circle the word to finish each sentence.

1. We spent a night in the _____ . — outdoors / (country) / house

2. My _____ and I saw many stars. — aunt / (cousin) / hound

3. They seemed close enough to _____ . — count / (touch) / bounce

4. A _____ of stars were very bright. — (couple) / group / outline

5. One group of stars looks like a _____ bear. — cute / (young) / proud

Notes for Home: Your child read words in which the short *u* sound is spelled *ou* as in *double*. *Home Activity:* Find words with *ou* as you read together. Have your child say each word aloud and tell whether it has the same vowel sound as *double*.

Level 2.2

Phonics: Short *u: ou* **95**

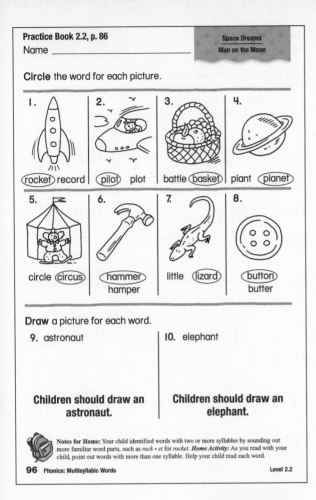

Practice Book 2.2, p. 86

Name _____

Man on the Moon

Circle the word for each picture.

1. rocket (circled) record
2. pilot (circled) plot
3. battle basket (circled)
4. plant planet (circled)

5. circle circus (circled)
6. hammer (circled) hamper
7. little lizard (circled)
8. button (circled) butter

Draw a picture for each word.

9. astronaut

10. elephant

Children should draw an astronaut.

Children should draw an elephant.

Notes for Home: Your child identified words with two or more syllables by sounding out more familiar word parts, such as *rock • et* for *rocket*. Home Activity: As you read with your child, point out words with more than one syllable. Help your child read each word.

96 Phonics: Multisyllabic Words

Level 2.2

Practice Book 2.2, p. 87

Name _____

Space Dreams
Man on the Moon

Pick a word from the box to finish each sentence.
Write the word on the line.

began   Earth   ever   remember   try

1. Nina **began** to build a rocket.

2. I will **try** to fly.

3. **Remember** to wear a seat belt.

4. Will you **ever** come back?

5. I'll come back to **Earth** soon!

Notes for Home: This week your child is learning to read the words *began, Earth, ever, remember,* and *try.* Home Activity: Have your child pretend that he or she is on the moon. Have your child use these words to write a letter home.

Level 2.2

High-Frequency Words **97**

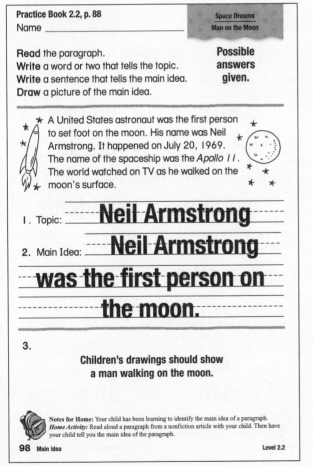

Practice Book 2.2, p. 88

Name _____

Space Dreams
Man on the Moon

Read the paragraph.
Write a word or two that tells the topic.
Write a sentence that tells the main idea.
Draw a picture of the main idea.

Possible answers given.

A United States astronaut was the first person to set foot on the moon. His name was Neil Armstrong. It happened on July 20, 1969. The name of the spaceship was the *Apollo 11.* The world watched on TV as he walked on the moon's surface.

1. Topic: **Neil Armstrong**

2. Main Idea: **Neil Armstrong was the first person on the moon.**

3.

Children's drawings should show a man walking on the moon.

Notes for Home: Your child has been learning to identify the main idea of a paragraph. Home Activity: Read aloud a paragraph from a nonfiction article with your child. Then have your child tell you the main idea of the paragraph.

98 Main Idea

Level 2.2

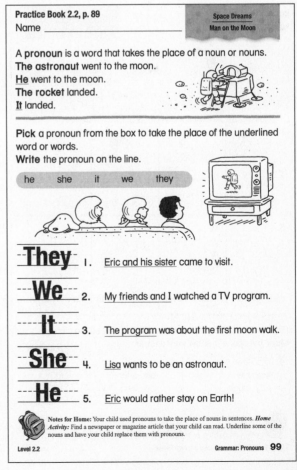

Practice Book 2.2, p. 89

Name _____

Space Dreams
Man on the Moon

A **pronoun** is a word that takes the place of a noun or nouns.
The astronaut went to the moon.
He went to the moon.
The rocket landed.
It landed.

Pick a pronoun from the box to take the place of the underlined word or words.
Write the pronoun on the line.

he   she   it   we   they

They 1. Eric and his sister came to visit.

We 2. My friends and I watched a TV program.

It 3. The program was about the first moon walk.

She 4. Lisa wants to be an astronaut.

He 5. Eric would rather stay on Earth!

Notes for Home: Your child used pronouns to take the place of nouns in sentences. Home Activity: Find a newspaper or magazine article that your child can read. Underline some of the nouns and have your child replace them with pronouns.

Level 2.2

Grammar: Pronouns **99**

Answers **357**

Pick a word from the box to finish the sentence.
Write the word on the line.

began circled Earth ever remember rockets try

1. Did I _____**ever**_____ tell you about my space trip?

2. Tell me again. I don't _____**remember**_____ it all.

3. My rocket _____**circled**_____ Earth three times.

4. I _____**began**_____ to get a little scared.

5. I was glad to get back to _____**Earth**_____!

6. I never wanted to _____**try**_____ flying again!

7. Now I watch _____**rockets**_____ launch only on TV.

Notes for Home: Your child used vocabulary words to complete sentences. *Home Activity:* Encourage your child to use some of the vocabulary words to write a description of a trip to space.

100 Vocabulary

Level 2.2

Put each group of words in **ABC order**.
Pick a word in ( ) that comes between the two words shown.
Write the word on the line.

1. tip (the/toy) **toy** try
2. chill (clap/cent) **clap** come
3. beg (bib/bug) **bib** black
4. wet (wring/why) **why** will
5. age (and/air) **air** all
6. glow (got/give) **got** grow
7. dizzy (dog/duty) **dog** dry
8. sick (sky/snow) **sky** smile
9. erase (ever/eye) **ever** extra
10. bad (brag/bed) **bed** boy

Notes for Home: Your child alphabetized words by looking at the second letter in words that begin with the same letter. This skill will help your child better use a glossary or dictionary. *Home Activity:* Help your child use the telephone book to look up the names of people you know.

Level 2.2

Research and Study Skills: Alphabetical Order to Second Letter (Glossary) **101**

str**aw**   b**ough**t

Circle the word for each picture.

1.	2.	3.	4.
say (saw)	lane (lawn)	(shawl) shell	(thought) thorn

5.	6.	7.	8.
cuff (cough)	(hook) hawk	(fought) foot	(dawn) down

Find the word that has the same vowel sound as the picture.
Mark the space to show your answer.

paw

9. ○ low
   ● law
   ○ laugh

10. ○ old
    ● ought
    ○ own

Notes for Home: Your child reviewed words spelled with *aw* or *ough* that have the vowel sound heard in *straw* and *bought*. *Home Activity:* Help your child write sentences using words with *aw* and *ough* listed above. Then have your child read the sentences aloud.

102 Phonics: /ô/ Vowel Patterns *aw, ough* Review

Level 2.2

---

camera carry follow lesson pretty suddenly

Write four words from the box that have two syllables.

1. _____**carry**_____   2. _____**follow**_____
3. _____**lesson**_____   4. _____**pretty**_____

Write two words from the box that have three syllables.

5. _____**camera**_____   6. _____**suddenly**_____

Pick a word from the box that is the opposite of each word below.
Write the word on the line.

7. ugly _____**pretty**_____   8. drop _____**carry**_____

Say the word for each picture.
Write the word from the box that has the same beginning sound.

ever began

9. bee
_____**began**_____

10. elephant
_____**ever**_____

Notes for Home: Your child spelled words that have more than one syllable, such as *suddenly*, and two frequently used words: *ever, began*. *Home Activity:* Help your child use these spelling words to write sentences. Have your child read each sentence aloud.

Level 2.2

Spelling: Multisyllabic Words **103**

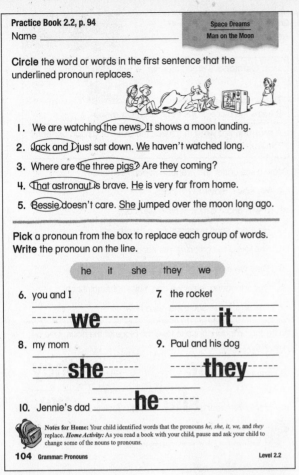

Circle the word or words in the first sentence that the underlined pronoun replaces.

1. We are watching (the news.) It shows a moon landing.

2. (Jack and I) just sat down. We haven't watched long.

3. Where are (the three pigs?) Are they coming?

4. (That astronaut) is brave. He is very far from home.

5. (Bessie) doesn't care. She jumped over the moon long ago.

Pick a pronoun from the box to replace each group of words.
Write the pronoun on the line.

he   it   she   they   we

6. you and I

   we

7. the rocket

   it

8. my mom

   she

9. Paul and his dog

   they

10. Jennie's dad

    he

Notes for Home: Your child identified words that the pronouns *he, she, it, we,* and *they* replace. **Home Activity:** As you read a book with your child, pause and ask your child to change some of the nouns to pronouns.

Part I: Vocabulary

Find the word that best fits in each sentence.
Mark the space for your answer.

1. Have you _____ looked at the moon?
   - ⬭ able
   - ⬛ ever
   - ⬭ done

2. Lee will _____ to come to the game.
   - ⬭ guess
   - ⬭ use
   - ⬛ try

3. The sun _____ to shine.
   - ⬛ began
   - ⬭ gathered
   - ⬭ circled

4. Three _____ fly into the sky.
   - ⬭ paws
   - ⬭ dinosaurs
   - ⬛ rockets

5. I can't _____ the cat's name.
   - ⬛ remember
   - ⬭ Earth
   - ⬭ try

GO ON ▶

Part 2: Comprehension

Read each question.
Mark the space for your answer.

6. Before 1969, no one had ever —
   - ⬭ gone into space.
   - ⬛ walked on the moon.
   - ⬭ made rockets fly.

7. What happened first?
   - ⬛ *Saturn 5* took off.
   - ⬭ Armstrong took pictures on the moon.
   - ⬭ The *Eagle* landed.

8. Collins did not walk on the moon because —
   - ⬭ he was sick.
   - ⬛ he had to fly *Columbia*.
   - ⬭ he did not want to.

9. The writer wanted mostly to tell about —
   - ⬛ the first walk on the moon.
   - ⬭ how to fly rockets.
   - ⬭ what we see on TV.

10. How do you know that men walked on the moon?
    - ⬭ The moon remembers the men.
    - ⬭ They came down in the Pacific Ocean.
    - ⬛ They brought moon rocks back to Earth.

STOP

gnats   **Wh**o's there?   **wr**ist

Circle the word for each picture.

1.	2.	3.	4.
(whole) will	(wrench) when	(wrapped) want	(write) white

5.	6.	7.	8.
(sign) sing	design (desk)	gown (gnaw)	breath (wreath)

Find the word that has the silent consonant.
Mark the space to show your answer.

9. ⬭ wind
   ⬛ who
   ⬭ wood

10. ⬛ wreck
    ⬭ wet
    ⬭ wig

Notes for Home: Your child reviewed words spelled with *gn, wh,* and *wr.* **Home Activity:** Write some of the following words on index cards and help your child practice reading them: *gnash, gnat, gnaw, gnome, sign, design, whole, who, whose, wholly, wrap, wreath, wrong.*

Answers **359**

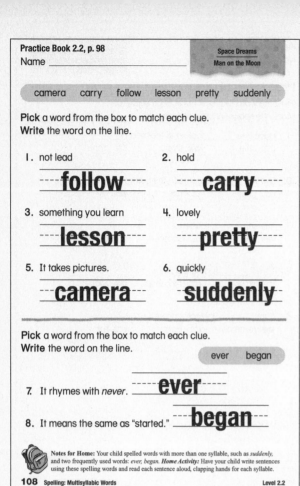

camera   carry   follow   lesson   pretty   suddenly

Pick a word from the box to match each clue.
Write the word on the line.

1. not lead

follow

2. hold

carry

3. something you learn

lesson

4. lovely

pretty

5. It takes pictures.

camera

6. quickly

suddenly

Pick a word from the box to match each clue.
Write the word on the line.

ever   began

7. It rhymes with *never*.

ever

8. It means the same as "started."

began

Notes for Home: Your child spelled words with more than one syllable, such as *suddenly*, and two frequently used words: *ever*, *began*. **Home Activity:** Have your child write sentences using these spelling words and read each sentence aloud, clapping hands for each syllable.

108 Spelling: Multisyllabic Words   Level 2.2

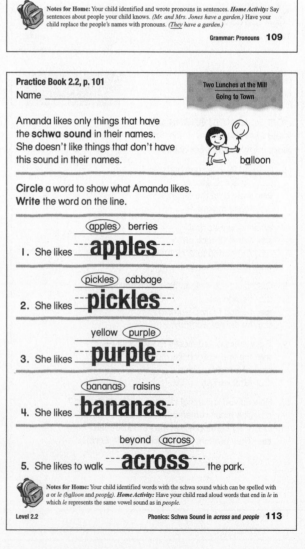

Mrs. Catalano is an art teacher.
She is an art teacher.

The word **she** is a pronoun.
It takes the place of the noun **Mrs. Catalano.**

A **pronoun** is a word that takes the place of a noun or nouns.
The words **he, she, it, we,** and **they** are pronouns.

Draw a line under the pronoun in each sentence.

1. We saw a movie in art class.

2. It was about a man in New Mexico.

3. He made sand paintings for a friend.

4. She loved the colors of the sand.

5. They were beautiful.

6. Our art teacher says we can make sand paintings.

7. She is going to show the class how.

Write the pronoun that can take the place of the noun. Use **he, she, we,** and **they.**

8. James Wolf **he**

9. Ed and Flo **they**

10. Ms. Silverwater **she**

11. Jack and I **we**

Notes for Home: Your child identified and wrote pronouns in sentences. **Home Activity:** Say sentences about people your child knows. *(Mr. and Mrs. Jones have a garden.)* Have your child replace the people's names with pronouns. *(They have a garden.)*

Grammar: Pronouns **109**

Circle the pronoun you can use in place of the word or words in ( ).

1. (Mrs. Choy) saves old newspapers.   He   (She)

2. (The papers) are in the garage.   (They)   It

3. (Dennis and I) put the papers in a car.   (We)   They

4. (Dennis) drives the car.   She   (He)

5. (The car) is filled with newspapers!   (It)   We

Write he, she, it, we, and they in the letter. One of the pronouns will be used twice.

Dear Alex,

I collect empty cans. **They** have to be cleaned. Then **we** take the cans to a special place. **It** makes the cans useful again. **They** will be used for many things. My brother said **he** will save cans too. Ask your mom if your family can help. I hope **she** says yes.

Your friend,
Eva

Notes for Home: Your child identified and wrote pronouns in sentences. **Home Activity:** Write the pronouns *he, she, we, it,* and *they* on cards. Have your child choose a card and say a sentence, using that pronoun.

110 Grammar: Pronouns

Amanda likes only things that have the **schwa sound** in their names. She doesn't like things that don't have this sound in their names.

balloon

Circle a word to show what Amanda likes.
Write the word on the line.

1. She likes (apples) berries

apples

2. She likes (pickles) cabbage

pickles

3. She likes yellow (purple)

purple

4. She likes (bananas) raisins

bananas

5. She likes to walk beyond (across) the park.

across

Notes for Home: Your child identified words with the schwa sound which can be spelled with *a* or *le* (*balloon* and *people*). **Home Activity:** Have your child read aloud words that end in *le* in which *le* represents the same vowel sound as in *people*.

Level 2.2   Phonics: Schwa Sound in *across* and *people* **113**

Add -s or **-es** to the noun in ( ) to show more than one.
Write the new noun on the line to finish each sentence.

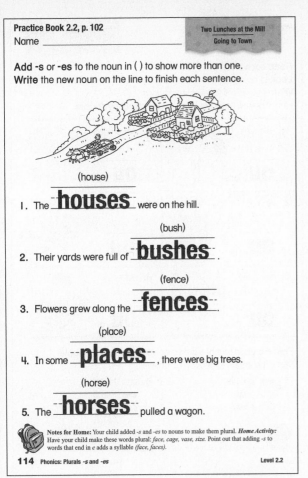

(house)

1. The **houses** were on the hill.

(bush)

2. Their yards were full of **bushes** .

(fence)

3. Flowers grew along the **fences** .

(place)

4. In some **places** , there were big trees.

(horse)

5. The **horses** pulled a wagon.

Notes for Home: Your child added -s and -es to nouns to make them plural. **Home Activity:** Have your child make these words plural: *face, cage, vase, size.* Point out that adding -s to words that end in *e* adds a syllable *(face, faces).*

Pick a word from the box to finish each sentence.
Write the word on the line.

| behind | only | sure | upon | word |

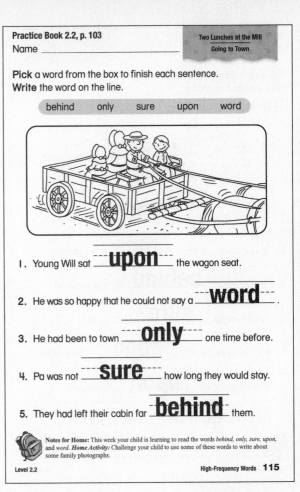

1. Young Will sat **upon** the wagon seat.

2. He was so happy that he could not say a **word** .

3. He had been to town **only** one time before.

4. Pa was not **sure** how long they would stay.

5. They had left their cabin far **behind** them.

Notes for Home: This week your child is learning to read the words *behind, only, sure, upon,* and *word.* **Home Activity:** Challenge your child to use some of these words to write about some family photographs.

Look at each picture to see what it shows about the person.
Pick a word from the box that tells what each person is like.
Write the word on the line.

| fair | funny | greedy | mean |
| nice | shy | smart | sneaky |

1. Amy gets good grades
   because she is **smart** .

2. Jack is a **nice** friend.

3. We let Matt judge the game
   because he is **fair** .

4. Sally is very **funny** .

5. Billy does not always raise his hand
   because he can be **shy** .

Notes for Home: Your child used word and picture clues to figure out what someone is like. **Home Activity:** When you read with your child, pause to ask her or him what a certain character is like. Then ask why your child thinks so.

He, she, and **it** are **pronouns**
that name only one.
He is eight years old.
We and **they** are **pronouns**
that name more than one.
They are friends.

Pick a pronoun from the box to take the place of the
underlined word or words.
Write the pronoun on the line.

| he | she | it | we | they |

They 1. Mary's family moved west in a big wagon.

It 2. The wagon top was like a round tent.

He 3. Mary's father drove the wagon all day.

we 4. Will my family and I ever get there?

She 5. Mary helped her mother fix meals.

Notes for Home: Your child used singular and plural pronouns to replace subjects in sentences. **Home Activity:** Ask your child questions about what his or her class did that day. Encourage your child to answer using the pronouns *he, she, it, we,* and *they.*

Answers **361**

Pick a word from the box to finish each sentence.
Write the word on the line.

| behind | crops | edge | sure | trade | upon | word |

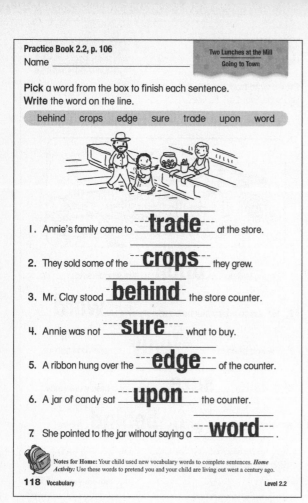

1. Annie's family came to __trade__ at the store.

2. They sold some of the __crops__ they grew.

3. Mr. Clay stood __behind__ the store counter.

4. Annie was not __sure__ what to buy.

5. A ribbon hung over the __edge__ of the counter.

6. A jar of candy sat __upon__ the counter.

7. She pointed to the jar without saying a __word__.

Notes for Home: Your child used new vocabulary words to complete sentences. **Home Activity:** Use these words to pretend you and your child are living out west a century ago.

118 Vocabulary   Level 2.2

Read each clue.
Look at each picture.
Write the letters to finish each word.   **dou**ble scoop
Hint: They all have the same vowel sound as **double**.

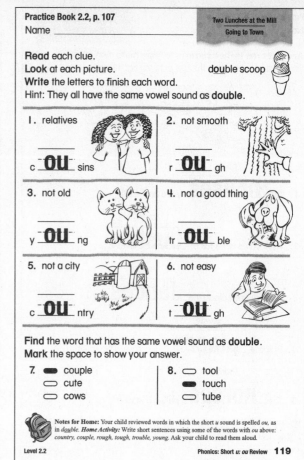

1. relatives   c__ou__sins

2. not smooth   r__ou__gh

3. not old   y__ou__ng

4. not a good thing   tr__ou__ble

5. not a city   c__ou__ntry

6. not easy   t__ou__gh

Find the word that has the same vowel sound as **double**.
Mark the space to show your answer.

7. ● couple
   ○ cute
   ○ cows

8. ○ tool
   ● touch
   ○ tube

Notes for Home: Your child reviewed words in which the short u sound is spelled ou, as in *double*. **Home Activity:** Write short sentences using some of the words with ou above: *country, couple, rough, tough, trouble, young*. Ask your child to read them aloud.

Level 2.2   Phonics: Short u: ou Review 119

| blouse | blouses | place | places | race | races |

Read the head at the top of each column.
Write the words from the box that belong in each column.

Names One	Names More Than One
1. __blouse__	2. __blouses__
3. __place__	4. __places__
5. __race__	6. __races__

Pick a word from the box to match each picture.
Write the word on the line.

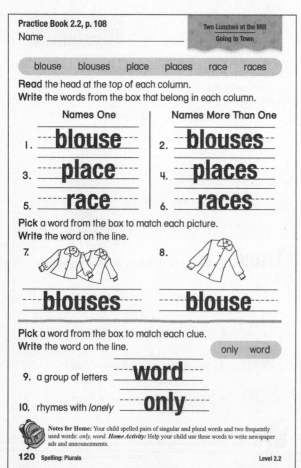

7. __blouses__

8. __blouse__

Pick a word from the box to match each clue.
Write the word on the line.

| only | word |

9. a group of letters __word__

10. rhymes with *lonely* __only__

Notes for Home: Your child spelled pairs of singular and plural words and two frequently used words: *only, word*. **Home Activity:** Help your child use these words to write newspaper ads and announcements.

120 Spelling: Plurals   Level 2.2

Circle a pronoun to take the place of the underlined words.

1. The children are playing ball.
   He   We   (They)

2. Tom throws the ball.
   (He)   We   They

3. Susan catches the ball from Tom.
   He   It   (She)

4. "Mary and I want the ball!"
   He   (We)   Her

5. The ball will be thrown to Mary and Nan.
   (It)   He   They

Circle the pronouns that name one.
Underline the pronouns that name more than one.

6.–10. (he)   we   they   (she)   (it)

Notes for Home: Your child reviewed using pronouns that name only one person, place, or thing and pronouns that name more than one. **Home Activity:** Find a picture that shows activity. Have your child use pronouns to describe what is happening in the picture.

Level 2.2   Grammar: Singular and Plural Pronouns 121

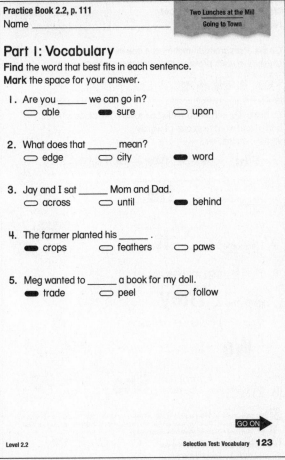

Part 1: Vocabulary

Find the word that best fits in each sentence.
Mark the space for your answer.

1. Are you _____ we can go in?
   ⬭ able ⬛ sure ⬭ upon

2. What does that _____ mean?
   ⬭ edge ⬭ city ⬛ word

3. Jay and I sat _____ Mom and Dad.
   ⬭ across ⬭ until ⬛ behind

4. The farmer planted his _____ .
   ⬛ crops ⬭ feathers ⬭ paws

5. Meg wanted to _____ a book for my doll.
   ⬛ trade ⬭ peel ⬭ follow

GO ON ➤

Level 2.2   Selection Test: Vocabulary **123**

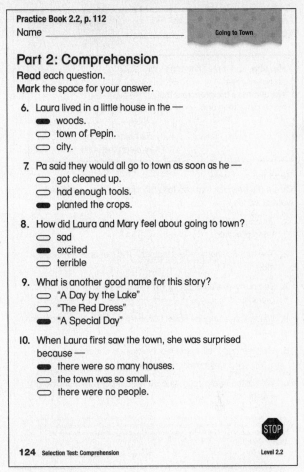

Part 2: Comprehension

Read each question.
Mark the space for your answer.

6. Laura lived in a little house in the —
   ⬛ woods.
   ⬭ town of Pepin.
   ⬭ city.

7. Pa said they would all go to town as soon as he —
   ⬭ got cleaned up.
   ⬭ had enough tools.
   ⬛ planted the crops.

8. How did Laura and Mary feel about going to town?
   ⬭ sad
   ⬛ excited
   ⬭ terrible

9. What is another good name for this story?
   ⬭ "A Day by the Lake"
   ⬭ "The Red Dress"
   ⬛ "A Special Day"

10. When Laura first saw the town, she was surprised
    because —
    ⬛ there were so many houses.
    ⬭ the town was so small.
    ⬭ there were no people.

STOP

124 Selection Test: Comprehension   Level 2.2

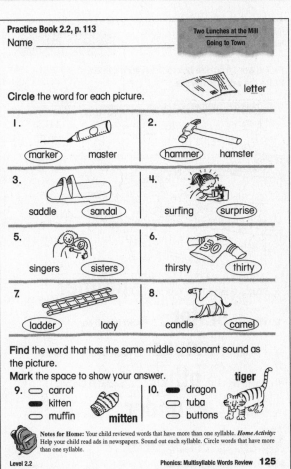

Circle the word for each picture.

letter

1. (marker) master	2. (hammer) hamster
3. saddle (sandal)	4. surfing (surprise)
5. singers (sisters)	6. thirsty (thirty)
7. (ladder) lady	8. candle (camel)

Find the word that has the same middle consonant sound as
the picture.

Mark the space to show your answer.

tiger

9. ⬭ carrot   10. ⬛ dragon
   ⬛ kitten   ⬭ tuba
   ⬭ muffin   ⬭ buttons

mitten

Notes for Home: Your child reviewed words that have more than one syllable. **Home Activity:**
Help your child read ads in newspapers. Sound out each syllable. Circle words that have more
than one syllable.

Level 2.2   Phonics: Multisyllabic Words Review **125**

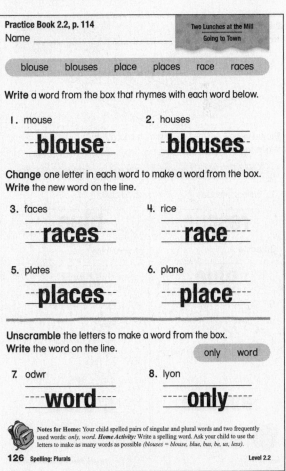

| blouse | blouses | place | places | race | races |

Write a word from the box that rhymes with each word below.

1. mouse   2. houses
   blouse   **blouses**

Change one letter in each word to make a word from the box.
Write the new word on the line.

3. faces   4. rice
   races   **race**

5. plates   6. plane
   places   **place**

Unscramble the letters to make a word from the box.
Write the word on the line.
only   word

7. odwr   8. lyon
   word   **only**

Notes for Home: Your child spelled pairs of singular and plural words and two frequently
used words: *only, word.* **Home Activity:** Write a spelling word. Ask your child to use the
letters to make as many words as possible (*blouses = blouse, blue, bus, be, us, less*).

126 Spelling: Plurals   Level 2.2

Answers **363**

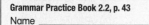

RETEACHING

He, she, and it are pronouns that name only one.
We and they are pronouns that name more than one.

He holds the bag.
They clean the yard.

Read the sentences.
Circle the pronoun that can take the place of the underlined word or words.

1. Jason and his friends go to a birthday party. (They)/ She) bring presents.

2. The birthday party is for Heather. (It /(She) is seven years old.

3. The party started at noon. (It)/ They) will end at three o'clock.

4. Jason loves birthday cake. (We /(He) asks if it is a chocolate cake.

5. Heather and I tell Jason that the cake is chocolate. (They /(We) laugh when he smiles.

6. We eat the whole cake, and we tell our parents that (she /(it) was good.

 Notes for Home: Your child matched noun phrases to singular and plural pronouns *(he, she, it, we, they)*. **Home Activity:** Together, make flashcards with sentences about friends, family, and your child. Help your child underline subjects and write pronouns on the other side of the cards.

Grammar: Singular and Plural Pronouns **127**

Circle each pronoun that means one person or thing.
Underline each pronoun that means more than one.

1. (he) 2. (she) 3. we 4. they 5. (it)

Choose a pronoun from the box to take the place of each underlined word or group of words.
Write it on the line.

| He | She | They | It | We |

6. Richard is crying. **He**

7. Her bugle is new. **It**

8. Sheri and Dan are blowing up balloons. **They**

9. Mom and I made a big sandwich. **We**

10. My sister wakes up early. **She**

 Notes for Home: Your child identified and used singular and plural pronouns in sentences. **Home Activity:** Have your child tell you about a movie or TV show he or she has seen. Help your child recognize the pronouns he or she uses.

128 Grammar: Singular and Plural Pronouns

---

glue

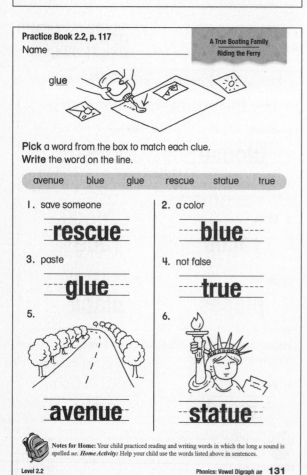

Pick a word from the box to match each clue.
Write the word on the line.

| avenue | blue | glue | rescue | statue | true |

1. save someone
rescue

2. a color
blue

3. paste
glue

4. not false
true

5.
avenue

6.
statue

 Notes for Home: Your child practiced reading and writing words in which the long *u* sound is spelled *ue*. **Home Activity:** Help your child use the words listed above in sentences.

Level 2.2

Phonics: Vowel Digraph *ue* **131**

Pick a word from the box to finish each sentence.
Write the word on the line.

| never | other | sister | summer | under |

1. May is visiting New York this **summer**

2. Her **sister** Becky is with her.

3. She has **never** been on a ferry before.

4. There are **other** boats on the bay.

5. The ferry goes **under** a bridge.

 Notes for Home: Your child read and wrote words ending in *-er* with the same ending sound as *weathçr*. **Home Activity:** Help your child write a list of words that end in *-er* that describe types of people, such as *worker* or *skater*.

132 Phonics: Schwa Sound in *weather*

Level 2.2

Pick a word from the box to finish each sentence.
Write the word on the line.

| course | hear | things | which | years |

1. Jed and Matt have been sailing for two __years__.

2. They know many __things__ about sailing.

3. Their boat stays on its __course__.

4. They __hear__ cheers from the shore.

5. __Which__ sailboat do you think will win the race?

Notes for Home: This week your child is learning to read the words *course, hear, things, which,* and *years.* **Home Activity:** Have your child use some of these words in a broadcast about a made-up sports contest.

Level 2.2   High-Frequency Words **133**

Write F before each sentence that gives a **fact.**
Write O before each sentence that gives an **opinion.**

1. __F__ I have been flying planes for ten years.

2. __F__ I flew from New York to Texas today.

3. __O__ I have a wonderful job.

4. __O__ More people should fly rather than drive.

Write a fact about planes.   **Possible answer given.**

5. __Planes are much faster than trains.__

Notes for Home: Your child practiced distinguishing between facts (statements that can be proven true or false) and opinions (statements that express a feeling or idea). **Home Activity:** As you read with your child, ask him or her to point out statements of fact and opinion.

134 Fact and Opinion   Level 2.2

Some pronouns are used as subjects of sentences.
They are: **I, he, she, we, they.**

Some pronouns are used after action verbs.
They are: **me, him, her, us, them.**

Some pronouns can be used anywhere in a sentence.
They are: **you, it.**

Circle a pronoun to take the place of
the underlined word or words.

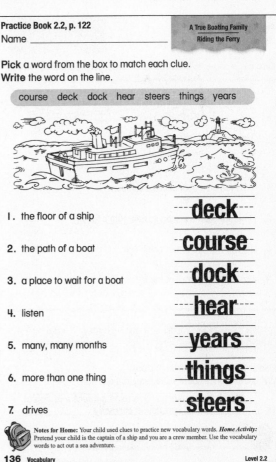

1. <u>My sisters and I</u> took Mike to the Statue of Liberty.
   (We)
   Us

2. Maria followed <u>Mike and me</u> inside.
   we
   (us)

3. Those stairs lead to the top of <u>the statue.</u>
   (it)
   you

4. <u>Mike</u> didn't want to climb the stairs.
   (He)
   Him

5. Julia and I followed <u>Maria</u> up the stairs.
   she
   (her)

Notes for Home: Your child chose pronouns to use as subjects or after action verbs. **Home Activity:** As you read to your child, point out nouns in sentences. Ask which pronouns he or she would use to replace these nouns.

Level 2.2   Grammar: Subject and Object Pronouns **135**

Pick a word from the box to match each clue.
Write the word on the line.

| course | deck | dock | hear | steers | things | years |

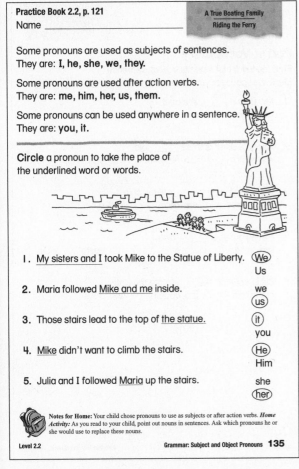

1. the floor of a ship   __deck__

2. the path of a boat   __course__

3. a place to wait for a boat __dock__

4. listen   __hear__

5. many, many months   __years__

6. more than one thing   __things__

7. drives   __steers__

Notes for Home: Your child used clues to practice new vocabulary words. **Home Activity:** Pretend your child is the captain of a ship and you are a crew member. Use the vocabulary words to act out a sea adventure.

136 Vocabulary   Level 2.2

Answers **365**

Say the word for each picture.
Write a or le to finish each word.

People ride across the river.

1. 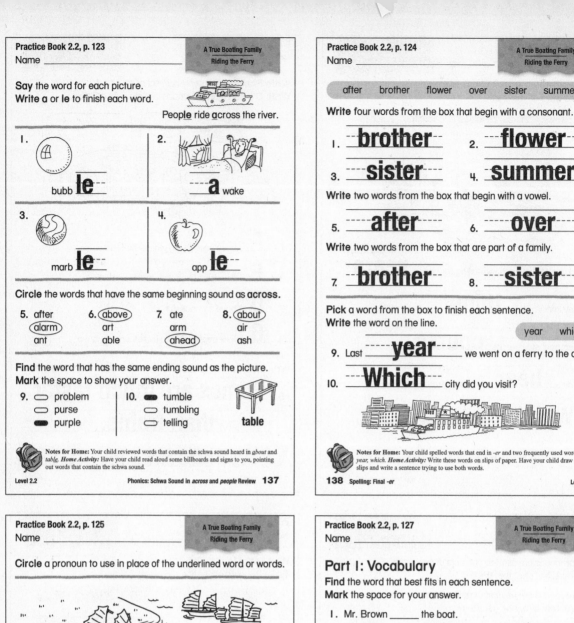 bubb**le**

2. **a** wake

3. marb**le**

4. app**le**

Circle the words that have the same beginning sound as **across**.

5. after
   (alarm)
   ant

6. (above)
   art
   able

7. ate
   arm
   (ahead)

8. (about)
   air
   ash

Find the word that has the same ending sound as the picture.
Mark the space to show your answer.

9. ○ problem
   ○ purse
   ● purple

10. ● tumble
    ○ tumbling
    ○ telling

table

Notes for Home: Your child reviewed words that contain the schwa sound heard in *about* and *table*. Home Activity: Have your child read aloud some billboards and signs to you, pointing out words that contain the schwa sound.

| after | brother | flower | over | sister | summer |

Write four words from the box that begin with a consonant.

1. **brother**   2. **flower**

3. **sister**   4. **summer**

Write two words from the box that begin with a vowel.

5. **after**   6. **over**

Write two words from the box that are part of a family.

7. **brother**   8. **sister**

Pick a word from the box to finish each sentence.
Write the word on the line.

year   which

9. Last **year** we went on a ferry to the city.

10. **Which** city did you visit?

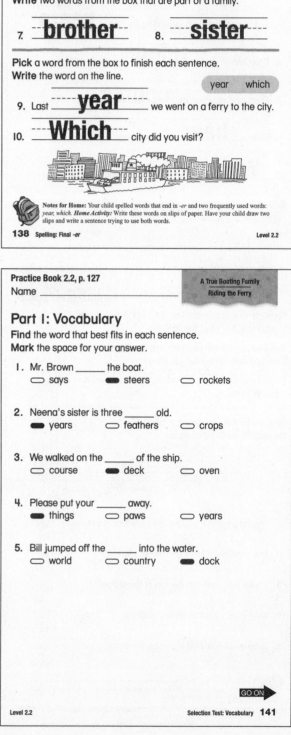

Notes for Home: Your child spelled words that end in *-er* and two frequently used words: *year, which*. Home Activity: Write these words on slips of paper. Have your child draw two slips and write a sentence trying to use both words.

Circle a pronoun to use in place of the underlined word or words.

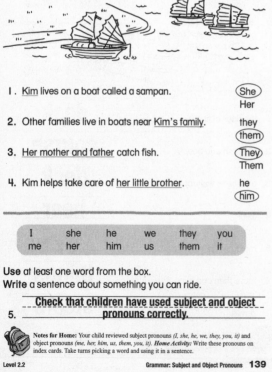

1. Kim lives on a boat called a sampan.
   (She)
   Her

2. Other families live in boats near Kim's family.
   they
   (them)

3. Her mother and father catch fish.
   (They)
   Them

4. Kim helps take care of her little brother.
   he
   (him)

| I | she | he | we | they | you |
| me | her | him | us | them | it |

Use at least one word from the box.
Write a sentence about something you can ride.

5. _Check that children have used subject and object_
   pronouns correctly.

Notes for Home: Your child reviewed subject pronouns (*I, she, he, we, they, you, it*) and object pronouns (*me, her, him, us, them, you, it*). Home Activity: Write these pronouns on index cards. Take turns picking a word and using it in a sentence.

Part 1: Vocabulary

Find the word that best fits in each sentence.
Mark the space for your answer.

1. Mr. Brown _____ the boat.
   ○ says   ● steers   ○ rockets

2. Neena's sister is three _____ old.
   ● years   ○ feathers   ○ crops

3. We walked on the _____ of the ship.
   ○ course   ● deck   ○ oven

4. Please put your _____ away.
   ● things   ○ paws   ○ years

5. Bill jumped off the _____ into the water.
   ○ world   ○ country   ● dock

GO ON

Part 2: Comprehension

Read each question.
Mark the space for your answer.

6. This story is mostly about —
   - ◯ the Statue of Liberty.
   - ◯ New York City.
   - ⬤ Captain Cruz.

7. Captain Cruz's ferry is for —
   - ◯ animals.
   - ⬤ people.
   - ◯ cars.

8. A captain's log is a kind of —
   - ⬤ book.
   - ◯ tree.
   - ◯ rope.

9. Captain Cruz is a good captain because —
   - ◯ a helper sits beside him.
   - ◯ he likes his job.
   - ⬤ he keeps everyone safe.

10. Which sentence is an opinion?
    - ◯ "Captain Cruz uses a radio."
    - ⬤ "The captain does his job well."
    - ◯ "That's Mr. Cruz, my neighbor."

STOP

---

birds   benches

Say the word for each picture.
Add -s or -es to finish each word.

1. nose **s**	2. dish **es**	3. box **es**	4. walrus **es**
5. horse **s**	6. face **s**	7. brush **es**	8. rose **s**

Find the word that names only one.
Mark the space to show your answer.

9. ⬤ glass
   ◯ places
   ◯ porches

10. ◯ foxes
    ⬤ mess
    ◯ spaces

Notes for Home: Your child reviewed adding -s or -es to nouns to show more than one. **Home Activity:** Have your child read aloud each word above with and without the -s or -es ending. Ask your child how many syllables are in each word.

---

after   brother   flower   over   sister   summer

Change one or two letters in each word to make a word from the box.
Write the new word on the line.

1. mister
   sister

2. offer
   after

3. oven
   over

4. supper
   summer

5. slower
   flower

6. mother
   brother

Write the word from the box that has the same beginning sound as the picture.

year   which

7. **whale**
   which

8. **yarn**
   year

Notes for Home: Your child spelled words that end in -er and two frequently used words: year, which. **Write:** Write each spelling word with its letters scrambled. Ask your child to unscramble and write each word.

RETEACHING

The pronouns **I, he, she, we,** and **they** are used as subjects of sentences.
The pronouns **me, him, her, us,** and **them** are used after action verbs.
The pronouns **you** and **it** can be used anywhere in a sentence.

Draw a line from the underlined word or group of words to the pronoun that can take its place.

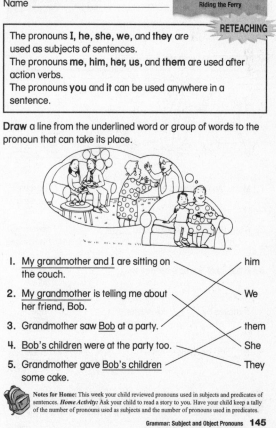

1. My grandmother and I are sitting on the couch. — him

2. My grandmother is telling me about her friend, Bob. — We

3. Grandmother saw Bob at a party. — them

4. Bob's children were at the party too. — She

5. Grandmother gave Bob's children some cake. — They

Notes for Home: This week your child reviewed pronouns used in subjects and predicates of sentences. **Home Activity:** Ask your child to read a story to you. Have your child keep a tally of the number of pronouns used as subjects and the number of pronouns used in predicates.

Answers **367**

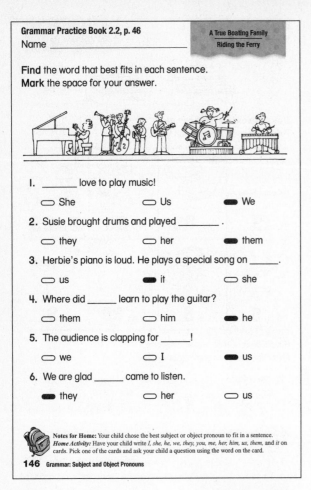

Find the word that best fits in each sentence.
Mark the space for your answer.

1. _____ love to play music!

   ⬭ She   ⬭ Us   ⬬ We

2. Susie brought drums and played _____ .

   ⬭ they   ⬭ her   ⬬ them

3. Herbie's piano is loud. He plays a special song on _____ .

   ⬭ us   ⬬ it   ⬭ she

4. Where did _____ learn to play the guitar?

   ⬭ them   ⬭ him   ⬬ he

5. The audience is clapping for _____!

   ⬭ we   ⬭ I   ⬬ us

6. We are glad _____ came to listen.

   ⬬ they   ⬭ her   ⬭ us

Notes for Home: Your child chose the best subject or object pronoun to fit in a sentence. **Home Activity:** Have your child write *I, she, he, we, they, you, me, her, him, us, them,* and *it* on cards. Pick one of the cards and ask your child a question using the word on the card.

146 Grammar: Subject and Object Pronouns

Pick the word that has the **long a** sound.
Write the word on the line.

freight train

1. piece / weigh / artichoke	2. talks / neighbors / friends
weigh	**neighbors**
3. neigh / nag / niece	4. eat / eight / candle
neigh	**eight**
5. veil / head / bride	6. sleigh / field / sled
veil	**sleigh**
7. head / animal / reins	8. deer / antlers / reindeer
reins	**reindeer**

Notes for Home: Your child wrote words in which the long *a* sound is spelled *ei*. **Home Activity:** List these word pairs: *weigh-way, rein-rain,* and *eight-ate.* Have your child read these words and use them in sentences.

Level 2.2   Phonics: Long *a: ei* **149**

Circle a word to finish each sentence.

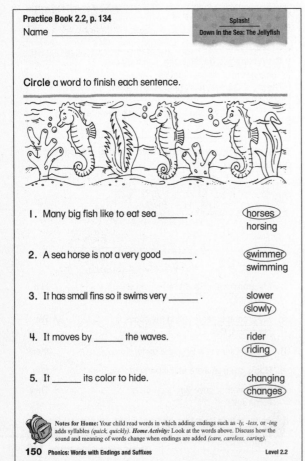

1. Many big fish like to eat sea _____ .   (horses) / horsing

2. A sea horse is not a very good _____ .   (swimmer) / swimming

3. It has small fins so it swims very _____ .   slower / (slowly)

4. It moves by _____ the waves.   rider / (riding)

5. It _____ its color to hide.   changing / (changes)

Notes for Home: Your child read words in which adding endings such as *-ly, -less,* or *-ing* adds syllables *(quick, quickly).* **Home Activity:** Look at the words above. Discuss how the sound and meaning of words change when endings are added *(care, careless, caring).*

150 Phonics: Words with Endings and Suffixes   Level 2.2

Pick a word from the box to finish each sentence.
Write the word on the line. Use each word only once.

cold   grow   most   move   near

1. **Most** seals live in the sea.

2. Some spend time on **cold** chunks of ice.

3. Seal pups **move** slowly on land.

4. They stay **near** their mothers.

5. They **grow** up fast.

Notes for Home: This week your child is learning to read the words *cold, grow, most, move,* and *near.* **Home Activity:** Have your child use some of these words to write a conversation between two animals that live in the sea.

Level 2.2   High-Frequency Words **151**

Read the sentences. **Look** at the pictures.
Answer the questions.

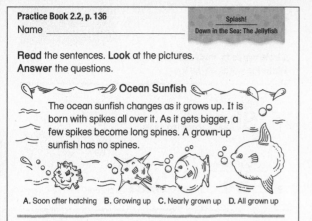

Ocean Sunfish

The ocean sunfish changes as it grows up. It is born with spikes all over it. As it gets bigger, a few spikes become long spines. A grown-up sunfish has no spines.

A. Soon after hatching   B. Growing up   C. Nearly grown up   D. All grown up

1. A baby sunfish has many spikes. What happens to them as the sunfish grows up?

Most of them go away.

2. Look at picture B.
How many long spikes does the sunfish have? **Five**

3. How is the fish in picture D different from the fish in picture C?

It is longer. It has two big fins. Its tail is not pointed.

 Notes for Home: Your child has been learning about looking at graphics, such as diagrams and charts, in order to better understand text. **Home Activity:** Check out library books that use graphics to give information. Discuss with your child the purpose of each graphic.

A **pronoun** takes the place of a noun or nouns. When you use pronouns, you don't need to use the same noun over and over.

Pick a pronoun from the box to finish the second sentence. Use each word only once. **Circle** the word or words in the first sentence that helped you decide which pronoun to use.

he   it   she   them   they

1. John took us to a tide pool. There **he** showed us a mole crab.

2. This crab has long feelers.
It uses **them** to catch food.

3. My sister picked up a stick.
Then **she** poked it in the sand.

4. Suddenly, all we saw was sand.
The crab was hidden under **it** .

5. My sister and I saw two tiny bumps.
John told us that **they** were its eyes.

 Notes for Home: For each pair of sentences, your child used a pronoun in place of a noun. **Home Activity:** Have your child pretend that he or she is visiting the bottom of the sea. Ask him or her to write you a postcard from there using several pronouns.

Pick a word from the box to match each clue.
Write the word on the line. Use each word once.

beach   cold   floating   flopped
grow   move   near   poke

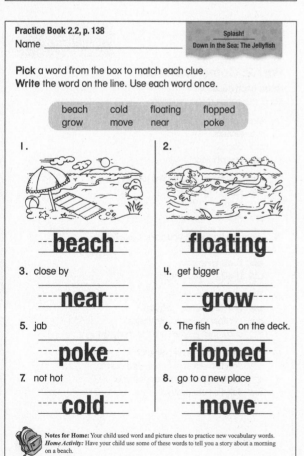

1. **beach**

2. **floating**

3. close by
near

4. get bigger
grow

5. jab
poke

6. The fish _____ on the deck.
flopped

7. not hot
cold

8. go to a new place
move

 Notes for Home: Your child used word and picture clues to practice new vocabulary words. **Home Activity:** Have your child use some of these words to tell you a story about a morning on a beach.

Circle the word that has the same vowel sound as clue.
Write the word on the line.

1. glue glee glad
glue

2. avenue about above
avenue

3. scrub rescue stuff
rescue

4. trust trouble threw
threw

5. true trip trouble
true

6. blush blue blur
blue

7. bark barbecue butter
barbecue

8. grape grew grain
grew

Find the picture that has the same vowel sound as **blue**.
Mark the space to show your answer.

9. ▬ statue   ▭ key   ▭ cat

10. ▭ tub   ▭ cup   ▬ glue

 Notes for Home: Your child reviewed words spelled with *ue* that have the vowel sound heard in *statue*. **Home Activity:** Write sentences using the words *Sue, blue, clue, glue,* and *true.* Help your child read them. Ask your child to draw pictures to match the sentences.

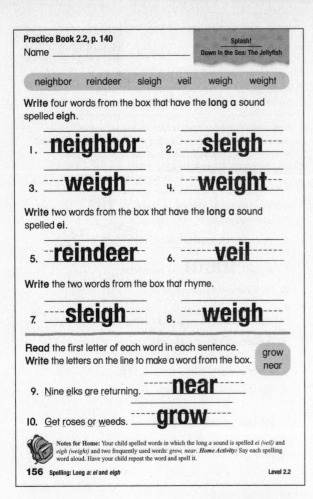

neighbor   reindeer   sleigh   veil   weigh   weight

Write four words from the box that have the **long a** sound spelled **eigh**.

1. **neighbor**   2. **sleigh**

3. **weigh**   4. **weight**

Write two words from the box that have the **long a** sound spelled **ei**.

5. **reindeer**   6. **veil**

Write the two words from the box that rhyme.

7. **sleigh**   8. **weigh**

Read the first letter of each word in each sentence.
Write the letters on the line to make a word from the box.

grow
near

9. Nine elks are returning. **near**

10. Get roses or weeds. **grow**

Notes for Home: Your child spelled words in which the long *a* sound is spelled *ei* (veil) and *eigh* (weight) and two frequently used words: *grow, near*. **Home Activity:** Say each spelling word aloud. Have your child repeat the word and spell it.

156 Spelling: Long *a: ei* and *eigh*   Level 2.2

Circle words to finish each sentence.
Write the words on the lines.

1. (She) Her
   She sees the seals.

2. (He) Him   he (him)
   He gives **him** a book.

3. (They) Them
   They watch one seal eat.

4. we (us)
   "Is the seal looking at **us** ?"

5. I (me)
   "The seal is feeding **me** !"

Notes for Home: Your child practiced using pronouns in sentences. **Home Activity:** Encourage your child to use pronouns to write about something that happened in school this week.

Level 2.2   Grammar: Writing with Pronouns **157**

Part 1: Vocabulary

Find the word that best fits in each sentence.
Mark the space for your answer.

1. Plants need water and sun to _____ .
   ⊙ trade   ⊙ keep   ● grow

2. When you _____ me, it hurts.
   ● poke   ⊙ follow   ⊙ beach

3. Will you sit _____ me today?
   ● near   ⊙ still   ⊙ between

4. A log was _____ in the water.
   ⊙ sealing   ● floating   ⊙ dashing

5. The dog _____ down on the grass.
   ⊙ drew   ● flopped   ⊙ gathered

GO ON →

Level 2.2   Selection Test: Vocabulary **159**

Part 2: Comprehension

Read each question.
Mark the space for your answer.

6. Many of the jellyfish in this story look like —
   ⊙ wheels.
   ⊙ ducks.
   ● parachutes.

7. Most jellyfish use tentacles to —
   ● catch food.
   ⊙ swim.
   ⊙ walk.

8. What will happen if you poke a jellyfish?
   ⊙ It will melt.
   ● It will sting you.
   ⊙ It will eat your finger.

9. The writer wanted to —
   ● give facts about jellyfish.
   ⊙ tell how to catch a jellyfish.
   ⊙ show that jellyfish are not really fish.

10. Which sentence is an opinion?
    ⊙ Jellyfish eat fish, crabs, and worms.
    ⊙ Each jellyfish lives about a year.
    ● Jellyfish are pretty.

STOP

160 Selection Test: Comprehension   Level 2.2

Name _____

Say the word for each picture.
Write the word on the line.
Use the words in the box if you need help.

baker	camper	catcher
marcher	mother	teacher

sing**er**

1. **teacher**
2. **baker**
3. **mother**
4. **camper**
5. **catcher**
6. **marcher**

Find the word that has the same ending sound as the picture.
Mark the space to show your answer.

7. ○ very
   ○ here
   ● after

8. ● weather
   ○ year
   ○ somewhere

singer

Notes for Home: Your child reviewed words ending in *-er* that have the schwa sound heard in *singer*. **Home Activity:** Many words ending in *-er* name people who do things, such as *singer*. Work with your child to list other words like this.

Name _____

neighbor	reindeer	sleigh	veil	weigh	weight

Write a word from the box that sounds the same as the word or words below.

1. way **weigh**
2. wait **weight**

Pick a word from the box to match each clue.
Write the word on the line.

3. rain + dear **reindeer**
4. like a sled **sleigh**

5. It is what a bride wears. **veil**

6. It is someone who lives near you. **neighbor**

Write the word from the box that means the opposite of each word below.

grow   near

7. far **near**
8. shrink **grow**

Notes for Home: Your child spelled words in which the long *a* sound is spelled *ei* (*veil*) and *eigh* (*weight*) and two frequently used words: *grow, near*. **Home Activity:** Encourage your child to draw a snowy scene and to use the spelling words to write about the picture.

Name _____

RETEACHING

A **pronoun** takes the place of a noun or nouns. When you use pronouns, you don't need to use the same noun over and over.

Joe likes **cats**. **He** plays with **them**.

Read each sentence.
Choose a pronoun from the box to finish the second sentence in each pair. **Write** it on the line.
Circle the word or words in the first sentence in each pair that helped you decide which pronoun to use.

He	She	It	them	They

1. (A woman) came to visit our class.
   She was from Guinea.

2. (Guinea) is a country in West Africa.
   It is on the coast of the Atlantic Ocean.

3. The (woman) and her (brother) told us about their country.
   They spoke to us in English.

4. They showed us (clothes) from Guinea.
   They even let us try **them** on!

Notes for Home: Your child replaced nouns and noun phrases with pronouns in sentences. **Home Activity:** Have your child pretend he or she is visiting another country. Ask him or her to write a postcard to you from the other country, using several pronouns.

Name _____

Read each sentence and question.
Answer each question by writing a pronoun from the box on the line. Some words are used more than once.

She	it	them	her	He	They

1. Sally has a messy room. What should Sally do?
   She should clean **it**.

2. There are toys everywhere. What should Sally do with the toys?
   She should put **them** away.

3. Sally can't find her homework. What should Sally do?
   She should look for **it**.

4. John wants to help Sally. What should John do?
   He should start helping **her**.

5. John and Sally finished cleaning. What should John and Sally do?
   They should have lunch!

Notes for Home: Your child used pronouns in sentences. **Home Activity:** Encourage your child to use pronouns to write about a day he or she really enjoyed.

Pick a word from the box to finish each sentence.
Write the word on the line.

| next   excited   expert   extra   explain |

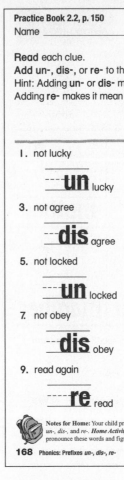

Texas

1. Dr. Sanchez is an **expert** on dinosaurs.

2. Her books **explain** how dinosaurs lived.

3. I can't wait for her **next** book about them.

4. I am **excited** about going to hear her talk tonight.

5. I have an **extra** ticket if you want to come!

Notes for Home: Your child read and wrote words that contain the letter combination *ex*. **Home Activity:** Help your child make up facts about someone named Rex, using a word containing *ex* in each sentence, for example: *Rex is an expert swimmer.*

Read each clue.
Add un-, dis-, or re- to the word to match each clue.
Hint: Adding **un-** or **dis-** makes a word mean the opposite.
Adding **re-** makes it mean "do again."

happy   **un**happy

1. not lucky **un** lucky	2. paint again **re** paint
3. not agree **dis** agree	4. opposite of *pack* **un** pack
5. not locked **un** locked	6. build again **re** build
7. not obey **dis** obey	8. not safe **un** safe
9. read again **re** read	10. not honest **dis** honest

Notes for Home: Your child practiced figuring out the meanings of words with the prefixes *un-*, *dis-*, and *re-*. **Home Activity:** Look for words like these in ads and signs. Help your child pronounce these words and figure out what they mean.

Circle a word to finish each sentence.

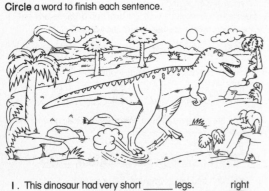

1. This dinosaur had very short _____ legs.
   right
   (front)

2. It moved _____ on its hind legs.
   (along)
   front

3. It was _____ a very scary creature.
   (probably)
   someday

4. I knew _____ away I wouldn't want to meet one.
   along
   (right)

5. _____ I'd like to dig up dinosaur bones.
   (Someday)
   Right

Notes for Home: This week your child is learning to read the words *along, front, probably, right,* and *someday.* **Home Activity:** Have your child use some of these words to write a news announcement about an imaginary and interesting discovery.

Read the paragraph.

Most reptiles lay their eggs and walk away. Scientists thought dinosaurs were like reptiles. Now some scientists think the dinosaur parents were there when the eggs hatched. They may have fed their babies. They may have kept them safe from harm. Perhaps dinosaurs were good parents after all.

1. Write a sentence that tells the main idea of the paragraph.

Some dinosaurs may have been good parents.

Possible answer given.

2. Draw a picture that shows the main idea.

Children's drawings should show a dinosaur parent taking care of its babies.

3. Write a title for the paragraph.

Titles will vary but should relate to the main idea.

Notes for Home: Your child found the most important idea of a paragraph. **Home Activity:** Read aloud paragraphs from a nature magazine or book to your child. Stop to talk about what the most important idea is in each paragraph.

Name _____

A **contraction** is a word made by putting two words together. An **apostrophe** ' shows where letters have been left out.

We **will see** the dinosaurs.
We'll see the dinosaurs.

Put the words together to make a contraction.
Write the contraction on the line.

1. is not

isn't

2. we are

we're

3. he is

he's

4. we have

we've

5. they are

they're

6. do not

don't

Pick a word from the box to finish each sentence.
Write the word on the line.

aren't   haven't

7. There **aren't** any dinosaurs alive today.

8. They **haven't** been here for millions of years.

Notes for Home: Your child wrote contractions by joining a pronoun and a verb or a verb with the word *not*. **Home Activity:** As you read, point out contractions. Have your child write the two words that were used to make each contraction.

Level 2.2   Grammar: Contractions **171**

Name _____

Pick a word from the box to match each clue.
Write the word on the line.

claws   front   giant   helmet
probably   someday   stone   right

1. huge

giant

2. a day in the future

someday

3. not back

front

4. Do it _____ away!

right

5. a hard hat

helmet

6. a rock

stone

7. a crab's "hands"

claws

8. likely

probably

Notes for Home: Your child used word and picture clues to practice new vocabulary words. **Home Activity:** Encourage your child to use these words to tell a fantasy story about a giant dinosaur or dragon with big claws.

172 Vocabulary   Level 2.2

Name _____

eight 8

Each word pair goes with the picture.
Circle the word that has the same **long a** sound as **eight**.
Write the word on the line.

1. (weigh) apple

weigh

2. (neighbor) talk

neighbor

3. (reindeer) antler

reindeer

4. (sleigh) dash

sleigh

5. hair (veil)

veil

6. (reins) saddle

reins

Find the word that has the same vowel sound as the picture.
Mark the space to show your answer.

7. ○ grass
● beige
○ taps

grapes

8. ● weight
○ white
○ whole

table

Notes for Home: Your child reviewed words with the long *a* sound spelled *ei* as heard in *eight*. **Home Activity:** Write the words with *ei* listed above on slips of paper. Take turns drawing words and using each word in a sentence.

Level 2.2   Phonics: Long a: ei Review **173**

Name _____

undo   unfair   unhappy   unlike   unlucky   untie

Write four words from the box that have two syllables.

1. **undo**

2. **unfair**

3. **unlike**

4. **untie**

Write two words from the box that have three syllables.

5. **unhappy**

6. **unlucky**

Pick a word from the box to match each clue.
Write the word on the line.

7. not glad

unhappy

8. not the same

unlike

Pick a word from the box to finish each sentence.
Write the word on the line.

front   probably

9. Mary will **probably** come to the show.

10. We will sit in the **front** row.

Notes for Home: Your child spelled words that begin with the prefix *un-* and two frequently used words: *front*, *probably*. **Home Activity:** Help your child write a clue for each word with *un-*. Discuss how this prefix changes the meaning of a word.

174 Spelling: Prefix *un-*   Level 2.2

Practice Book 2.2, p. 157

Name _____

Tex and the Big Bad T. Rex
Let's Go Dinosaur Tracking!

Take out sentences that don't belong
with the other sentences in a paragraph.

Dinosaurs lived a long time ago. They
were the largest animals on Earth then.
~~You can see dinosaur bones today.~~ Some
dinosaurs were bigger than houses.
Anklyosaurus could be up to 56 feet long!

Read the sentences.
Pick three sentences that belong together.
Draw a line through the one that doesn't belong.

1. Ankylosaurus looked a little like a turtle.
2. That is because it had a hard shell like a turtle.
3. ~~Turtles are very slow animals.~~
4. However, Ankylosaurus was much larger than a turtle.

Write three sentences that belong together about dinosaurs.

5. **Children should write three related sentences**

that tell about the same idea.

Notes for Home: Your child identified and wrote sentences that belong together.
Home Activity: Copy a few sentences each from several paragraphs of a story and cut them
up. Have your child group the sentences that make sense together.

Level 2.2

Writing Process: Revise **175**

Practice Book 2.2, p. 158

Name _____

Tex and the Big Bad T. Rex
Let's Go Dinosaur Tracking!

Use the words in ( ) to make a contraction.
Write the contraction on the line to finish each sentence.

(had not)
1. They ___**hadn't**___ seen a dinosaur before.

(It is)
2. ___**It's**___ much bigger than an elephant.

(They are)
3. ___**They're**___ glad to see this one.

(would not)
4. They ___**wouldn't**___ like to meet a live one.

(They will)
5. ___**They'll**___ dream of dinosaurs tonight.

Notes for Home: Your child wrote contractions. **Home Activity:** Read with your child and
point out pairs of words that can be made into contractions. Have him or her write the
contractions and reread the sentences with the contractions in place.

176 Grammar: Contractions

Level 2.2

Practice Book 2.2, p. 159

Name _____

Tex and the Big Bad T. Rex
Let's Go Dinosaur Tracking!

Part 1: Vocabulary

Find the word that best fits in each sentence.
Mark the space for your answer.

1. Jason puts on a _____ when he rides his bike.
   ⬭ surface　⬛ helmet　⬭ someday

2. The bear's _____ are sharp.
   ⬛ claws　⬭ rockets　⬭ tools

3. The wall was made of _____ .
   ⬭ giant　⬛ stone　⬭ beach

4. Mina lost her _____ tooth.
   ⬛ front　⬭ word　⬭ poke

5. We will _____ go to the zoo.
   ⬭ since　⬭ should　⬛ probably

GO ON

Level 2.2

Selection Test: Vocabulary **177**

Practice Book 2.2, p. 160

Name _____

Let's Go Dinosaur Tracking!

Part 2: Comprehension

Read each question.
Mark the space for your answer.

6. What happened first?
   ⬭ The tracks turned to stone.
   ⬛ A dinosaur left some tracks.
   ⬭ Sand covered the tracks.

7. This story is mostly about —
   ⬭ finding a real dinosaur.
   ⬭ Roland Bird.
   ⬛ looking for dinosaur tracks.

8. You can tell that sauropods were —
   ⬛ very large.
   ⬭ three-legged.
   ⬭ meat eaters.

9. What did you learn about dinosaurs from this story?
   ⬭ Most dinosaurs were shaped like birds.
   ⬛ There were many different kinds.
   ⬭ All dinosaurs were very large.

10. Where is the best place to look for dinosaur tracks?
    ⬭ in a field of grass
    ⬭ in a lake
    ⬛ on flat stone

STOP

178 Selection Test: Comprehension

Level 2.2

Tex and the Big Bad T. Rex
Let's Go Dinosaur Tracking!

Circle a word to finish each sentence.

1. It looks around _____ .
   careless (carefully) caring

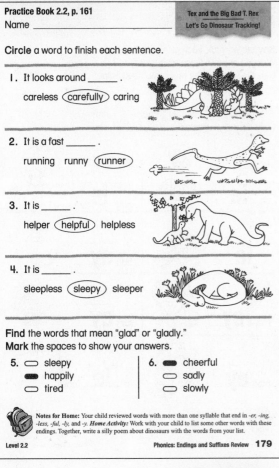

2. It is a fast _____ .
   running runny (runner)

3. It is _____ .
   helper (helpful) helpless

4. It is _____ .
   sleepless (sleepy) sleeper

Find the words that mean "glad" or "gladly."
Mark the spaces to show your answers.

5. ○ sleepy
   ● happily
   ○ tired

6. ● cheerful
   ○ sadly
   ○ slowly

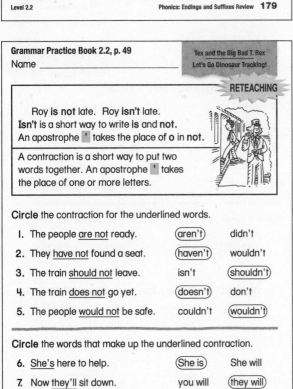

Notes for Home: Your child reviewed words with more than one syllable that end in *-er, -ing, -less, -ful, -ly,* and *-y.* **Home Activity:** Work with your child to list some other words with these endings. Together, write a silly poem about dinosaurs with the words from your list.

Level 2.2   Phonics: Endings and Suffixes Review **179**

Tex and the Big Bad T. Rex
Let's Go Dinosaur Tracking!

undo   unfair   unhappy   unlike   unlucky   untie

Add un- to each word to make a word from the box.
Write the new word on the line.

1. do
   undo

2. happy
   unhappy

3. tie
   untie

4. lucky
   unlucky

5. like
   unlike

6. fair
   unfair

Pick a word from the box to match each clue.   front   probably
Write the word on the line.

7. likely **probably**

8. opposite of *back* **front**

Notes for Home: Your child spelled words with the prefix *un-* and two frequently used words: *front, probably.* **Home Activity:** Help your child make crossword puzzles that include these spelling words. Work together to think of clues for each word.

180 Spelling: Prefix *un-*   Level 2.2

Tex and the Big Bad T. Rex
Let's Go Dinosaur Tracking!

RETEACHING

> Roy **is not** late. Roy **isn't** late.
> **Isn't** is a short way to write **is** and **not**.
> An apostrophe **'** takes the place of **o** in **not**.

A contraction is a short way to put two words together. An apostrophe **'** takes the place of one or more letters.

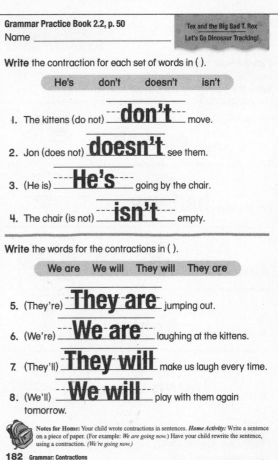

Circle the contraction for the underlined words.

1. The people <u>are not</u> ready.   (aren't)   didn't
2. They <u>have not</u> found a seat.   (haven't)   wouldn't
3. The train <u>should not</u> leave.   isn't   (shouldn't)
4. The train <u>does not</u> go yet.   (doesn't)   don't
5. The people <u>would not</u> be safe.   couldn't   (wouldn't)

Circle the words that make up the underlined contraction.

6. <u>She's</u> here to help.   (She is)   She will
7. Now <u>they'll</u> sit down.   you will   (they will)
8. Then <u>we'll</u> hear the whistle.   (we will)   we are
9. At last <u>we're</u> on our way.   they are   (we are)

Notes for Home: Your child identified contractions correctly in sentences. **Home Activity:** Write contractions, such as *isn't, doesn't,* or *we're,* on cards. Choose a card and have your child use that contraction in a sentence. Then change roles.

Grammar: Contractions **181**

Tex and the Big Bad T. Rex
Let's Go Dinosaur Tracking!

Write the contraction for each set of words in ( ).

He's   don't   doesn't   isn't

1. The kittens (do not) **don't** move.
2. Jon (does not) **doesn't** see them.
3. (He is) **He's** going by the chair.
4. The chair (is not) **isn't** empty.

Write the words for the contractions in ( ).

We are   We will   They will   They are

5. (They're) **They are** jumping out.
6. (We're) **We are** laughing at the kittens.
7. (They'll) **They will** make us laugh every time.
8. (We'll) **We will** play with them again tomorrow.

Notes for Home: Your child wrote contractions in sentences. **Home Activity:** Write a sentence on a piece of paper. (For example: *We are going now.*) Have your child rewrite the sentence, using a contraction. (*We're going now.*)

182 Grammar: Contractions

Answers **375**

Correct each sentence.
Write it on the line.
Hint: Check that all pronouns are used correctly.

1. Me wrote a report on dinosaurs.

I wrote a report on dinosaurs.

2. Them were big animals.

They were big animals.

3. Mrs. Lee said he liked it.

Mrs. Lee said she liked it.

4. Her liked my pictures.

She liked my pictures.

5. My dad was proud of I.

My dad was proud of me.

Notes for Home: Your child corrected pronouns in sentences. **Home Activity:** Read a story together. Look for sentences with nouns that can be replaced with pronouns. Have your child read the sentences using the proper pronouns. *(Mike threw the ball. He threw it.)*

Level 2.2 — Writing Process: Edit **183**

Say the word for each picture.
Write ie or ey to finish each word.
Use the words in the box if you need help.

thi**ef**   key

| briefcase | chief | cookie | honey |
| money | monkey | piece | turkey |

1. ch **ie** f

2. cook **ie**

3. p **ie** ce

4. hon **ey**

5. monk **ey**

6. turk **ey**

7. mon **ey**

8. br **ie** fcase

Notes for Home: Your child wrote words with the long *e* sound spelled *ie* and *ey* as in *thief* and *key*. **Home Activity:** Work with your child to write a story using as many of the pictured words as possible.

Level 2.2 — Phonics: Long *e*: *ie*, *ey* **187**

Pick the word that has the same consonant sound heard at the end of **graph**.
Write the word on the line to finish each sentence.

graph

(enough)   some

1. Did we make **enough** ?

up   (halfway)

2. It is filled **halfway** .

(cough)   sneeze

3. Don't **cough** , please.

(trophy)   medal

4. We deserve a **trophy** .

smile   (laugh)

5. Don't **laugh** , it's true.

Notes for Home: Your child finished sentences using words with the consonants *gh*, *ph*, and *lf* that represent the sound /f/. **Home Activity:** Make up rhymes with your child using the words with *gh*, *ph*, and *lf* shown above.

188 Phonics: Consonants *gh*, *ph*, *lf* — Level 2.2

Draw a line to match each word to a clue.

1. above ——————— a. something you hear
2. few ——————— b. not below
3. kept ——————— c. not many
4. number ——————— d. tells how many
5. sound ——————— e. the opposite of "gave away"

Write a sentence for each word in the box on the lines below.

| above | few | kept | number | sound |

6. Children's sentences should use each word correctly.

7. _____

8. _____

9. _____

10. _____

Notes for Home: This week your child is learning to read the words *above, few, kept, number,* and *sound*. **Home Activity:** Have your child tell you about an experience buying or selling something using as many of the listed words as possible.

Level 2.2 — High-Frequency Words **189**

Look at each picture.
Circle **R** if the picture shows something that could really happen.
Circle **F** if the picture shows something that could not really happen.

1. ⓇF	2. ⓇF	3. RⒻ
4. RⒻ	5. RⒻ	6. RⒻ
7. ⓇF	8. ⓇF	9. ⓇF

Draw a picture of something that could happen in a fantasy.
10.

Children's drawings should show something that could happen in a fantasy.

 Notes for Home: Your child identified things that could happen in a realistic story and things that could happen in a fantasy. *Home Activity:* Read a story. Ask your child to identify realistic events (real people doing ordinary things) and fantasy events (animals talking).

A **sentence** is a group of words that tell a complete idea.

Sentence: Toby likes to drink lemonade.
Not a sentence: A hot and thirsty Toby.

Read the words.
Write an **S** on the line if the words are a complete sentence.
Write an **N** on the line if the words are **not** a complete sentence.

S 1. Chris has a plan.

N 2. Wants to sell.

S 3. I love lemonade and cookies!

N 4. More cookies.

Write a sentence to go with the picture above.

5. **They sell lemonade.**

Possible answer given.

 Notes for Home: Your child identified and wrote complete sentences. *Home Activity:* Ask your child to tell you a story about solving a problem. Encourage him or her to use complete sentences.

Pick a word from the box to finish each sentence.
Write the word on the line.

| above | few | ice | kept |
| lemonade | number | sound | |

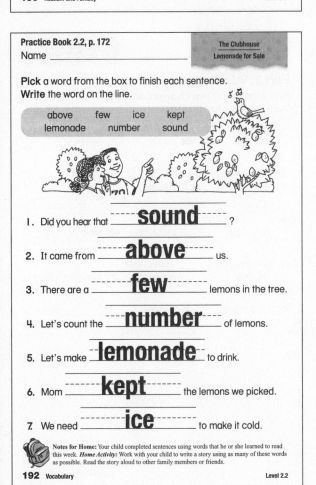

1. Did you hear that **sound** ?

2. It came from **above** us.

3. There are a **few** lemons in the tree.

4. Let's count the **number** of lemons.

5. Let's make **lemonade** to drink.

6. Mom **kept** the lemons we picked.

7. We need **ice** to make it cold.

Notes for Home: Your child completed sentences using words that he or she learned to read this week. *Home Activity:* Work with your child to write a story using as many of these words as possible. Read the story aloud to other family members or friends.

Use the graphs to answer the questions.

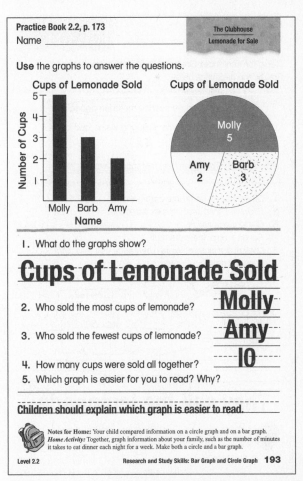

1. What do the graphs show?

Cups of Lemonade Sold

2. Who sold the most cups of lemonade? **Molly**

3. Who sold the fewest cups of lemonade? **Amy**

4. How many cups were sold all together? **10**

5. Which graph is easier for you to read? Why?

Children should explain which graph is easier to read.

Notes for Home: Your child compared information on a circle graph and on a bar graph. *Home Activity:* Together, graph information about your family, such as the number of minutes it takes to eat dinner each night for a week. Make both a circle and a bar graph.

Answers **377**

Texas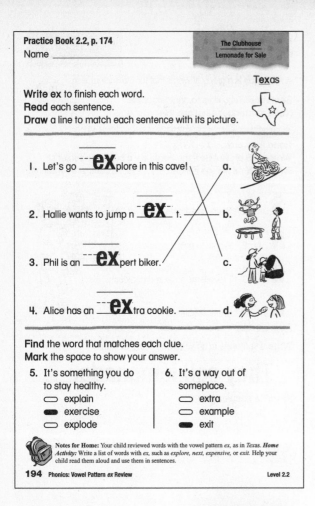

Write ex to finish each word.
Read each sentence.
Draw a line to match each sentence with its picture.

1. Let's go **ex**plore in this cave!   a.

2. Hallie wants to jump n **ex** t.   b.

3. Phil is an **ex**pert biker.   c.

4. Alice has an **ex**tra cookie. ——— d.

Find the word that matches each clue.
Mark the space to show your answer.

5. It's something you do
to stay healthy.
- explain
- ● exercise
- explode

6. It's a way out of
someplace.
- extra
- example
- ● exit

Notes for Home: Your child reviewed words with the vowel pattern *ex*, as in *Texas*. **Home Activity:** Write a list of words with *ex*, such as *explore, next, expensive,* or *exit*. Help your child read them aloud and use them in sentences.

| calf | half | laugh | phone | rough | tough |

Write three words from the box spelled with **gh**.

1. **laugh**   2. **rough**   3. **tough**

Write the word from the box that rhymes with  .
bone

4. **phone**

Change one letter in each word to make a word from the box.
Write the new word on the line.

5. halt **half**   6. calm **calf**

Pick a word from the box to finish each sentence.
Write the word on the line.

sound
kept

7. I hear the **sound** of popcorn popping.

8. Dean **kept** it all for himself.

Notes for Home: Your child spelled words with the consonants *gh, ph,* and *lf* and two frequently used words: *sound, kept*. **Home Activity:** Say each spelling word. Have your child use it in a sentence. Say the spelling word again, and have your child write it.

Read the sentences Greg and Diane say to each other.
Follow the directions below.

Greg: (What do we need to make lemonade?)

Diane: We need lemons, sugar, water, and ice. X

Diane: Stir it.

Greg: This is the best lemonade I've ever had!

1. Draw one line under the command.
2. Draw two lines under the exclamation.
3. Circle the question.
4. Put an X after the statement.
5. Look at the picture. Write a sentence that tells what
happens next.

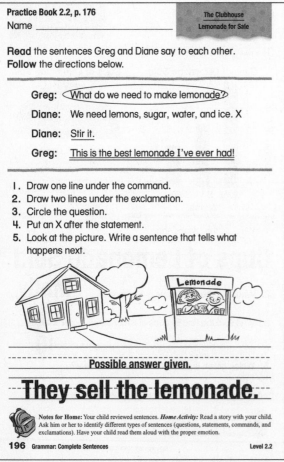

Possible answer given.

They sell the lemonade.

Notes for Home: Your child reviewed sentences. **Home Activity:** Read a story with your child. Ask him or her to identify different types of sentences (questions, statements, commands, and exclamations). Have your child read them aloud with the proper emotion.

Part I: Vocabulary

Find the word that best fits in each sentence.
Mark the space for your answer.

1. Write your name _____ the line.
- ever
- ● above
- behind

2. The bird made a beautiful _____ .
- ● sound
- number
- garbage

3. Jill _____ all her toys in a box.
- began
- exclaimed
- ● kept

4. We have only a _____ cups of milk.
- ● few
- whole
- enough

5. I like lots of _____ in my water.
- paper
- ● ice
- room

GO ON ➡

Part 2: Comprehension

Read each question.
Mark the space for your answer.

6. The club members decided to make some money by —
   - ● selling lemonade.
   - ○ having a bake sale.
   - ○ getting more members.

7. The kids wanted the money to —
   - ○ buy lemons.
   - ○ set up a corner stand.
   - ● fix their clubhouse.

8. Few people got lemonade on Thursday because —
   - ○ the lemonade did not taste good.
   - ● everyone went to watch Jed the juggler.
   - ○ Thursday's bar was way down low.

9. Sheri must have asked Jed to —
   - ● do his act next to the lemonade stand.
   - ○ leave so they could sell more lemonade.
   - ○ never juggle again.

10. The Elm Street kids learned that —
    - ○ selling lemonade is no fun.
    - ○ they could not fix the clubhouse.
    - ● a job is easier when everyone works together.

STOP

| disappear | dislike | remake | repaint | untie | unwrap |

Pick a word from the box that is the opposite of each word below.
Write the word on the line.

1. tie
   untie
2. wrap
   unwrap
3. like
   dislike
4. appear
   disappear

Pick a word from the box that means the same as each group of words.
Write the word on the line.

5. paint again
   repaint
6. make again
   remake

Find the word that matches each clue.
Mark the space to show your answer.

7. not lucky
   - ● unlucky
   - ○ lucky
   - ○ unkind

8. read again
   - ○ understand
   - ● reread
   - ○ return

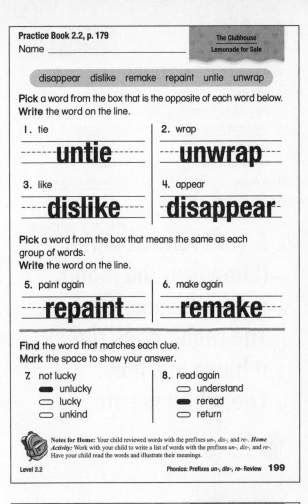

Notes for Home: Your child reviewed words with the prefixes *un-*, *dis-*, and *re-*. **Home Activity:** Work with your child to write a list of words with the prefixes *un-*, *dis-*, and *re-*. Have your child read the words and illustrate their meanings.

| calf | half | laugh | phone | rough | tough |

Pick a word from the box to match each picture.
Write the word on the line.

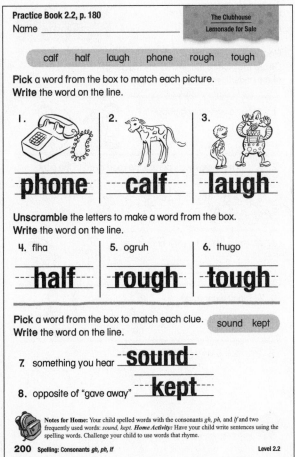

1. **phone**
2. **calf**
3. **laugh**

Unscramble the letters to make a word from the box.
Write the word on the line.

4. flha
   half
5. ogruh
   rough
6. thugo
   tough

Pick a word from the box to match each clue.
Write the word on the line.   sound   kept

7. something you hear   **sound**

8. opposite of "gave away"   **kept**

Notes for Home: Your child spelled words with the consonants *gh*, *ph*, and *lf* and two frequently used words: *sound, kept*. **Home Activity:** Have your child write sentences using the spelling words. Challenge your child to use words that rhyme.

RETEACHING

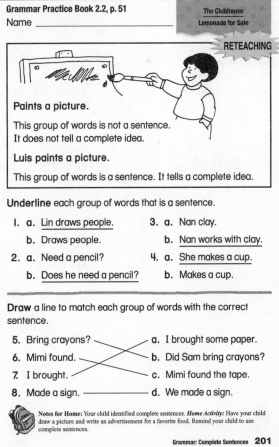

Paints a picture.

This group of words is not a sentence.
It does not tell a complete idea.

Luis paints a picture.

This group of words is a sentence. It tells a complete idea.

Underline each group of words that is a sentence.

1. a. <u>Lin draws people.</u>
   b. Draws people.

2. a. Need a pencil?
   b. <u>Does he need a pencil?</u>

3. a. Nan clay.
   b. <u>Nan works with clay.</u>

4. a. <u>She makes a cup.</u>
   b. Makes a cup.

Draw a line to match each group of words with the correct sentence.

5. Bring crayons? — b. Did Sam bring crayons?
6. Mimi found. — a. I brought some paper.
7. I brought. — c. Mimi found the tape.
8. Made a sign. — d. We made a sign.

Notes for Home: Your child identified complete sentences. **Home Activity:** Have your child draw a picture and write an advertisement for a favorite food. Remind your child to use complete sentences.

Underline each group of words that is a sentence.

1. <u>Animals live in the woods.</u>
2. <u>A rabbit hears the call.</u>
3. <u>Some animals may hunt.</u>
4. Does run.
5. <u>They hunt in the dark.</u>
6. <u>Can it get away?</u>
7. Runs at night.
8. In a hole.
9. Howls at the moon.
10. Rabbit is.
11. A rabbit.
12. <u>Will the rabbit sleep?</u>

Now **write** the other groups of words in complete sentences.
Possible answers given.

13. **A wolf runs at night.**
14. **It howls at the moon.**
15. **A rabbit is nearby.**
16. **The rabbit does run.**
17. **It hides in a hole.**
18. **The rabbit is safe.**

 Notes for Home: Your child wrote complete sentences. *Home Activity:* Together, write a sentence. Cut the paper between the subject and predicate. *(The rabbit/hopped away.)* Have your child write two new sentences, using the subject in one and the predicate in another.

Practice Book 2.2, p. 183
Name _____

Start Collecting! It's Fun!
The Puddle Pail

Pick a word from the box to finish each sentence.
Write the word on the line.

| either | neither | receive | ceiling |

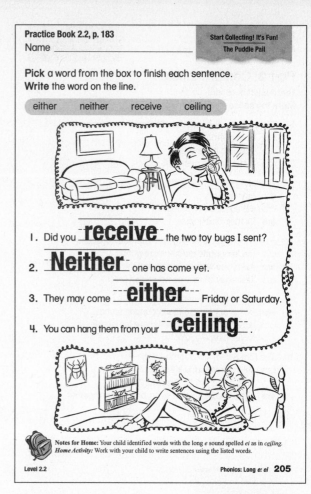

1. Did you **receive** the two toy bugs I sent?
2. **Neither** one has come yet.
3. They may come **either** Friday or Saturday.
4. You can hang them from your **ceiling**.

 Notes for Home: Your child identified words with the long *e* sound spelled *ei* as in *ceiling*. *Home Activity:* Work with your child to write sentences using the listed words.

Practice Book 2.2, p. 184
Name _____

Start Collecting! It's Fun!
The Puddle Pail

Write the word for each picture.
Use the word in ( ) to help you.

leaf   leaves

1. (calf) **calves**
2. (knife) **knives**
3. (loaf) **loaves**
4. (shelf) **shelves**

Draw a picture of the word below.

5. wolves

**Children should draw
more than one wolf.**

 Notes for Home: Your child wrote plural words in which *f* is changed to *v* before adding *-es*. *Home Activity:* Ask your child to write a sentence using each of the plural words above.

Practice Book 2.2, p. 185
Name _____

Start Collecting! It's Fun!
The Puddle Pail

Read each sentence.
Circle the picture that shows the meaning
of the underlined word.

1. Al has a very <u>young</u> puppy.
2. Al and his puppy walk across the <u>road</u> to go to the park.
3. Al wants to <u>start</u> a rock collection.
4. Al found <u>eight</u> rocks.
5. This rock is very <u>round</u> and smooth.

Notes for Home: This week your child is learning to read the words *eight, road, round, start,* and *young*. *Home Activity:* Write these words on slips of paper and have your child practice reading them aloud and using them in sentences.

Practice Book 2.2, p. 186
Name _____

Start Collecting! It's Fun!
The Puddle Pail

Read each sentence.
Use the other words in the sentence and the pictures to help you figure out the meaning of the underlined word.
Circle the meaning of the word.

1. Carrie added a British pound to her collection.
   a. (a kind of money or coin)
   b. a scale

2. She likes to collect currency.
   a. type of food
   b. (money)

3. She stores her collection in a box.
   a. (keeps)
   b. shops

4. Carrie is eager to get more coins.
   a. not careful
   b. (looking forward to)

5. She adores collecting coins!
   a. decorates
   b. (loves)

 Notes for Home: Your child used context clues—pictures or words that surround an unfamiliar word—to figure out a word's meaning. **Home Activity:** Read a story to your child. Ask him or her to use context clues to figure out the meanings of unfamiliar words.

Practice Book 2.2, p. 187
Name _____

Start Collecting! It's Fun!
The Puddle Pail

Quotation marks " " show the beginning and the end of what someone says.

Tim said, "Do you like my shells?"
"Yes, I do," Greta answered.

Put a ✓ on the line if the sentence does not need quotation marks.
Put an X on the line if the sentence needs quotation marks.
Then add quotation marks to the sentence.

✓ 1. Gus asked Nan to look at his baseball cards.

X 2. Nan said,"You have a lot of cards."

X 3. Gus said,"I've collected over 50 cards."

✓ 4. Nan asked her mom if she could collect cards too.

X 5. Her mom said,"I'll help you get started."

 Notes for Home: Your child identified sentences that use quotation marks. **Home Activity:** Write a simple conversation between two characters or family members. Have your child help you put the quotation marks where they belong.

Practice Book 2.2, p. 188
Name _____

Start Collecting! It's Fun!
The Puddle Pail

Pick a word from the box to match each clue.
Write the word on the line.

castle	crocodile	eight	puddle
road	round	shadows	young

1. **crocodile**

2. **road**

3. **castle**

4. **puddle**

5. They go everywhere you go!
   shadows

6. seven, _____, nine, ten
   eight

7. not old, but _____
   young

8. A square is not, but a circle is.
   round

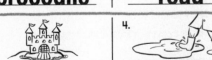 **Notes for Home:** Your child matched clues with vocabulary words that he or she learned to read this week. **Home Activity:** Work with your child to write a story using as many of these words as possible.

Practice Book 2.2, p. 189
Name _____

Start Collecting! It's Fun!
The Puddle Pail

monk**ey**   cook**ie**s

Circle the word for each picture.

1. (piece) peas
2. moan (money)
3. turkey (turtle)
4. (honey) hotter

5. keep (key)
6. (donkey) done
7. cheek (chief)
8. three (thief)

Find the word that has the same **long e** sound as the picture.
Mark the space to show your answer.

9. ○ veil
   ○ vase
   ● valley

10. ○ felt
    ● field
    ○ fried

cookie

 Notes for Home: Your child reviewed words with long e spelled *ie* and *ey* as in *cookies* and *monkey*. **Home Activity:** Write a list of long e words spelled *ie* and *ey*. Have your child tell you a story using as many of the words as possible.

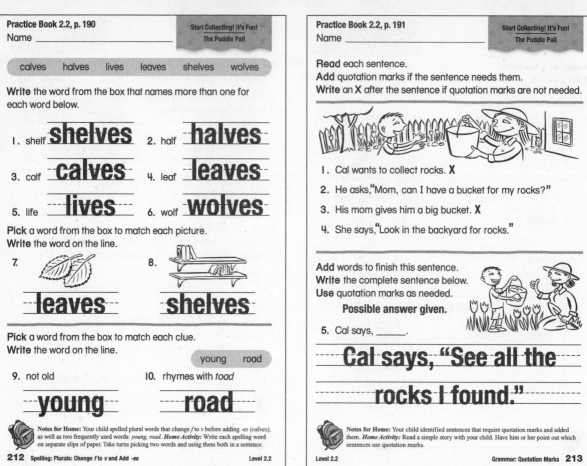

Practice Book 2.2, p. 190
Name _____

| calves | halves | lives | leaves | shelves | wolves |

Write the word from the box that names more than one for each word below.

1. shelf **shelves**
2. half **halves**
3. calf **calves**
4. leaf **leaves**
5. life **lives**
6. wolf **wolves**

Pick a word from the box to match each picture.
Write the word on the line.

7. **leaves**
8. **shelves**

Pick a word from the box to match each clue.
Write the word on the line.

| young | road |

9. not old **young**
10. rhymes with *toad* **road**

Notes for Home: Your child spelled plural words that change *f* to *v* before adding *-es (calves)*, as well as two frequently used words: *young, road*. Home Activity: Write each spelling word on separate slips of paper. Take turns picking two words and using them both in a sentence.

212 Spelling: Plurals: Change *f* to *v* and Add *-es*   Level 2.2

Practice Book 2.2, p. 191
Name _____

Read each sentence.
Add quotation marks if the sentence needs them.
Write an **X** after the sentence if quotation marks are not needed.

1. Cal wants to collect rocks. **X**
2. He asks, "Mom, can I have a bucket for my rocks?"
3. His mom gives him a big bucket. **X**
4. She says, "Look in the backyard for rocks."

Add words to finish this sentence.
Write the complete sentence below.
Use quotation marks as needed.
Possible answer given.

5. Cal says, _____.

Cal says, "See all the rocks I found."

Notes for Home: Your child identified sentences that require quotation marks and added them. Home Activity: Read a simple story with your child. Have him or her point out which sentences use quotation marks.

Level 2.2   Grammar: Quotation Marks **213**

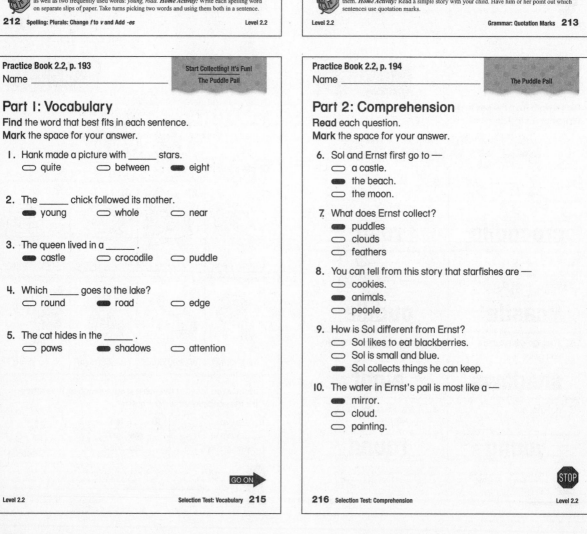

Practice Book 2.2, p. 193
Name _____

Part 1: Vocabulary
Find the word that best fits in each sentence.
Mark the space for your answer.

1. Hank made a picture with _____ stars.
   - ○ quite
   - ○ between
   - ● eight

2. The _____ chick followed its mother.
   - ● young
   - ○ whole
   - ○ near

3. The queen lived in a _____ .
   - ● castle
   - ○ crocodile
   - ○ puddle

4. Which _____ goes to the lake?
   - ○ round
   - ● road
   - ○ edge

5. The cat hides in the _____ .
   - ○ paws
   - ● shadows
   - ○ attention

GO ON

Level 2.2   Selection Test: Vocabulary **215**

Practice Book 2.2, p. 194
Name _____

Part 2: Comprehension
Read each question.
Mark the space for your answer.

6. Sol and Ernst first go to —
   - ○ a castle.
   - ● the beach.
   - ○ the moon.

7. What does Ernst collect?
   - ● puddles
   - ○ clouds
   - ○ feathers

8. You can tell from this story that starfishes are —
   - ○ cookies.
   - ● animals.
   - ○ people.

9. How is Sol different from Ernst?
   - ○ Sol likes to eat blackberries.
   - ○ Sol is small and blue.
   - ● Sol collects things he can keep.

10. The water in Ernst's pail is most like a —
    - ● mirror.
    - ○ cloud.
    - ○ painting.

STOP

216 Selection Test: Comprehension   Level 2.2

Practice Book 2.2, p. 195
Name _____

Start Collecting! It's Fun!
The Puddle Pail

Say the word for each picture.
Write gh, ph, or lf to finish each word.
Use the words in the box if you need help.

| calf | cough | half |
| laugh | photos | trophy |

phone

| 1. tro **ph** y | 2. cou **gh** | 3. ha **lf** |
| 4. ca **lf** | 5. **ph** otos | 6. lau **gh** |

Pick the word that has the same ending sound as the picture.
Mark the space to show your answer.

7. ● rough
   ○ rugs
   ○ rush

8. ○ thought
   ● tough
   ○ tugs

graph

Notes for Home: Your child reviewed words with the sound /f/ spelled *gh*, *ph*, and *lf* (*laugh*, *graph*, and *half*). **Home Activity:** Make a set of cards. Write words with the /f/ sound on half the cards. Illustrate the words on the other half. Have your child match the pairs of cards.

Practice Book 2.2, p. 196
Name _____

Start Collecting! It's Fun!
The Puddle Pail

| calves | halves | lives | leaves | shelves | wolves |

Pick a word from the box to match each clue.
Write the word on the line.

1. grows on trees
   leaves

2. more than one life
   lives

3. like dogs
   wolves

4. baby cows
   calves

5. where you find
   library books
   shelves

6. 1 half + 1 half = 2
   halves

Pick a word from the box to finish each sentence.
Write the word on the line.

| young |
| road |

7. The bus drives down the **road** .

8. It takes **young** children to school.

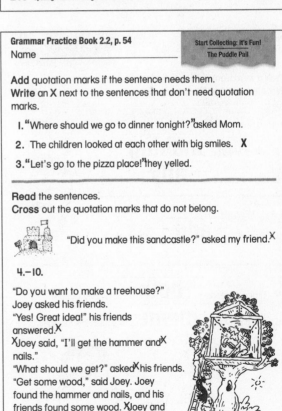

Notes for Home: Your child spelled plural words that change *f* to *v* before adding *-es* and two frequently used words: *young*, *road*. **Home Activity:** Help your child write sentences that use the spelling words. Together draw pictures to illustrate each sentence.

Grammar Practice Book 2.2, p. 53
Name _____

Start Collecting! It's Fun!
The Puddle Pail

RETEACHING

Quotation marks show the beginning and ending of what someone says.

"How much is this?" asked Nancy.

The saleswoman said, "It is one dollar."

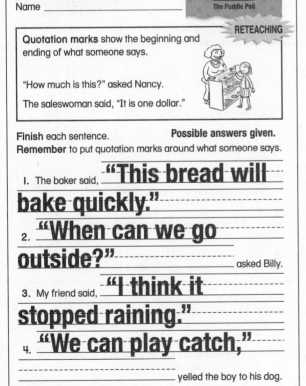

Finish each sentence.   **Possible answers given.**
Remember to put quotation marks around what someone says.

1. The baker said, **"This bread will bake quickly."**

2. **"When can we go outside?"** asked Billy.

3. My friend said, **"I think it stopped raining."**

4. **"We can play catch,"** yelled the boy to his dog.

Notes for Home: Your child used quotation marks to show a speaker's exact words in sentences. **Home Activity:** Have your child tell you about a conversation he or she had. Write it, leaving out the quotation marks. Have your child insert quotation marks.

Grammar Practice Book 2.2, p. 54
Name _____

Start Collecting! It's Fun!
The Puddle Pail

Add quotation marks if the sentence needs them.
Write an X next to the sentences that don't need quotation marks.

1. "Where should we go to dinner tonight?" asked Mom.

2. The children looked at each other with big smiles. **X**

3. "Let's go to the pizza place!" they yelled.

Read the sentences.
Cross out the quotation marks that do not belong.

"Did you make this sandcastle?" asked my friend. X

4.–10.

"Do you want to make a treehouse?"
Joey asked his friends.
"Yes! Great idea!" his friends
answered. X
X Joey said, "I'll get the hammer and X
nails."
"What should we get?" asked X his friends.
"Get some wood," said Joey. Joey
found the hammer and nails, and his
friends found some wood. X Joey and
his friends built a great treehouse. X

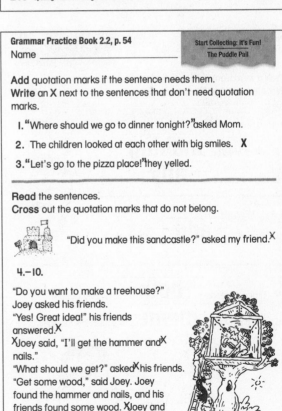

Notes for Home: Your child made decisions about where quotation marks belong in sentences. **Home Activity:** Have your child look through a newspaper and find sentences with quotation marks.

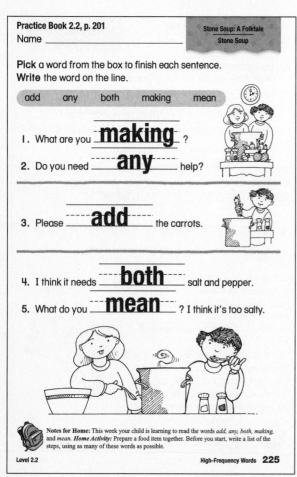

Stone Soup: A Folktale
Stone Soup

Here are some places where **commas** are used:

6 Morrow Court, Apt. 2B ←— in addresses
Salem, MA 01944

May 29, 2000 ←— in dates

Dear Harry, ←— to start a letter
How are you? → to separate three or more things
Liz, Jan, and Phil are going to the game next Saturday. Do
you want to go with me?

Your friend, ←— to end a letter
Jimmy

1.–8. Add eight commas to this letter.

19 East Lake Dr.
Gladstone, MI 49837

June 5, 2000

Dear Uncle Sid,

Sarah and I made soup for lunch. Sarah put carrots, peas,
and mushrooms into a pot of water. I added salt, pepper, and
garlic.

Love,
Jake

Notes for Home: Your child placed commas in a letter. **Home Activity:** Together, write a
postcard to a friend. Help your child place the commas in addresses, in dates, after the
opening and closing, and when listing more than two items.

Stone Soup: A Folktale
Stone Soup

Pick a word from the box to match each clue.
Write the word on the line.

ANNUAL
BAKING
CONTEST

| add | both | contest | delicious |
| judges | making | mean | stranger |

1. something you enter to
   win a prize .... **contest**

2. We are _____ pies. .... **making**

3. two together .... **both**

4. people who choose
   the winner .... **judges**

5. a person you don't know ... **stranger**

6. Did you _____ to call my
   cooking bad? .... **mean**

7. tastes great .... **delicious**

8. join one thing to another ... **add**

Notes for Home: Your child matched vocabulary words to clues. **Home Activity:** Write each
word on an index card. Take turns drawing a card, saying the word aloud, and using it in a
sentence.

Stone Soup: A Folktale
Stone Soup

Pick a **long e** word from the box to finish each sentence.
Write the word on the line.

ceiling   either   Neil   receive

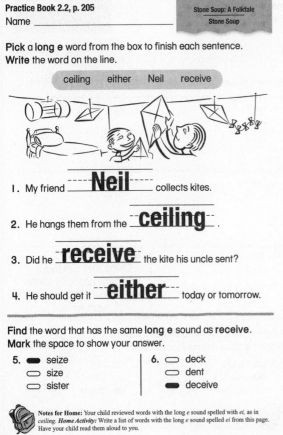

1. My friend ___**Neil**___ collects kites.

2. He hangs them from the ___**ceiling**___.

3. Did he ___**receive**___ the kite his uncle sent?

4. He should get it ___**either**___ today or tomorrow.

Find the word that has the same **long e** sound as **receive**.
Mark the space to show your answer.

5. ● seize   6. ◯ deck
   ◯ size   ◯ dent
   ◯ sister   ● deceive

Notes for Home: Your child reviewed words with the long e sound spelled with ei, as in
ceiling. **Home Activity:** Write a list of words with the long e sound spelled ei from this page.
Have your child read them aloud to you.

Stone Soup: A Folktale
Stone Soup

airplane   care   chair   hair   pair   share

Write four words from the box spelled with **air**.

1. **airplane**   2. **chair**

3. **hair**   4. **pair**

Write two words from the box spelled with **are**.

5. **care**   6. **share**

Pick a word from the box to match each clue.
Write the word on the line.

making
mean

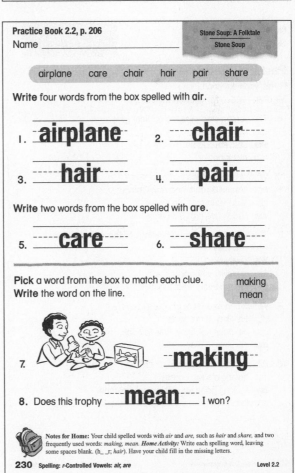

7. **making**

8. Does this trophy **mean** I won?

Notes for Home: Your child spelled words with air and are, such as hair and share, and two
frequently used words: making, mean. **Home Activity:** Write each spelling word, leaving
some spaces blank. (h__r; hair). Have your child fill in the missing letters.

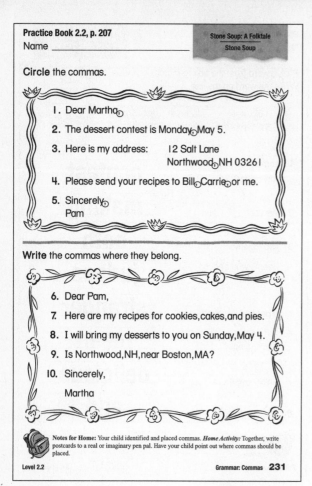

Practice Book 2.2, p. 207
Name _____

Stone Soup: A Folktale
Stone Soup

Circle the commas.

1. Dear Martha,

2. The dessert contest is Monday, May 5.

3. Here is my address: 12 Salt Lane
                                        Northwood, NH 03261

4. Please send your recipes to Bill, Carrie, or me.

5. Sincerely,
   Pam

Write the commas where they belong.

6. Dear Pam,

7. Here are my recipes for cookies, cakes, and pies.

8. I will bring my desserts to you on Sunday, May 4.

9. Is Northwood, NH, near Boston, MA?

10. Sincerely,

    Martha

Notes for Home: Your child identified and placed commas. **Home Activity:** Together, write postcards to a real or imaginary pen pal. Have your child point out where commas should be placed.

Level 2.2   Grammar: Commas **231**

Practice Book 2.2, p. 209
Name _____

Stone Soup: A Folktale
Stone Soup

Part I: Vocabulary
Find the word that best fits in each sentence.
Mark the space for your answer.

1. Holly loves _____ cookies.
   ● making   ○ sealing   ○ dashing

2. Julio won the baking _____ .
   ● contest   ○ stranger   ○ deck

3. They _____ like to paint.
   ○ mean   ● both   ○ add

4. The _____ say my soup is the best.
   ○ Earth   ○ spiders   ● judges

5. What a _____ cake!
   ○ few   ● delicious   ○ young

GO ON

Level 2.2   Selection Test: Vocabulary **233**

Practice Book 2.2, p. 210
Name _____

Stone Soup

Part 2: Comprehension
Read each question.
Mark the space for your answer.

6. The person who wins the contest gets a —
   ○ bowl of soup.
   ● gold soup ladle.
   ○ black pot.

7. Who are the judges in the contest?
   ○ Minnie Stronie and Ann Chovie
   ○ Vida Minn and Ida Know
   ● Brock Lee and Sal Lamie

8. The judges had second helpings of Ida Know's soup because they —
   ● really liked it.
   ○ were very hungry.
   ○ did not know what was in it.

9. Which sentence tells about Bill Lownie?
   ○ He likes to eat soup.
   ○ He does not know how to cook.
   ● He likes to play tricks.

10. Which could **not** really happen?
    ○ having a soup contest
    ● making good soup from only a stone
    ○ living in a town called Bellie Acres

STOP

234 Selection Test: Comprehension   Level 2.2

Practice Book 2.2, p. 211
Name _____

Stone Soup: A Folktale
Stone Soup

lea**f**
lea**ves**

Draw a picture for each word.

1. wolf	2. shelf
3. calves	4. wolves
5. shelves	6. calf

Check that children's drawings correctly show one or more than one for each word.

Find the word that matches each picture.
Mark the space to show your answer.

7. ○ scars
   ● scarf
   ○ scarves

8. ○ loaf
   ○ loans
   ● loaves

Notes for Home: Your child reviewed words that change *f* to *v* and add *-es* to mean more than one. **Home Activity:** Write a list of singular words such as *half, calf, knife, loaf, shelf,* and *wolf.* Have your child write the plural spelling for each word.

Level 2.2   Phonics: Plural *-es* Review **235**

---

386 Answers

Practice Book 2.2, p. 212

Name _____

Stone Soup: A Folktale
Stone Soup

| airplane | care | chair | hair | pair | share |

Change one letter of each word to make a word from the box.
Write the word on the line.

1. chain

chair

2. pail

pair

3. shore

share

4. cart

care

Pick a word from the box to match each clue.
Write the word on the line.

5. something a pilot flies

airplane

6. grows on your head

hair

Pick a word from the box to finish each rhyme.
Write the word on the line.

making
mean

7. What do you **mean** ?
That frog isn't green!

8. Is it a pie you are **making** ?
Or a cake you are baking?

Notes for Home: Your child spelled words with *air* and *are*, such as *hair* and *share*, and two frequently used words: *making, mean*. **Home Activity:** Mix up the letters of each spelling word. Have your child unscramble and spell each word correctly.

236 Spelling *r*-Controlled Vowels: *air, are*

Level 2.2

Grammar Practice Book 2.2, p. 55

Name _____

Stone Soup: A Folktale
Stone Soup

Commas are used in addresses:
6000 Michigan Avenue, Apt. 3
Chicago, IL 60615

Commas are used in dates: March 15, 2001

Commas are used to start letters: Dear Marge,

Commas are used to separate three or more things:
I need to buy rice, sugar, and milk.

Commas are used to end a letter: Your friend,
Jimmy

Add commas where they belong in this letter.

1.–10.

Jake Fountain
321 Miller Court, Apt. 6A
Boulder, CO 83009

July 6, 2001

Dear Dad,
Summer camp is great! Today we went hiking,
swimming, and biking. Tomorrow we will cook
hamburgers, hot dogs, fries, and sweet corn.

Love,
Tabitha

Notes for Home: Your child inserted commas into the following parts of a letter: the address, the date, the greeting, items in a series, and the closing. **Home Activity:** Have your child write a letter to you about something funny that happened at school.

Grammar: Commas **237**

Grammar Practice Book 2.2, p. 56

Name _____

Stone Soup: A Folktale
Stone Soup

Read this letter.

44 Dixie Lane
New Orleans, LA 70003
June 3, 2000

Dear Friend,

Hi. I just moved into this neighborhood. I come from
Lincoln, Nebraska. I have a cat, a dog, and a bird. I was
wondering if you would like to come over for lunch on
Saturday, June 10.

Sincerely,
Mindy

Write a letter in response to the letter above.
Remember to use commas.   **Check for commas.**

_____
_____
_____
_____
_____
_____

Notes for Home: Your child read and wrote letters with commas. **Home Activity:** Write a letter to your child, and have him or her circle the commas and then write back to you.

238 Grammar: Commas

Practice Book 2.2, p. 215

Name _____

A Good Idea
Annie's Gifts

Say the word for each picture.
Write a, e, i, o, or u on the line to finish the word.

to**ma**to

1.
r **a** dio

2.
z **e** bra

3.
comp **u** ter

4.
m **u** sic

5.
p **i** lot

6.
b **a** by

7.
t **i** ger

8.
m **o** tor

Notes for Home: Your child completed words with long vowel sounds at the end of syllables as in *to•ma•to*. **Home Activity:** Write these words: *navy, lazy, zebra, tiny, lion, total, October, tuba*. Help your child say each word and identify the long vowel sounds.

Level 2.2

Phonics: Long Vowels at the Ends of Syllables **241**

A Good Idea
Annie's Gifts

Circle the word for each picture.

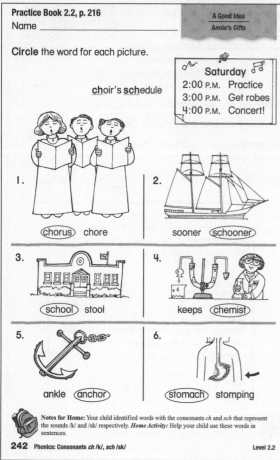

Saturday
2:00 P.M. Practice
3:00 P.M. Get robes
4:00 P.M. Concert!

<u>ch</u>oir's <u>sch</u>edule

1. (chorus) chore
2. sooner (schooner)
3. (school) stool
4. keeps (chemist)
5. ankle (anchor)
6. (stomach) stomping

Notes for Home: Your child identified words with the consonants *ch* and *sch* that represent the sounds /k/ and /sk/ respectively. Home Activity: Help your child use these words in sentences.

242 Phonics: Consonants *ch* /k/, *sch* /sk/   Level 2.2

A Good Idea
Annie's Gifts

Pick a word from the box to finish each sentence.
Write the word on the line.

| also | group | soon | though | tried |

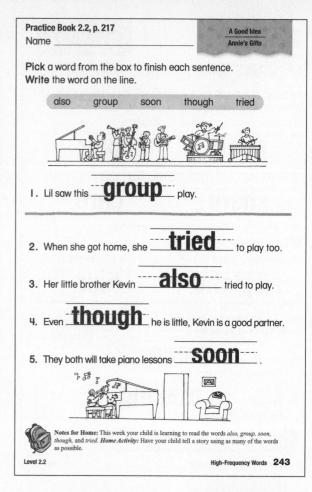

1. Lil saw this **group** play.

2. When she got home, she **tried** to play too.

3. Her little brother Kevin **also** tried to play.

4. Even **though** he is little, Kevin is a good partner.

5. They both will take piano lessons **soon**.

Notes for Home: This week your child is learning to read the words *also, group, soon, though,* and *tried.* Home Activity: Have your child tell a story using as many of the words as possible.

Level 2.2   High-Frequency Words **243**

A Good Idea
Annie's Gifts

Read the story.
Follow the directions below.

You may wish to read the story aloud.

Max wanted to be in a club. He tried out for the school play. But he didn't get a part. Max thought about joining the school chorus. But he sounds like a frog when he sings.

Max was sad. <u>His mom told him to keep trying because everyone is good at something.</u>

One day, Max saw the soccer club playing soccer. He liked sports. Maybe he would like soccer. Max joined the game. He was surprised when he scored a goal. The other players asked Max to play with them every afternoon. Max was happy to say "Yes!"

1. Underline the sentence that tells the story's big idea.
2. Write a sentence that tells what you learned from the story.

Possible answer: **Keep trying new things.**

Draw two pictures. One should show how Max felt at the beginning of the story, and one should show how he felt at the end.

3.   4.

Children's drawings should show first a boy looking sad and then the boy happily playing soccer.

Notes for Home: Your child identified the theme of a story. Home Activity: Read a story to your child. Discuss the theme. Ask your child to tell you what the big idea is in the story and to share anything he or she learned from the story.

244 Theme   Level 2.2

A Good Idea
Annie's Gifts

Commas are placed between the date and the year.
They also go between the day of the week and the date.

Hannah was born on May 5, 1991.
She will have a party on Saturday, May 3.

Commas are also used to join two complete sentences with a connecting word like *and*.

Harry likes to play the drums, and he likes to sing.

Read each sentence.
Add commas where they are missing.

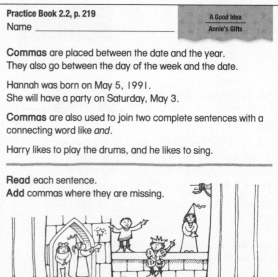

1. The play is on June 26, 2000.

2. Tryouts will begin Sunday, April 5.

3. They will start to practice on Tuesday, April 7.

4. Everyone got a part, so all the children were happy.

5. The play was great, and everyone wants to do it again!

Notes for Home: Your child added commas to dates and compound sentences. Home Activity: Read a story with your child. Ask your child to point out the commas in the sentences. Talk about why these commas are used where they are.

Level 2.2   Grammar: Commas **245**

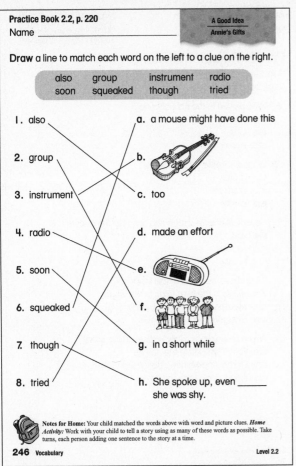

Draw a line to match each word on the left to a clue on the right.

| also | group | instrument | radio |
| soon | squeaked | though | tried |

1. also   a. a mouse might have done this

2. group   b. [violin]

3. instrument   c. too

4. radio   d. made an effort

5. soon   e. [radio]

6. squeaked   f. [group of people]

7. though   g. in a short while

8. tried   h. She spoke up, even _____ she was shy.

Notes for Home: Your child matched the words above with word and picture clues. **Home Activity:** Work with your child to tell a story using as many of these words as possible. Take turns, each person adding one sentence to the story at a time.

246 Vocabulary   Level 2.2

hare   chair

Say the word for each picture.
Write air or are to finish each word.

| 1. p**air** | 2. st**air**s | 3. c**are** | 4. st**are** |
| 5. squ**are** | 6. f**air** | 7. h**air** | 8. **air**plane |

Find the word that has the same vowel sound as **chair**.
Mark the space to show your answer.

9. ● dare   10. ◯ sprain
    ◯ dark   ◯ spark
    ◯ drain   ● spare

Notes for Home: Your child reviewed words with *air* and *are* where the letter *r* changes the vowel sounds, such as *hare* and *chair*. **Home Activity:** Challenge your child to make up sentences that rhyme using the words on this page. *(There's a hare on the chair!)*

Level 2.2   Phonics: *r*-Controlled Vowels: *air, are* Review **247**

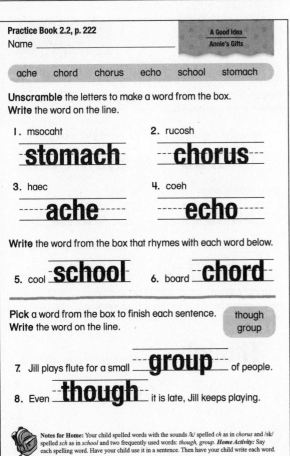

| ache | chord | chorus | echo | school | stomach |

Unscramble the letters to make a word from the box.
Write the word on the line.

1. msocaht   2. rucosh
stomach   **chorus**

3. haec   4. coeh
ache   **echo**

Write the word from the box that rhymes with each word below.

5. cool **school**   6. board **chord**

Pick a word from the box to finish each sentence.
Write the word on the line.

though
group

7. Jill plays flute for a small **group** of people.

8. Even **though** it is late, Jill keeps playing.

Notes for Home: Your child spelled words with the sounds /k/ spelled *ch* as in *chorus* and /sk/ spelled *sch* as in *school* and two frequently used words: *though, group*. **Home Activity:** Say each spelling word. Have your child use it in a sentence. Then have your child write each word.

248 Spelling: Consonants /k/: *ch*, /sk/: *sch*   Level 2.2

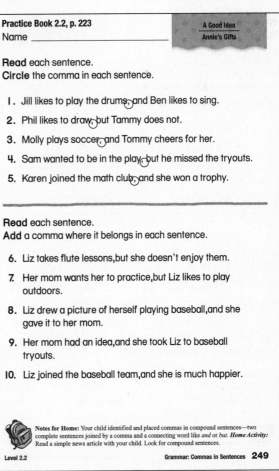

Read each sentence.
Circle the comma in each sentence.

1. Jill likes to play the drums, and Ben likes to sing.

2. Phil likes to draw, but Tammy does not.

3. Molly plays soccer, and Tommy cheers for her.

4. Sam wanted to be in the play, but he missed the tryouts.

5. Karen joined the math club, and she won a trophy.

Read each sentence.
Add a comma where it belongs in each sentence.

6. Liz takes flute lessons, but she doesn't enjoy them.

7. Her mom wants her to practice, but Liz likes to play outdoors.

8. Liz drew a picture of herself playing baseball, and she gave it to her mom.

9. Her mom had an idea, and she took Liz to baseball tryouts.

10. Liz joined the baseball team, and she is much happier.

Notes for Home: Your child identified and placed commas in compound sentences—two complete sentences joined by a comma and a connecting word like *and* or *but*. **Home Activity:** Read a simple news article with your child. Look for compound sentences.

Level 2.2   Grammar: Commas in Sentences **249**

Part 1: Vocabulary

Find the word that best fits in each sentence.
Mark the space for your answer.

1. Ed went to school, and I went _____ .
   ○ friend   ● also   ○ thumb

2. Anya _____ to read her brother's book.
   ● tried   ○ squeaked   ○ exclaimed

3. A _____ of children marched down the street.
   ○ spray   ● group   ○ patch

4. Jack eats peas even _____ he doesn't really like them.
   ○ until   ○ both   ● though

5. Please turn off the _____ .
   ○ garbage   ○ homework   ● radio

GO ON

Part 2: Comprehension

Read each question.
Mark the space for your answer.

6. Who played in the school band?
   ○ Patty
   ● Lee
   ○ Annie

7. What did Annie try to play last?
   ○ drums
   ○ recorder
   ● piano

8. How did Annie feel after she sang for the guests?
   ● sad
   ○ excited
   ○ happy

9. What did Annie learn in this story?
   ○ Music is the best thing in the world.
   ○ Most people don't try hard enough.
   ● Everyone has special gifts.

10. Which one did **not** really happen in the story?
    ● Frogs jumped in the house.
    ○ Daddy and Momma danced at night.
    ○ Annie drew some pictures.

STOP

---

ba**dge**

Circle the word for each picture.

1. (ledge) leave

2. (bridge) bring

3. (fudge) funnel

4. jug (judge)

Find the word that has the same ending sound as **badge**.
Mark the space to show your answer.

5. ● edge
   ○ egg
   ○ end

6. ○ plug
   ○ plaid
   ● pledge

Notes for Home: Your child reviewed the sound /j/ spelled *dge* as in *badge*. **Home Activity:** Challenge your child to use the words with *dge* listed above in sentences. Work together to illustrate each sentence.

| ache | chord | chorus | echo | school | stomach |

Pick a word from the box to match each clue.
Write the word on the line.

1. a group of singers
   chorus

2. where your food goes
   stomach

3. a place to learn
   school

4. a hurt
   ache

5. rhymes with *sword*
   chord

6. a sound you hear again
   echo

Pick a word from the box to finish each sentence.
Write the word on the line.

though
group

7. **Though** Tim likes tennis, he likes baseball more.

8. Tim likes to play with a **group** of people.

Notes for Home: Your child spelled words with the consonant sound /k/ spelled *ch* and two frequently used words: *though, group*. **Home Activity:** Have your child write the spelling words on paper. Cut and mix the letters. Have your child use the letters to rebuild the words.

RETEACHING

A **comma** is placed between the date and the year.

A **comma** is also placed between the day of the week and the date.

Priscilla will be seven years old on May 5, 2003.
We're going to Miami on Sunday, April 19.

Commas are also used to join two complete sentences with a connecting word, such as *and*.

I like to swim, and my brother likes to hike.

1.–4. Circle the commas in this paragraph.

Max's sister is the smartest girl in the school. She is graduating on June 22, 2002. She will read a speech to her classmates, and they will all sing a song. Max can bring one friend to her party on Monday, June 23. Max is going to buy his sister a book, and he is going to give her a card.

Add commas where they belong.

5. Call me on Monday, March 11.

6. I am going to summer camp on Tuesday, July 22, and he is going on vacation.

 Notes for Home: Your child identified and placed commas in dates and in sentences with connecting words. **Home Activity:** Have your child show you his or her work on this page. Ask your child to explain why the commas are used where they are.

Grammar: Commas in Sentences 255

Read each sentence.
Add a comma where it belongs in each sentence.

1. Alisa wrote a story, and she drew a picture.
2. Mom ran a race, and we watched.
3. The students like to play outside, but today it is raining.
4. My birthday is in March, and I am having a party.
5. We lost our cat, but she came home on her own.

Write three sentences about a family dinner. **Check for**
Use and or **but** with a comma in each sentence. **commas.**

6. _____
_____
_____

7. _____
_____
_____

8. _____
_____

 Notes for Home: Your child placed commas in sentences and wrote sentences using commas. **Home Activity:** Read a story with your child. Ask him or her to point out the commas and to explain why they are there.

256 Grammar: Commas in Sentences   Level 2.2

Read the word at the top of each column.
Write the words from the box that have the same vowel sound.

flour   Earth   heard   pearls   sour

early	hour
1. **Earth**	4. **flour**
2. **heard**	5. **sour**
3. **pearls**	

Pick a word from the box to match each clue.
Write the word on the line.

6.

Earth

7.

pearls

8. It sounds the same as *flower*.

flour

9. not sweet, but _____

sour

10.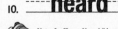

heard

 Notes for Home: Your child read and wrote words where the letter *r* changes the vowel sound as in (*heard*, *sour*). **Home Activity:** Ask your child to write and then read a sentence using each of the following words: *earn, search, hour, sour.*

Level 2.2   Phonics: *r*-Controlled Vowels: *ear /ĕr/* and *our /our/* **259**

Circle a word to finish each sentence.

1. The stream near the school was full of _____.   (pollution) / pollute

2. The children wanted to take _____ to clean it up.   acting / (action)

3. They held a clean-up day during their _____.   (vacation) / vacate

4. They spent the day _____ garbage.   (collecting) / collection

5. Then they asked people to sign a _____ .   petting / (petition)

 **Notes for Home:** Your child read words that include the syllable *-tion* as in *lotion.* **Home Activity:** Write or say words with *-tion* (*attention, solution, prediction, fiction, creation*). Give your child clues about the word to help him or her guess the meaning.

260 Phonics: Syllable Pattern *-tion*   Level 2.2

Answers **391**

Read each sentence.
Circle the picture that shows the meaning for each underlined word.

1. Beth picked an empty <u>piece</u> of the garden to use.

2. Dave went to <u>buy</u> some seeds.

3. Beth and Dave <u>used</u> tools to dig a hole in the soil.

4. At first, <u>nothing</u> grew.

5. Now, only a week later, the plants have <u>already</u> sprouted.

Notes for Home: This week your child is learning to read the words *already, buy, nothing, piece,* and *used*. **Home Activity:** Have your child write or tell a story about working together using these words.

Read each sentence.
Write H if the person is doing something helpful.
Write N if the person is doing something that is **not** helpful.

N 1. Tommy threw his wrapper on the ground.

H 2. Sue collected money to buy a new slide.

N 3. Tal used the money to buy himself a snack.

H 4. Jason fixed the broken swing.

Draw a picture to show something helpful that one of the children did.

5.

Children should draw a girl collecting money or a boy fixing a swing.

Notes for Home: Your child made judgments about actions that are helpful and those that are not. **Home Activity:** As you read, ask your child whether the characters are acting in a good way or a bad way. Ask your child why he or she thinks a particular action is good or bad.

Circle the sentences that tell about the same idea.
Put these sentences in order to make a paragraph.
Write numbers in front of these sentences to show the order.

5 1. (The children waited for the plants to grow.)

2 2. (It was time to plant a garden.)

___ 3. Chris and Tina went for a walk.

4 4. (Chris planted the seeds and watered them.)

___ 5. Tim played football in the park.

___ 6. We went to visit Grandma.

1 7. (Spring had come.)

3 8. (Everyone had a job to do.)

You may want children to write their paragraphs on a separate sheet of paper. The order of some sentences may vary, but they should make sense as a paragraph.

Notes for Home: Your child identified sentences that can be grouped into a paragraph. **Home Activity:** Have your child write sentences about a time he or she did something as part of the neighborhood or community. Help your child put the sentences into paragraphs.

Pick a word from the box to match each clue.
Write the word on the line.

| already | buy | empty | nothing |
| piece | property | soil | used |

1. not full

empty

2. She ____ a shovel to dig.

used

3. I ____ planted my garden.

already

4. dirt

soil

5.

piece

6.

buy

7. the opposite of *everything*

nothing

8. something you own

property

Notes for Home: Your child completed sentences using words that he or she learned to read this week. **Home Activity:** Play act that you and your child are planting a garden. Try to use as many words from the list above as you can.

Practice Book 2.2, p. 237

Wicker School Takes Action
City Green

Say the word for the picture.
Write **a, e, i, o,** or **u** to finish each word.

tiger

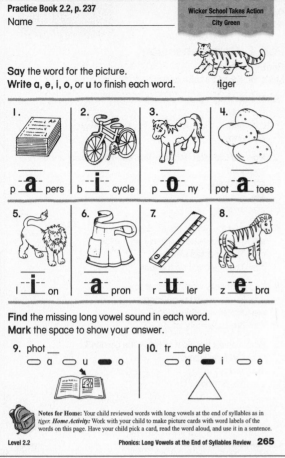

1. p **a** pers
2. b **i** cycle
3. p **o** ny
4. pot **a** toes

5. l **i** on
6. **a** pron
7. r **u** ler
8. z **e** bra

Find the missing long vowel sound in each word.
Mark the space to show your answer.

9. phot __
○ a ○ u ● o

10. tr __ angle
○ a ● i ○ e

Notes for Home: Your child reviewed words with long vowels at the end of syllables as in *tiger*. **Home Activity:** Work with your child to make picture cards with word labels of the words on this page. Have your child pick a card, read the word aloud, and use it in a sentence.

Level 2.2 — Phonics: Long Vowels at the End of Syllables Review **265**

Practice Book 2.2, p. 238

Wicker School Takes Action
City Green

earn flour heard hour learn sour

Write three words from the box spelled with **ear**.

1. **earn** 2. **heard** 3. **learn**

Write three words from the box spelled with **our**.

4. **flour** 5. **hour** 6. **sour**

Write two words from the box that rhyme with **burn**.

7. **earn** 8. **learn**

Pick a word from the box to finish each sentence.
Write the word on the line.

piece
already

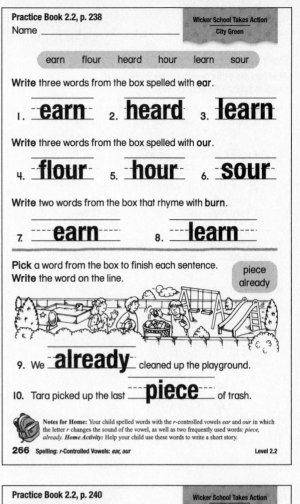

9. We **already** cleaned up the playground.

10. Tara picked up the last **piece** of trash.

Notes for Home: Your child spelled words with the *r*-controlled vowels *ear* and *our* in which the letter *r* changes the sound of the vowel, as well as two frequently used words: *piece, already*. **Home Activity:** Help your child use these words to write a short story.

266 Spelling: *r*-Controlled Vowels: *ear, our* — Level 2.2

Practice Book 2.2, p. 239

Wicker School Takes Action
City Green

Leave out details that do **not** support the main idea.

Main Idea: We need to clean the park.
John will pick up trash.
~~Pat will go for a bike ride.~~

Read the sentence that tells the main idea.
Cross out the sentence that does **not** support the main idea.

1. **Main Idea:** Our city needs a skateboard park.
   Many people enjoy using skateboards.
   ~~Skateboards don't cost very much.~~
   It isn't safe to skateboard in the streets.

2. **Main Idea:** Do something besides watching TV.
   ~~There are too many ads on TV.~~
   You can make something with your hands.
   You can play make-believe with a friend.

3. **Main Idea:** Dogs are smart animals.
   Dogs can understand commands.
   ~~Some dogs have long hair.~~
   A dog remembers what you teach it.

Write a sentence to go with this main idea:

Possible answer given.

4. A cow does not make a very good pet.

A cow can't sit inside.

Notes for Home: Your child identified sentences that did not belong with the main idea of a paragraph. **Home Activity:** Have your child give you a main idea. Make up sentences that go with it and one that does not. Ask your child which sentence does not belong. Switch roles.

Level 2.2 — Writing Process: Revise **267**

Practice Book 2.2, p. 240

Wicker School Takes Action
City Green

Read the paragraph.
Underline a sentence if it belongs in the paragraph.
Draw a line through it if it does **not** belong in the paragraph.

1. Jess wants to plant a garden.
2. Jess picks a spot for the garden.
3. ~~She dusts the shelves.~~
4. She digs in the dirt.
5. She plants the seeds.
6. ~~Jess brushes her hair.~~
7. She waters her seeds.
8. ~~Jess loves to read books.~~

Add two sentences of your own to finish the paragraph.

9. **Children should write two sentences related to Jess planting a garden.**

10. _____

Notes for Home: Your child identified sentences that can be grouped into a paragraph. **Home Activity:** Help your child write a story. Work together to group the sentences together into paragraphs.

268 Grammar: Paragraphs — Level 2.2

Part 1: Vocabulary

Find the word that best fits in each sentence.
Mark the space for your answer.

1. I need a _____ of tape.
   ○ word ● piece ○ number

2. The cookie jar is _____ again.
   ● empty ○ nothing ○ calm

3. Are you done _____ ?
   ○ between ○ never ● already

4. The Changs bought a _____ car.
   ● used ○ round ○ pleased

5. We planted the seeds in the _____ .
   ○ tool ○ wheel ● soil

GO ON ➡

Part 2: Comprehension

Read each question.
Mark the space for your answer.

6. The building was torn down because it was —
   ○ ugly.
   ○ new.
   ● unsafe.

7. How did Old Man Hammer feel when he looked at the empty lot?
   ○ pleased
   ● upset
   ○ excited

8. What did the neighbors do first?
   ● They paid one dollar to rent the lot.
   ○ They planted seeds.
   ○ They cleaned up the junk.

9. The neighbors work together to —
   ○ knock down the building.
   ● make something good.
   ○ buy the empty lot.

10. Who worked the most to make the garden?
    ○ Old Man Hammer
    ● Marcy
    ○ Mr. Bennett

STOP

Say the word for each picture.
Write ch or sch to finish each word.

anchor

1. **sch** ool

2. **ch** orus

3. stoma **ch**

4. e **ch** o

Find the word where **ch** has the same sound heard in **anchor**.
Mark the space to show your answer.

5. ○ lunch
   ○ chair
   ● ache

6. ● character
   ○ branches
   ○ chin

Notes for Home: Your child reviewed the consonant sounds /k/ spelled *ch* (*chorus*) and /sk/ spelled *sch* (*school*). **Home Activity:** Write each word from this page on an index card. Place them around a room. When your child finds a card, have him or her read the word to you.

---

earn   flour   heard   hour   learn   sour

Write a word from the box to match each picture.

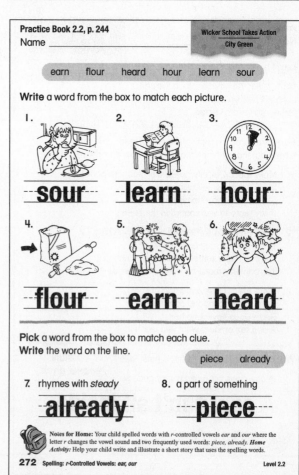

1. **sour**

2. **learn**

3. **hour**

4. **flour**

5. **earn**

6. **heard**

Pick a word from the box to match each clue.
Write the word on the line.

piece   already

7. rhymes with *steady*
   already

8. a part of something
   piece

Notes for Home: Your child spelled words with *r*-controlled vowels *ear* and *our* where the letter *r* changes the vowel sound and two frequently used words: *piece, already*. **Home Activity:** Help your child write and illustrate a short story that uses the spelling words.

RETEACHING

Circle the sentences that tell about the same idea. **Draw** a line through the sentence that does not tell about the same idea.

(I like to play with my friends) (We play games and sports)

~~Dogs can be small or big.~~

A **paragraph** is a group of sentences that tell about the same idea. The sentences are in an order that makes sense.

Circle the sentences that tell about the same idea.
Put these sentences in order to make a paragraph.
Write numbers in front of these sentences to show order.

__3__ 1. (Other people keep stamps that are their favorite colors.)

__1__ 2. (Many people collect stamps.)

_____ 3. My brother likes to buy baseball cards.

__2__ 4. (Some people like stamps that show places.)

__4__ 5. (Whatever their reasons are, people who collect stamps enjoy their hobby.)

 Notes for Home: Your child identified sentences that can be grouped into a paragraph. **Home Activity:** Look at a favorite story with your child. Have your child choose an interesting sentence or idea from the story, and help him or her write a paragraph about that sentence or idea.

Draw a box around the group of sentences that is in paragraph order. **Write** another sentence that fits in the paragraph.

Responses will vary.

1. Doug took the toy away from Rollo. Doug's dog Rollo broke a new toy car. Rollo put his head down on his paws.

2. Willa's mom got a new car. It was bright blue. Mom took Willa for a ride. Willa waved to the neighbors as they drove along.

Then Willa and her mother rode to the supermarket.

Number each sentence in paragraph order. **Draw** a line through the sentence that doesn't belong in the paragraph.

__1__ Roxanne was waiting for her little sister Sue.

__4__ Finally Roxanne saw her sister walking outside.

_____ ~~Roxanne and her sister like to go swimming.~~

__2__ First she saw her sister go into the library.

__3__ Next Sue returned a book.

__5__ Then the girls rode home on their bikes.

 Notes for Home: Your child identified a paragraph and rearranged sentences in paragraph order. **Home Activity:** Talk with your child about what he or she did today. Then help your child write a paragraph to describe his or her day.

Correct each sentence.
Write it on the line.
Hint: Use capital letters and the correct end marks.

1. i help mrs. woo

I help Mrs. Woo.

2. how do you help her

How do you help her?

3. we pick up trash in oak park

We pick up trash in Oak Park.

4. a clean park is nice

A clean park is nice.

5. flowers grow there in may

Flowers grow there in May.

 Notes for Home: Your child capitalized the beginning of sentences and proper nouns and wrote end marks for sentences. **Home Activity:** Write sentences for your child to check. Have him or her tell you if the sentences are written correctly.

Teacher's Notes

Teacher's Notes

Teacher's Notes

Teacher's Notes

Teacher's Notes

Credits

Level 2.1

Illustrations

Joe Bartos: pp. 56, 130, 186; **Bill Basso:** p. 2; **Joe Boddy:** pp. 27, 28, 29, 33, 34, 45, 46, 47, 192; **Priscilla Burris:** pp. 51, 52, 63, 64, 65, 66, 69, 70, 81, 82, 84, 87, 88, 96, 135, 136, 150, 151, 152, 153, 154, 167, 168, 169, 170, 171, 172, 187, 188, 189, 190, 191, 205, 206, 207, 208, 209, 210, 224, 225; **Penny Carter:** pp. 75, 76, 77, 78, 79, 80, 226, 227, 228, 241, 242, 243, 244, 245, 246, 259, 260, 261, 263, 264; **Eldon Doty:** pp. 113, 114, 240, 258; **Julie Durell:** pp. 139, 141, 143, 144, 149, 155, 156, 157, 161, 162, 173, 174, 179, 180; **Ruth J. Flanagan:** pp. 12, 30, 66, 74, 92, 122, 140, 158, 184, 196, 214, 232, 276; **Collin Fry:** pp. 97, 98, 99, 99, 100, 115, 116, 117, 118, 132, 133, 134; **Rachel Geswaldo:** pp. 112, 222; **Jerry Gonzalez:** p. 20; **Susan Hall:** pp. 83, 91, 95, 175, 183, 267, 275; **Kersti Mack:** pp. 148, 204, 258; **Patrick Merrell:** pp. 43, 44, 57, 58, 59, 61, 62; **John Nez:** pp. 38, 94; **Doug Roy:** pp. 3, 4, 5, 6, 7, 8, 21, 22, 23, 24, 193, 194, 199, 211, 213, 217, 218, 221, 229, 230, 235; **John Sanford:** cover; **Terry Sirrell:** pp. 25, 26, 39, 40, 41, 42, 166; **Jessica W. Stanley:** pp. 11, 15, 16; **George Ulrich:** pp. 236, 247, 248, 249, 250, 254, 265, 266, 268, 271, 272; **Ronnie Walter:** pp. 101, 102, 103, 107, 108, 119, 120, 125, 126, 131, 137, 138

Level 2.2

Illustrations

Elizabeth Allen: pp. 42, 43, 44, 51, 57, 58, 59, 60, 61, 62, 75, 77, 78, 79, 80; **Bill Basso:** p. 2; **Joe Boddy:** pp. 9, 10, 11, 15, 27, 28, 29, 45, 46, 47; **Penny Carter:** pp. 151, 157, 161; **Bill Colorus:** pp. 187, 188, 190, 192, 223, 224; **Mena Dolobowsky:** pp. 136, 139, 140, 149, 150, 153, 154, 155, 156, 157, 170, 171, 172, 253, 265, 266, 268, 271, 272; **Eldon Doty:** pp. 76, 97, 102, 103, 104, 107, 119, 130, 148, 204; **Ruth J. Flanagan:** pp. 12, 30, 66, 92, 122, 140, 158, 184, 196, 214, 232, 276; **Tom Garcia:** pp. 166, 240; **Jerry Gonzales:** p. 94; **Susan Hall:** pp. 3, 4, 5, 6, 7, 8, 21, 22, 23, 24, 25, 26, 39, 40, 41, 52, 63, 64, 65, 69, 70, 81, 83, 84, 87, 88, 91, 173, 175, 176, 179, 183, 275; **Olga Jakim:** p. 74; **Patrick Merrell:** pp. 95, 96, 98, 99, 100, 113, 114, 115, 116, 117, 118, 131, 132, 133, 134, 135, 143, 144; **John Nez:** p. 20; **Melanie Reim:** p. 56, 112, 222; **Doug Roy:** pp. 225, 226, 228, 241, 242, 243, 245, 246, 259, 260, 261, 263, 264; **Joanna Roy:** pp. 38, 186, 258; **John Sanford:** cover; **Jessica W. Stanley:** pp. 194, 195, 196, 200, 205, 206, 207, 208, 209, 210, 211, 212, 213, 217, 218, 229, 230, 231, 235, 247; **George Ulrich:** pp. 121, 125